WITHDRAWN

PROGRESS IN

Nucleic Acid Research and Molecular Biology

Volume 30

PROGRESS IN

Nucleic Acid Research and Molecular Biology

edited by

WALDO E. COHN

Biology Division
Oak Ridge National Laboratory
Oak Ridge, Tennessee

KIVIE MOLDAVE

Department of Biological Chemistry
College of Medicine
University of California
Irvine, California

Volume 30

1983

ACADEMIC PRESS

A Subsidiary of Harcourt Brace Jovanovich, Publishers

New York   London
Paris   San Diego   San Francisco   São Paulo   Tokyo   Toronto

ACADEMIC PRESS, INC.
111 Fifth Avenue, New York, New York 10003

United Kingdom Edition published by
ACADEMIC PRESS, INC. (LONDON) LTD.
24/28 Oval Road, London NW1 7DX

LIBRARY OF CONGRESS CATALOG CARD NUMBER: 63-15847

ISBN 0-12-540030-6

PRINTED IN THE UNITED STATES OF AMERICA

83 84 85 86   9 8 7 6 5 4 3 2 1

Contents

RNA Processing in a Unicellular Microorganism: Implications for Eukaryotic Cells

David Apirion

Nearest-Neighbor Effects in the Structure and Function of Nucleic Acids

E. Bubienko, P. Cruz, J. F. Thomason, and P. N. Borer

The Elongation Factor EF-Tu and Its Two Encoding Genes

L. Bosch, B. Kraal, P. H. Van der Meide, F. J. Duisterwinkel, and J. M. Van Noort

Small Nuclear RNAs and RNA Processing

Ram Reddy and Harris Busch

Ribosome Evolution: The Structural Bases of Protein Synthesis in Archaebacteria, Eubacteria, and Eukaryotes

James A. Lake

Analysis of the Expression of Genes Encoding Animal mRNA by *in Vitro* Techniques

James L. Manley

Synthesis, Processing, and Gene Structure of Vasopressin and Oxytocin

Dietmar Richter

Contributors

Numbers in parentheses indicate the pages on which the authors' contributions begin.

DAVID APIRION (1), *Department of Microbiology and Immunology, Washington University School of Medicine, St. Louis, Missouri 63110*

P. N. BORER[1] (41), *Department of Chemistry, University of California at Irvine, Irvine, California 92717*

L. BOSCH (91), *Department of Biochemistry, State University of Leiden, 2333 AL Leiden, The Netherlands*

E. BUBIENKO[2] (41), *Department of Chemistry, University of California at Irvine, Irvine, California 92717*

HARRIS BUSCH (127), *Department of Pharmacology, Baylor College of Medicine, Houston, Texas 77030*

P. CRUZ[3] (41), *Department of Chemistry, University of California at Irvine, Irvine, California 92717*

F. J. DUISTERWINKEL (91), *Department of Biochemistry, State University of Leiden, 2333 AL Leiden, The Netherlands*

B. KRAAL (91), *Department of Biochemistry, State University of Leiden, 2333 AL Leiden, The Netherlands*

JAMES A. LAKE (163), *The Molecular Biology Institute and Department of Biology, University of California, Los Angeles, Los Angeles, California 90024*

JAMES L. MANLEY (195), *Department of Biology, Columbia University, New York, New York 10027*

RAM REDDY (127), *Department of Pharmacology, Baylor College of Medicine, Houston, Texas 77030*

DIETMAR RICHTER (245), *Institut für Physiologische Chemie, Abteilung Zellbiochemie, Universität Hamburg, 2000 Hamburg 20, Federal Republic of Germany*

J. F. THOMASON[4] (41), *Department of Chemistry, University of California at Irvine, Irvine, California 92717*

J. M. VAN NOORT (91), *Department of Biochemistry, State University of Leiden, 2333 AL Leiden, The Netherlands*

P. H. VAN DER MEIDE (91), *Department of Biochemistry, State University of Leiden, 2333 AL Leiden, The Netherlands*

[1] Present address: Department of Chemistry, Syracuse University, Syracuse, New York 13210.

[2] Present address: Department of Pharmaceutical Chemistry, University of California at San Francisco, San Francisco, California 94143.

[3] Present address: Department of Chemistry, University of California at Berkeley, Berkeley, California 94720.

[4] Present address: Department of Pharmaceutical Chemistry, University of California at San Francisco, San Francisco, California 94143.

Preface

Progress in Nucleic Acid Research (and Molecular Biology, added in 1964) was begun in 1963 as a serial publication updating the three-volume treatise "The Nucleic Acids," edited by E. Chargaff and J. N. Davidson (Volumes I and II published in 1955 and Volume III in 1960). Davidson and Waldo E. Cohn were the editors of the first thirteen volumes (1963–1973) with the latter continuing to serve as editor after Davidson's untimely death in 1972 (see the Obituary in Volume 13). With this volume, Kivie Moldave joins Cohn, and the publication now has, as originally, a dual editorship.

Dr. Moldave is no newcomer to the editor's chair. In addition to many years as a member of the Editorial Boards of *The Journal of Biological Chemistry* and *Biochemistry*, as well as of the *Biological Regulation and Development* series, he has been, and still is, a coeditor, since 1967, of the volumes of *Methods in Enzymology* devoted to nucleic acids and protein synthesis. But even more than editorial experience, Kivie Moldave's involvement with this publication underlines the gradual, if spasmodic, shift in emphasis from nucleic acid chemistry per se to the role of nucleic acids in molecular biology, genetics, virology, and immunology. Not that chemistry is abandoned; the appearance of "processing" in the titles of papers in this volume attests to that. But the chemistry of concern is that taking place *in vivo* in biochemical and biological pathways or phenomena. Twenty years of progress are reflected in "Progress"!

Yet the major aims of this serial publication, set out in the Preface to Volume 1, remain the same: "We seek . . . to encourage the writing of 'essays in circumscribed areas' in which recent developments in particular aspects . . . are discussed by workers provided with an opportunity for more personal interpretation than is normally provided in review articles. . . . we [encourage] more discussion and speculation than is customary . . . and the expression of points of view that are perhaps controversial and certainly individualistic. We [do not attempt] to define or restrict any author's approach to his chosen subject and [confine] our editing to ensuring maximum clarity to [persons] active in or concerned with the general field. . . . We seek to provide a forum for discussion and debate."

As in the past, we welcome comments and advice from colleagues as to how this publication may be made more valuable to them.

WALDO E. COHN
KIVIE MOLDAVE

Abbreviations and Symbols

All contributors to this Series are asked to use the terminology (abbreviations and symbols) recommended by the IUPAC-IUB Commission on Biochemical Nomenclature (CBN) and approved by IUPAC and IUB, and the Editor endeavors to assure conformity. These Recommendations have been published in many journals (*1, 2*) and compendia (*3*) in four languages and are available in reprint form from the Office of Biochemical Nomenclature (OBN), as stated in each publication, and are therefore considered to be generally known. Those used in nucleic acid work, originally set out in section 5 of the first Recommendations (*1*) and subsequently revised and expanded (*2, 3*), are given in condensed form (I–V) below for the convenience of the reader. Authors may use them without definition, when necessary.

I. Bases, Nucleosides, Mononucleotides

1. *Bases* (in tables, figures, equations, or chromatograms) are symbolized by Ade, Gua, Hyp, Xan, Cyt, Thy, Oro, Ura; Pur = any purine, Pyr = any pyrimidine, Base = any base. The prefixes S-, H_2, F-, Br, Me, etc., may be used for modifications of these.

2. *Ribonucleosides* (in tables, figures, equations, or chromatograms) are symbolized, in the same order, by Ado, Guo, Ino, Xao, Cyd, Thd, Ord, Urd (Ψrd), Puo, Pyd, Nuc. Modifications may be expressed as indicated in (1) above. Sugar residues may be specified by the prefixes r (optional), d (=deoxyribo), a, x, l, etc., to these, or by two three-letter symbols, as in Ara-Cyt (for aCyd) or dRib-Ade (for dAdo).

3. *Mono-, di-, and triphosphates of nucleosides* (5′) are designated by NMP, NDP, NTP. The N (for "nucleoside") may be replaced by any one of the nucleoside symbols given in II-1 below. 2′-, 3′-, and 5′- are used as prefixes when necessary. The prefix d signifies "deoxy." [Alternatively, nucleotides may be expressed by attaching P to the symbols in (2) above. Thus: P-Ado = AMP; Ado-P = 3′-AMP] cNMP = cyclic 3′:5′-NMP; Bt₂cAMP = dibutyryl cAMP, etc.

II. Oligonucleotides and Polynucleotides

1. Ribonucleoside Residues

(a) Common: A, G, I, X, C, T, O, U, Ψ, R, Y, N (in the order of I-2 above).

(b) Base-modified: sI or M for thioinosine = 6-mercaptopurine ribonucleoside; sU or S for thiouridine; brU or B for 5-bromouridine; hU or D for 5,6-dihydrouridine; i for isopentenyl; f for formyl. Other modifications are similarly indicated by appropriate *lower-case* prefixes (in contrast to I-1 above) (*2, 3*).

(c) Sugar-modified: prefixes are d, a, x, or l as in I-2 above; alternatively, by *italics* or boldface type (with definition) unless the entire chain is specified by an appropriate prefix. The 2′-*O*-methyl group is indicated by *suffix* m (e.g., -Am- for 2′-*O*-methyladenosine, but -mA- for 6-methyladenosine).

(d) Locants and multipliers, when necessary, are indicated by superscripts and subscripts, respectively, e.g., -m₂⁶A- = 6-dimethyladenosine; -s⁴U- or -⁴S- = 4-thiouridine; -ac⁴Cm- = 2′-*O*-methyl-4-acetylcytidine.

(e) When space is limited, as in two-dimensional arrays or in aligning homologous sequences, the prefixes may be placed *over the capital letter*, the suffixes *over the phosphodiester symbol*.

2. Phosphoric Residues [left side = 5′, right side = 3′ (or 2′)]

(a) Terminal: p; e.g., pppN . . . is a polynucleotide with a 5′-triphosphate at one end; Ap is adenosine 3′-phosphate; C > p is cytidine 2′:3′-cyclic phosphate (*1, 2, 3*); p < A is adenosine 3′:5′-cyclic phosphate.

xiii

(b) Internal: hyphen (for known sequence), comma (for unknown sequence); unknown sequences are enclosed in parentheses. E.g., pA-G-A-C(C$_2$,A,U)A-U-G-C > p is a sequence with a (5') phosphate at one end, a 2':3'-cyclic phosphate at the other, and a tetranucleotide of unknown sequence in the middle. (**Only codon triplets should be written without some punctuation separating the residues.**)

3. Polarity, or Direction of Chain

The symbol for the phosphodiester group (whether hyphen or comma or parentheses, as in 2b) represents a 3'-5' link (i.e., a 5' ... 3' chain) unless otherwise indicated by appropriate numbers. "Reverse polarity" (a chain proceeding from a 3' terminus at left to a 5' terminus at right) may be shown by numerals or by right-to-left arrows. Polarity in any direction, as in a two-dimensional array, may be shown by appropriate rotation of the (capital) letters so that 5' is at left, 3' at right when the letter is viewed right-side-up.

4. Synthetic Polymers

The complete name or the appropriate group of symbols (see II-1 above) of the repeating unit, **enclosed in parentheses if complex or a symbol,** is either (a) preceded by "poly," or (b) followed by a subscript "n" or appropriate number. **No space follows "poly"** (2, 5).

The conventions of II-2b are used to specify known or unknown (random) sequence, e.g.,

polyadenylate = poly(A) or A$_n$, a simple homopolymer;

poly(3 adenylate, 2 cytidylate) = poly(A$_3$C$_2$) or (A$_3$,C$_2$)$_n$, an *irregular* copolymer of A and C in 3:2 proportions;

poly(deoxyadenylate-deoxythymidylate) = poly[d(A-T)] or poly(dA-dT) or (dA-dT)$_n$ or d(A-T)$_n$, an *alternating* copolymer of dA and dT;

poly(adenylate,guanylate,cytidylate,uridylate) = poly(A,G,C,U) or (A,G,C,U)$_n$, a random assortment of A, G, C, and U residues, proportions unspecified.

The prefix copoly or oligo may replace poly, if desired. The subscript "n" may be replaced by numerals indicating actual size, e.g., A$_n \cdot$ dT$_{12\text{-}18}$.

III. Association of Polynucleotide Chains

1. *Associated* (e.g., H-bonded) chains, or bases within chains, are indicated by a *center dot* (not a hyphen or a plus sign) separating the *complete* names or symbols, e.g.:

poly(A) $\cdot$ poly(U)   or   A$_n$ $\cdot$ U$_m$

poly(A) $\cdot$ 2 poly(U)   or   A$_n$ $\cdot$ 2U$_m$

poly(dA-dC) $\cdot$ poly(dG-dT)   or   (dA-dC)$_n$ $\cdot$ (dG-dT)$_m$.

2. *Nonassociated* chains are separated by the plus sign, e.g.:

2[poly(A) $\cdot$ poly(U)] $\rightarrow$ poly(A) $\cdot$ 2 poly(U) + poly(A)

or   2[A$_n$ $\cdot$ U$_m$] $\rightarrow$ A$_n$ $\cdot$ 2U$_m$ + A$_n$.

3. Unspecified or unknown association is expressed by a comma (again meaning "unknown") between the completely specified chains.

Note: In all cases, each chain is completely specified in one or the other of the two systems described in II-4 above.

IV. Natural Nucleic Acids

RNA	ribonucleic acid or ribonucleate
DNA	deoxyribonucleic acid or deoxyribonucleate
mRNA; rRNA; nRNA	messenger RNA; ribosomal RNA; nuclear RNA
hnRNA	heterogeneous nuclear RNA
D-RNA; cRNA	"DNA-like" RNA; complementary RNA

mtDNA	mitochondrial DNA
tRNA	transfer (or acceptor or amino-acid-accepting) RNA; replaces sRNA, which is not to be used for any purpose
aminoacyl-tRNA	"charged" tRNA (i.e., tRNA's carrying aminoacyl residues); may be abbreviated to AA-tRNA
alanine tRNA or tRNA^{Ala}, etc.	tRNA normally capable of accepting alanine, to form alanyl-tRNA, etc.
alanyl-tRNA or alanyl-tRNA^{Ala}	The same, with alanyl residue covalently attached. [*Note:* fMet = formylmethionyl; hence tRNA^{fMet}, identical with tRNA$_f^{Met}$]

Isoacceptors are indicated by appropriate subscripts, i.e., tRNA$_1^{Ala}$, tRNA$_2^{Ala}$, etc.

V. Miscellaneous Abbreviations

P_i, PP_i	inorganic orthophosphate, pyrophosphate
RNase, DNase	ribonuclease, deoxyribonuclease
t_m (not T_m)	melting temperature (°C)

Others listed in Table II of Reference 1 may also be used without definition. No others, with or without definition, are used unless, in the opinion of the editor, they increase the ease of reading.

Enzymes

In naming enzymes, the 1978 recommendations of the IUB Commission on Biochemical Nomenclature (4) are followed as far as possible. At first mention, each enzyme is described *either* by its systematic name *or* by the equation for the reaction catalyzed *or* by the recommended trivial name, followed by its EC number in parentheses. Thereafter, a trivial name may be used. Enzyme names are not to be abbreviated except when the substrate has an approved abbreviation (e.g., ATPase, but not LDH, is acceptable).

REFERENCES*

1. *JBC* **241**, 527 (1966); *Bchem* **5**, 1445 (1966); *BJ* **101**, 1 (1966); *ABB* **115**, 1 (1966), **129**, 1 (1969); and elsewhere.†
2. *EJB* **15**, 203 (1970); *JBC* **245**, 5171 (1970); *JMB* **55**, 299 (1971); and elsewhere.†
3. "Handbook of Biochemistry" (G. Fasman, ed.), 3rd ed. Chemical Rubber Co., Cleveland, Ohio, 1970, 1975, Nucleic Acids, Vols. I and II, pp. 3–59.
4. "Enzyme Nomenclature" [Recommendations (1978) of the Nomenclature Committee of the IUB]. Academic Press, New York, 1979.
5. "Nomenclature of Synthetic Polypeptides," *JBC* **247**, 323 (1972); *Biopolymers* **11**, 321 (1972); and elsewhere.†

Abbreviations of Journal Titles

Journals	Abbreviations used
Annu. Rev. Biochem.	ARB
Arch. Biochem. Biophys.	ABB
Biochem. Biophys. Res. Commun.	BBRC

*Contractions for names of journals follow.

†Reprints of all CBN Recommendations are available from the Office of Biochemical Nomenclature (W. E. Cohn, Director), Biology Division, Oak Ridge National Laboratory, Box Y, Oak Ridge, Tennessee 37830, USA.

Biochemistry	Bchem
Biochem. J.	BJ
Biochim. Biophys. Acta	BBA
Cold Spring Harbor Symp. Quant. Biol.	CSHSQB
Eur. J. Biochem.	EJB
Fed. Proc.	FP
Hoppe-Seyler's Z. physiol. Chem.	ZpChem
J. Amer. Chem. Soc.	JACS
J. Bacteriol.	J. Bact.
J. Biol. Chem.	JBC
J. Chem. Soc.	JCS
J. Mol. Biol.	JMB
Nature, New Biology	Nature NB
Nucleic Acid Research	NARes
Proc. Nat. Acad. Sci. U.S.	PNAS
Proc. Soc. Exp. Biol. Med.	PSEBM
Progr. Nucl. Acid Res. Mol. Biol.	This Series

Some Articles Planned for Future Volumes

Dynamics of Nucleosome Structure in Transcriptional Control
V. ALLFREY

Immunoassay of Carcinogen-Modified DNA
J. M. BOYLE AND P. P. STRICKLAND

The Hypoxanthine-Guanine Phosphoribosyltransferase Gene: A Model for the Study of Mutation in Mammalian Cells
C. T. CASKEY

Role of DNA Methylation in Gene Expression
V. INGRAM

Biological Significance of Modifications of tRNA
H. KERSTEN

Optimization of Translational Accuracy
C. G. KURLAND

Eukaryotic rRNA Genes: Organization and Transcription
R. K. MANDAL

Recent Progress in Structure and Function of rRNA
H. NOLLER

The Recombination-like Activities of *E. coli recA* Protein
C. M. RADDING

Site-Specific Mutagenesis
V. RAJBHANDARY

Translational Control Involving Novel RNA and Ribonucleoprotein
S. SARKAR

Arrangement of Genes in Chloroplast DNA of Higher Plants
K. TEWARI

Molecular Aspects of Development in *Artemia salina*
A. WAHBA

Molecular Genetics of Human Hemoglobin
S. W. WEISSMAN

RNA Processing in a Unicellular Microorganism: Implications for Eukaryotic Cells

DAVID APIRION

Department of Microbiology and
   Immunology,
Washington University School of
   Medicine,
St. Louis, Missouri

Processing of RNA is a feature of RNA metabolism that contributes to the determination of the final population of active RNA molecules in the cell. Processing is the sum of events that convert a primary RNA transcript into a functional molecule.

The immediate transcription products of prokaryotic genes are frequently not identical with the RNA molecules that function in the cell. The stable RNA species, the ribosomal and transfer RNAs (tRNAs) as well as a few of the messenger RNAs, of *Escherichia coli* differ from the primary transcription products of their genes in one or more aspects. For example, rRNA transcription units of *E. coli* contain sequences that specify the three rRNAs 16 S, 23 S, and 5 S as well as one or more tRNAs. Similarly, tRNA genes are frequently clustered and cotranscribed in multimers of up to seven identical or different tRNAs. Moreover, tRNA genes are located in the "spacer" region of every rRNA transcription unit of *E. coli* and in the "trailer" regions of some of these gene clusters.

Progress in Nucleic Acid Research
and Molecular Biology, Vol. 30

In order to produce functional RNA molecules from the immediate products of transcription, prokaryotic cells carry out three basic types of RNA maturation reactions: separation of polycistronic transcripts into monocistronic precursor RNAs; accurate recognition of the mature 5' and 3' termini, removing extraneous nucleotides without altering the terminal sequences themselves; and modification of the base or the ribose moiety of the four primary nucleosides in an RNA chain. Not every RNA molecule is subject to all three of these processes. Certain polycistronic tRNA transcripts do require all three; many—probably most—messenger RNAs require no processing for their functional expression.

Because I have coauthored a number of reviews on RNA processing in prokaryotic cells and bacteriophages (1–3), this article deals mainly with studies on RNA processing in E. coli carried out in my laboratory. These concentrate primarily on the endonucleolytic cleavages that lead from RNA precursors to the mature molecules. The article follows more or less chronologically our development of this topic.

Since one of the major aspects of RNA processing that separate prokaryotic from eukaryotic cells is the existence of intervening sequences in the latter but not in the former, as a student of RNA processing I could not avoid contemplating this issue, and I wish to share some of my thoughts that suggest a way in which the complex mosaic eukaryotic gene could have evolved from the "streamlined" prokaryotic gene. I consider that the evolution of the nucleus played a major role in this transition.

I. Early Studies

The first studies on processing of RNA in my laboratory were carried out on the conversion of p16 (17 S), the immediate precursor of 16 S rRNA, to 16 S rRNA. At that time we were studying a strain that contained a large number of mutations, including one affecting the enzyme RNase II, and we found that we could isolate a strain that still contained the mutation affecting RNase II but that could grow at higher temperatures and mature 17 S to 16 S rRNA normally (4). This indicated that RNase II is unlikely to be essential for any vital function in the cell. The appearance at this time of two papers concluding that RNase II is the enzyme that processes p16 (17 S) to 16 S rRNA (5, 6) prompted us to search for an enzyme in E. coli distinct from RNase II that can process 17 S to 16 S rRNA. We found such an activity, but the reaction would proceed only if the substrate was a ribonucleoprotein particle (7). Later studies (8, 9) corroborated our findings and indicate that there is a soluble protein(s) in the cell that is required to convert 17 S to 16 S rRNA, and that it is effective only if the 17 S RNA is in an RNP particle.

II. Processing of rRNA in an RNase-III⁻ Strain

Our interest in RNase III was initiated by studies on the degradation of rRNA during starvation, which led us to the conclusion that the breakdown of rRNA in various kinds of starvation starts with an endonucleolytic activity that is not RNase I (10–12). At the time, the only other known nonspecific endoribonuclease in E. coli was RNase III. As soon as a mutant in this enzyme became available (13) we wanted to compare rRNA breakdown in an isogenic rnc, rnc⁺ (RNase III⁻, RNase III⁺) pair and to find out if RNase III is the endoribonuclease that initiates rRNA decay during starvation. However, the strain containing the rnc-105 mutation (AB301-105) contained at least seven mutations other than the RNase-III lesion (14). To study the effect of the RNase-III mutation (rnc-105) by itself, the mutation was first mapped at minute 54.5 (see Fig. 1); isogenic rnc⁺/rnc-105 pairs were then constructed by transducing the rnc-105 mutation into a different genetic background (15), which allowed further study of the roles of RNase III.

Electrophoretic analysis of RNAs from an rnc-105 strain demonstrated a dramatic effect on rRNA production (16, 17). The mutant synthesizes a variety of RNAs (30 S, 25 S, and 18 S) whose presence is solely dependent upon the rnc-105 mutation (18). This was deduced by isolating revertants from the rnc-105 mutant. Some of the revertants were true revertants and no longer harbored the rnc-105 mutation. In these revertants, rRNA metabolism became normal (18). Thus, analysis of an RNase-III mutant started our more recent interst in RNA processing.

As soon as the RNase-III mutant was analyzed in different laboratories, it became obvious that it accumulates large rRNA molecules, such as 30 S, that contain 16 S and 23 S rRNA sequences not observed in wild-type strains (19, 20). Such large rRNA molecules do not appear in wild-type cells. The notion was then put forward that the large rRNA, 30 S, is a precursor that is processed to 16 S and 23 S rRNA (19, 20). However, in a quantitative analysis of precursor–product relationships between the large rRNA molecules and the mature rRNA, we found that even in an RNase-III⁻ strain, rRNAs are not cut from the 30 S RNA (16). These findings therefore suggested that there must be some other

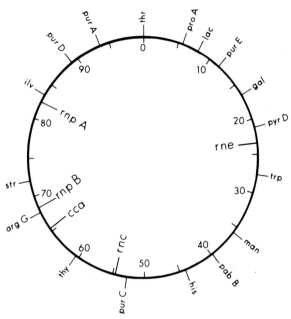

FIG. 1. Genetic map of RNA-processing mutations in *Escherichia coli* K12. The RNA-processing genes are inside the circle. The loci are discussed in the text. *rnc*, RNase III (15, 107); *rne*, RNase E (46); *rnp*, RNase P (35, 85–87); *cca*, nucleotidyl-transferase (108, 109). A mutation that affects RNase D (*rnd*) was mapped at 39.8 min (110).

enzyme(s) besides RNase III that can process the nascent rRNA chain into precursors of the mature rRNAs.

It was suggested at that time that the available RNase-III mutant (*rnc-105*) is leaky, and that the residual activity of this enzyme is responsible for maturation of rRNA in an *rnc-105* mutant. To deal with this issue, we measured RNase-III-like activity in extracts of an isogenic pair of strains, one *rnc* and the other *rnc⁺*. We found that the extract of the *rnc* strain contained some RNase-III-like activity, but this activity had properties different from the activity observed in an extract of an *rnc⁺* strain. The residual activity was not enhanced by assaying it at a higher pH (21), whereas the activity of RNase III is increased at higher pHs (22). Moreover, the residual activity is less temperature-sensitive than the activity in extracts of the *rnc⁺* strain (18). Therefore, we concluded that strains carrying the *rnc-105* mutation have no detectable level of RNase III, and we argued that the maturation of rRNA taking place *in vivo* in an *rnc* mutant is unlikely to be a result of residual RNase-III activity.

This prompted us to investigate in detail the precursor product relationship among the rRNA species appearing in an isogenic *rnc* and *rnc*+ pair of strains. While one can observe 17 S and 16 S rRNA as well as 23 S rRNA in a wild-type (*rnc*+) strain, in an *rnc* strain one can observe 30 S, 25 S, 23 S, 18 S, 17 S, and 16 S rRNA molecules (*17*). We showed that the biochemical phenotype of an *rnc* mutant is not temperature-dependent; i.e., all these different molecules appear at all temperatures where the *rnc* mutant can grow (*18*). We also showed that all this complex phenotype is caused by a single point mutation, since one can isolate true revertants that have become indistinguishable from a wild-type *rnc*+ strain (*18*). Revertants could be selected, since *rnc-105* mutants grow considerably slower than their *rnc*+ counterpart strains; at elevated temperatures, such as 45°C, the growth differential between the two strains is sufficient to permit selection (*14, 15, 21, 23*). *Rnc*+ revertants were also isolated by growth of *rnc* cells in a medium containing adenine analogs (*18*).

Analysis of precursor–product relationships among the various rRNA species appearing in the *rnc* mutant (*17*) showed that the large RNAs (30 S and 25 S) do not contribute significantly to the mature rRNA and are probably degraded. Whereas 23 S rRNA is matured from a precursor (p23) that is only slightly larger than p23 in an *rnc*+ strain (*24*), 16 S rRNA is derived from 18 S and 17 S rRNA. The 18 S rRNA (Fig. 2) appearing in the *rnc* mutant is obviously a new rRNA species, but also the 17 S rRNA found in an *rnc* mutant is slightly larger than the 17 S rRNA appearing in an *rnc*+ strain (*24*). We suggested that these slightly abnormal precursors can be recognized by the normal cellular machinery that processes 16 S and 23 S rRNA from their immediate precursors, and that maturation of rRNA can take place in the absence of RNase III (*17, 24*). However, the larger rRNA molecules (25 S), which contain 23 S and 5 S rRNA (*25*), and 30 S RNA cannot be processed by this machinery.

While these findings clearly established the function of RNase III in the maturation of rRNA, they also indicated that there must be cellular enzymes besides RNase III that can process (separate) 16 S from 23 S rRNA in the nascent rRNA transcript. These findings also indicated that RNase III is not involved in the maturation of 5 S rRNA, since the metabolism of 5 S rRNA was not affected in the RNase-III⁻ mutant. All these findings suggested a specific model for the maturation of rRNA in *E. coli*, which was first published in 1976 (*26*) and has been modified only slightly since (Fig. 3).

In order to carry out the various analyses necessary to establish precursor–product relationships, it was obvious that we need to de-

6   DAVID APIRION

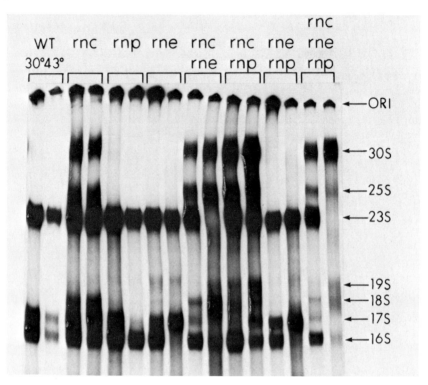

FIG. 2. Ribosomal RNAs produced in different RNA-processing mutants. For each of
the genotypes indicated, cultures of the corresponding strain were labeled with $^{32}P_i$ at
30°C or at 43°C, and nucleic acids were fractionated on a 3% polyacrylamide gel (details
as in 17 and 36). For each strain, the left lane represents RNA from cells grown at 30°C,
and the right lane represents RNA from cells labeled at 43°C. The rne mutant behaves
like a classical ts mutant, but the rnc mutant does not. Strains carrying the rnc-105
allele are completely missing RNase III (24), and therefore the patterns observed at 30°C
and 43°C are similar. The rnpA49 mutation used here is apparently defective in the
synthesis, but not in the function, of RNase P (89), and certain features of this mutation
are already expressed at temperatures where the mutant can grow (35, 36). The rne and
rne rnp strains used here contain an additional ts mutation(s) that blocks protein synthesis (46), and therefore 16 S rRNA, the product of secondary rRNA processing, is not
observed in these strains at the elevated temperature. It can be seen that 16 S rRNA
appears in the rnc rne double mutant and in the rnc rne rnp triple mutant. The difference between p16 and m16 is substantial (~150 nucleotides) and can be easily detected
in gels, but the difference between p23 and m23 is only 15 nucleotides (24) and cannot
be observed in the gel. The size differences between p16a and p16b, and p23a and p23b
(see text and Ref. 24) are also not readily observed in gels.

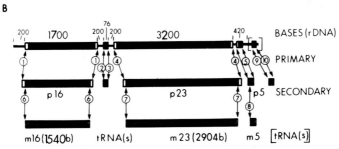

FIG. 3. Structure and processing map of ribosomal RNA transcripts. (A) Structure and cleavage sites of the rRNA primary transcript (not to scale). Derived from data from a number of laboratories (summarized in *17* and *57*). Distal ("trailer") tRNAs are bracketed, since not all ribosomal RNA gene clusters contain them. Transcripts may contain one or two spacer tRNAs, and zero, one, or two trailer RNAs. Arrows indicate endonucleolytic cleavage sites. Each cutting event is given a separate number, referring to the enzyme involved: A and B, where used, indicate that two (or more) separate cuts might be required. (Cut No. 8 is now known to be composed of two cuts, on either side of the 5 S rRNA.) Thick solid segments represent mature rRNA sequences, thick open segments represent precursor-specific sequences removed during secondary processing steps, stippled segments are sequences found only in p16b and p23b of RNase III⁻ cells, and thin lines (except for tRNAs) represent nonconserved sequences discarded during primary processing. Enzymes are discussed in the text. (B) Processing in wild-type strains. The first line shows the transcriptional map of a representative rDNA unit, approximately to scale. Distances in bases are between vertical bars above the map. The primary and secondary cuts, numbered as in panel A, are shown above the products they generate. Open and solid segments are as in panel A.

velop a relatively simple and efficient method to analyze quantitatively large numbers of samples of cells labeled with radioisotopes for various lengths of time. We chose to use $^{32}P_i$ since it was relatively cheap and could be easily detected by short autoradiographic expo-

sure of polyacrylamide gels. However, to manipulate a large number
of cultures rapidly and economically without losing information about
the RNA molecules of the cell, we found it useful to subject whole-cell
lysates to electrophoresis in thin-slab polyacrylamide gels that could
be quantitated by techniques we developed earlier (11). We were
concerned, however, with the various macromolecules that might be
labeled with $^{32}P_i$. Therefore, we set up a series of investigations to find
out what are the various ^{32}P-labeled bands that appear in polyacrylamide gels when whole-cell lysates prepared from cells labeled
with $^{32}P_i$ were subjected to electrophoresis.

Doing these experiments we found that most of the bands contain
RNA, that it is possible to get all the DNA of the cell to migrate as a
single band in polyacrylamide gels containing sodium dodecyl sulfate
(27), that it is possible to separate the lipopolysaccharides and phos-
pholipids from DNA and RNA (28), and that DNA, RNA, phos-
pholipids, and lipopolysaccharides are the four major classes of macromolecules that appeared as bands after labeling cells with $^{32}P_i$.
Besides being very instrumental in helping us to analyze the
precursor–product relationships among RNA molecules in rnc^+ and
rnc strains (17), these techniques are also very useful for assessing the
level of these various macromolecules in a variety of physiological
situations—for instance, ratios of various classes of RNAs to DNA (28).
Thus we could easily determine relationships among a variety of
macromolecules in exponential growth and amino-acid starvation in
both relaxed and stringent strains (29).

While the rnc-105 mutation was instrumental in establishing the
role of RNase III in the processing of rRNA, the analysis of an isogenic
rnc, rnc^+ pair of strains showed that RNase III is not the endonuclease
that initiates the turnover of rRNA during starvations (21).

III. Processing of rRNA in an RNase-III⁻, RNase-P⁻ Double Mutant

Studies with the RNase-III⁻ mutant suggested that other enzymes
besides RNase III are involved in cutting the growing rRNA chain
between 16 S and 23 S rRNA. However, they gave no clue to what the
enzyme(s) might be. At this time, it was already known that there are
spacer tRNAs in the rRNA gene cluster between 16 S and 23 S rRNA
(30, 31); it was also known that RNase P is involved in the maturation
of many tRNA precursors to form their 5′ ends (32). However, none of
these precursors was a very large RNA, and there was also the notion

that RNase P may require a free CCA in the tRNA to be active (33). Therefore, it was not obvious that RNase P could be involved in the maturation of rRNA. Nonetheless, since there were mutants defective in RNase P, it seemed to us worthwhile to construct rnc, rnp double mutants, and to find out if RNase P participates in the maturation of rRNA.

In order to build up rnc, rnp double mutants, we wanted to know the map location of the rnpA49 mutation (34). Therefore, the rnpA49 mutation was mapped (35; see Fig. 1) and double rnc, rnp strains were constructed (36), and their rRNA metabolism was analyzed.

To our delight, the rnc, rnp double mutant (see Figs. 2 and 3) accumulated a larger precursor of 16 S rRNA than the rnc mutant itself. This larger molecule, named 19 S RNA, contained all the three "spacer" tRNAs, tRNA^{Glu}, tRNA^{Ile}, and tRNA^{Ala} (36, 37), that could be found in the region between 16 S and 23 S rRNA, in rRNA gene clusters (30, 31). Moreover, purified RNase P could process these three tRNAs from the 19 S RNA (37). Thus, it became obvious that RNase P is participating in the processing of rRNA in E. coli (see Figs. 2 and 3). Later, this conclusion was further supported by the finding that the 30 S rRNA that accumulates in the RNase-III$^-$ strain can be cleaved specifically by purified RNase P (38). Moreover, the 19 S RNA as well as the 18 S RNA contained 5 ′ triphosphates (37). Furthermore, analysis of the 17 S (p16) and 23 S (p23) RNA that accumulate in an rnc mutant showed that they contain stems that RNase III could cleave to create the immediate precursors of 16 S and 23 S rRNAs (24). In sum, all these results show that the enzyme RNase III is the first to cleave the nascent growing rRNA chain, followed by enzymes that remove the tRNA from the transcript. This is all summarized in Fig. 3. The studies on the rRNA stems also showed that in an rnc mutant there is no detectable level of RNase III in vivo, since no normal p16 or p23 (generated by RNase III) could be found. Thus, these studies helped to formulate the more detailed model for rRNA processing presented in Fig. 3.

It was suggested that RNase III might be cleaving RNA molecules near or at rho termination sites (39). To test for this possibility, rnc, rho double mutants were constructed (40). We found that RNA metabolism in rnc, rho double mutants was very similar or identical to RNA metabolism in rnc strains (40). Therefore, one cannot argue that the rnc-105 strain survived because the rho factor can replace RNase-III activity in producing 3′ ends of RNA molecules. We concluded from this study that rho and RNase III do not recognize the same sequences, and that they act independently. Moreover, rho acts to stop transcription whereas RNase III as well as all other processing enzymes act on an existing RNA chain.

IV. The *rne* Mutant and the RNase-E Enzyme

The analysis of maturation of 5 S rRNA in *rnc* and *rnc, rnp* strains strongly suggested that 5 S rRNA is processed by at least one, or perhaps two, endoribonucleases that were neither RNase III nor RNase P (*17, 36, 37*). Also we anticipated that if only a single enzyme participates in the cleavage of the 5 S rRNA, a loss of this enzyme would be lethal. Therefore, we isolated conditional (temperature-sensitive) mutants, starting with an *rnc* mutant, and analyzed their RNA metabolism. We expected that in a mutant defective in this enzyme, which we called RNase E, only 25 S rRNA should accumulate at the nonpermissive temperature, and no 23 S and 5 S rRNA should appear (see Fig. 3). Indeed, we found such a strain among temperature-sensitive mutants isolated from an *rnc* strain (*41*). As we expected, when we replaced in the *rnc, rne* double mutant the *rnc* mutation with the *rnc*+ allele, the 23 S rRNA reappeared, but 5 S rRNA still was not produced; instead, a larger RNA molecule was found. This RNA molecule, which we called 9 S RNA, contained 5 S rRNA sequences (*42, 43*), and it could be used as a substrate from which 5 S rRNA could be matured *in vitro* (*43*). Using this 9 S RNA, it was possible partially to purify an enzyme, RNase E, that matures 9 S RNA to 5 S RNA (*44*). This maturation takes place in two steps, apparently by a single enzyme. The first cleavage occurs proximal to 5 S rRNA, and the second distal to it. The enzyme is thermolabile in an *rne-3071* mutant (*45*).

The *rne* mutation was mapped and found to reside at 24 minutes in the *E. coli* map (Fig. 1), and isogenic *rne,rne*+ strains were prepared (*46*). The ability to transfer the *rne* mutation by P1-mediated transduction, and the ability to isolate Ts+ revertants from the *rne* mutants, suggested that the *rne-3071* is a point mutation (*46*).

With a partially purified RNase E and 9 S rRNA, cleavages are introduced three nucleotides prior to 5 S rRNA and three nucleotides past 5 S rRNA (*47;* see Fig. 4). *In vitro,* the product of the RNase-E reaction is a 5 S rRNA precursor that contains six extra nucleotides, three at each end.

Using extracts from an *rne*+ and *rne* isogenic pair of strains, both cleavages, before and after the 5 S rRNA (Fig. 4) are thermolabile in extracts of the RNase-E− mutant (*47*). Thus, barring the possibility that the *rne* gene specifies a polypeptide that participates in two different enzymes, each processing on one side of the 5 S rRNA, the evidence

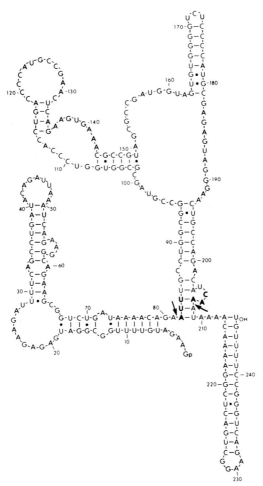

FIG. 4. Sequence and partial secondary structure of an RNase-E substrate, the 9 S rRNA of *Escherichia coli*. The sequence presented here is from a hybrid *rrnD* gene (J. Szeberenyi and D. Apirion, unpublished observations; a few base changes are found in the *rrnA*, *rrnB*, *rrnE*, and *rrnG* gene clusters). The last two stems, starting with nucleotides 82 and 213, respectively, were verified experimentally (49). These stems as well as the structure starting with nucleotide 29 were also indicated by computer analysis of the sequence (R. J. Feldmann, National Institutes of Health). The secondary structure involving sequences from the 5' end of the molecule was suggested by the finding that molecules missing the first eight nucleotides were not cleaved by RNase E (47). The arrows show the positions of RNase E cleavages (43, 47). The six bases near the arrows, indicated in bold letters, are not included in the mature 5 S rRNA. The structure shown is transcribed from the four rRNA gene clusters that do not contain trailer tRNAs. An almost identical RNA, up to nucleotide 209, is also transcribed from the other rRNA gene clusters, which do contain trailer tRNAs.

strongly indicates that RNase E is the enzyme that processes 5 S rRNA at both ends. As can be seen in Fig. 4, 9 S RNA contains sequences before and after the 5 S rRNA.

Interestingly, it seems from DNA and RNA analysis that the sequences between 23 S rRNA and 5 S rRNA are very much conserved in all the seven rRNA gene clusters. [The 5' end of the 9 S RNA is created by an RNase-III cleavage (Fig. 3).] I suggest that this region is conserved because it contains information for the processing reaction by RNase E. This notion is strongly supported by the finding that the portion of the 9 S RNA without the termination stem (see Fig. 4) is an excellent substrate for RNase E; however, when the first eight nucleotides are removed, it is hardly a substrate (47). This suggested that the 9 S rRNA might exist in a particular secondary structure depicted in Fig. 4, where nucleotides from the 5' end pair with the nucleotides in proximity to the RNase-E cleavage site. Removing a few nucleotides from the 5' end of 9 S RNA would disrupt this part of the secondary structure and in this way could interfere with the reaction. The situation is even more interesting when one realizes that the sequences at the 5' end of 9 S RNA participate in the RNase-III cleavage site that is involved in the production of 23 S rRNA (Figs. 3 and 4 and Ref. 24); they are part of the stem of the giant 23 S rRNA loop (see Fig. 3). Thus, it seems that, as in the case of attenuation, where the same sequence of RNA can participate in two different base-pairing schemes (48), in rRNA processing the same RNA sequence can participate in two different reactions by base-pairing with RNA sequences in two different regions. However, since the RNase-III stem, created after 23 S rRNA, can contain 29 base-pairs, while the stem next to 5 S can contain only 12 or 13 base-pairs, it is obvious that the RNase-III site will be formed first, and only after it is cleaved can the RNase-E site be formed.

Parts of the secondary structure of the 9 S RNA were determined experimentally (49). Here, as in the case of the stems of the RNase-III cleavage sites (24), we relied on the sensitivity of single-stranded RNA and the resistance of double-stranded RNA under certain conditions (high salt) to particular nucleases, such as T1 and pancreatic RNase. This particular technique is adequate only to detect relatively large uninterrupted stems, ten base-pairs and longer.

The 9 S RNA isolated from the *rne* mutant does not contain distal tRNAs (50); therefore, it probably represents 5 S RNA from rRNA gene clusters that do not contain distal (trailer) tRNAs (49). However, other RNAs that contain 5 S rRNA also accumulate in an *rne* mutant at the nonpermissive temperature, and we identified a molecule, "10 S

RNA," that contains 5 S and tRNA^{Asp} (51). Moreover, using an *rne, rnp* double mutant, it was possible to detect RNA molecules containing 5 S rRNA as well as tRNA^{Asp} and tRNA^{Trp} (52). Therefore, it is apparent that RNase E participates in the processing of the 5 S rRNA from all the rRNA genes. This is further indicated by the fact that, in an *rne* mutant at the nonpermissive temperature, no mature 5 S rRNA was detected (42). Also, these experiments showed that RNase P participates in the processing of the distal tRNAs. Therefore, all the tRNAs co-transcribed with rRNA are processed by RNase P.

To get some further understanding of RNase E, the *rne* gene was cloned in a λ vector (53) and in a plasmid vector (54), but in no case did the cell carrying this cloned DNA overproduce RNase E. This could be because, e.g., RNase E could be composed of two polypeptides, only one of them coded for by the *rne* gene, or the clone might have not contained a promoter. One important observation made using the *rne* DNA was that it did hybridize only to a single locus on the *E. coli* chromosome (54). This observation suggests that the RNA processing enzymes do not constitute a multigene family.

Strains carrying the *rnc-105* mutation are viable, but strains carrying the *rnpA49* or the *rne 3071* mutations are not, and with the last two, one is compelled to analyze transient situations. However, the *rnpA49* mutant has a very distinctive biochemical phenotype also at temperatures where the cell grows (35, 36), and the *rne* mutant continues to synthesize macromolecules for about two hours after the cells are transferred to a nonpermissive temperature (55). Therefore, it is possible to analyze RNA synthesis in each of these strains. In fact, the *rne* mutant, when transferred to 43°C, kept growing linearly (55) as expected from a cell when all its preexisting machinery is perfectly normal, but which cannot synthesize any new cellular machinery, such as ribosomes. The unique patterns of small RNAs in the *rnc, rne,* and *rnp* mutants can be all observed in a single picture (see 56). Each of these mutants has unique characteristics.

V. Processing of rRNA in Multiple RNA-Processing Mutants

In order to ascertain the effects of the three enzymes RNase III, RNase E, and RNase P on rRNA metabolism, all the possible double and triple mutants were constructed (56) and investigated (57). A summary is shown in Figs. 2 and 3. Only the loss of RNase III causes the appearance of the large rRNA molecules. Ribosomal RNA transcripts in the cell take the form of giant ribonucleoprotein loops held together by duplex stems; p16 and p23 rRNA precursors arise by cleavages within these stems (Fig. 3).

A. Processing in Wild-Type Cells

The detailed sequence of processing events discussed here is illustrated by the model presented in Fig. 3. An RNA polymerase, which initiates transcription of a ribosomal RNA gene cluster, continues to synthesize the various components of the polycistronic rRNA primary transcript: leader sequences; p16 rRNA; spacer sequences containing tRNAs; p23 rRNA; p5 rRNA; and distal sequences that in some gene clusters contain tRNAs. Before transcription is terminated, however, processing endonucleases are already acting on the nascent transcript. As polymerase molecules complete synthesis of p16 rRNA, the complementary sequences flanking the m16 transcript anneal to form a double-stranded stem from which m16 sequences loop out. As Fig. 3 shows, the stem so formed is cleaved by RNase III, which cuts within it (Fig. 3, cuts 1A and 1B) to release p16 precursor rRNA plus a 5′ leader fragment from the growing RNA chain. As the spacer region is synthesized, tRNAs are removed by endonucleolytic cleavage (RNase "F") at or near the 3′ side, and at the 5′ end by RNase P (cuts 2 and 3 in Fig. 3). Trimming of the 3′ end, perhaps by RNase D (58), might be also required to produce mature spacer tRNAs. As the RNA polymerase completes transcription of 23 S rRNA genes, RNase III excises p23 sequences, again by cleaving in the double-stranded stem formed by complementary sequences surrounding m23 (Fig. 3, cuts 4A and 4B). Transcription of the distal portion of the gene cluster now proceeds into the 5 S gene (Fig. 3). As soon as p5 rRNA sequences are formed and have folded into the appropriate conformation, they are excised by RNase E (Fig. 3, cuts 5 A and 5B), and distal (trailer) tRNAs are removed by RNase P (cut 9) and another activity (cut 10) possibly identical with RNase "F."

That p23 and p5 rRNA are excised from rRNA transcripts prior to transcription termination is evidenced by the failure to detect 25 S rRNA (p23 plus p5) in wild-type strains (see Fig. 2), and by the demonstration that no material in the 9 S region of a polyacrylamide gel prepared from RNA isolated from wild-type cells contains p5 sequences (42). It is clear, then, that the primary processing cleavages by RNase III and RNase E are exceedingly rapid events, such that virtually all sites are cleaved within seconds after synthesis of the sequences that comprise them.

It is interesting to mention here a major difference between processing of rRNA in prokaryotic and eukaryotic cells. As emphasized here, in prokaryotic cells most of the rRNA processing occurs during transcription, whereas in all the eukaryotic systems studied thus far, most of the rRNA species are transcribed in a single molecule that is processed posttranscriptionally (59).

B. Processing in Mutant Strains

The origin of rRNA species seen in mutants defective in RNA processing enzymes (Fig. 2) can readily be described by reference to the model shown in Fig. 3. In strains lacking the processing endonuclease RNase III, scission of nascent rRNA transcripts is initiated by RNase P and another enzyme(s) that cut in the spacer region to remove the tRNA sequences (cuts 2 and 3). The single-stranded region between cut 2 and the p16 stem is removed, possibly by enzyme(s) such as RNase II or polynucleotide phosphorylase, giving rise to 18 S RNA. Subsequently, the 5' leader sequence is removed from 18 S RNA in a slower process by single-strand specific nucleases that leave intact the duplex stem (see Fig. 3 and Ref. 24). The final rRNA product, a p16b molecule that contains the entire duplex stem and is thus slightly larger than normal p16a (24), is converted to normal m16 rRNA by the maturation enzyme(s) RNase(s) M16 (cuts 6A and 6B). RNase-E cleavage in the distal portion of the nascent rRNA transcript generates p5 rRNA and a p23-like molecule. The latter contains extra single-stranded spacer sequences extending from cleavage 3 to 5A, which could be rapidly and nonspecifically removed, giving rise to the p23b rRNA of the rnc strain (24). This p23b RNA might be further processed to mature rRNA (m23) via the maturation enzyme(s) RNase(s) "M23" (cuts 7A and 7B).

When RNase E is inactivated in the rne mutant, p5 rRNA is not removed from the distal portion of the transcript, which instead accumulates as 9 S RNA. If RNase P is also inactivated, trailer tRNAs are found linked to 5 S rRNA (51, 52; cuts 4B to 10). Failure to perform RNase-E and RNase-III cleavages in the rnc, rne strain at nonpermissive temperatures yields p5 sequences linked to p23 rRNA. A 25 S RNA thus accumulates at the expense of p23 and p5 (see Figs. 2 and 3). In these rnc, rne double-mutant cells, unlike in rnc single-mutant strains, no 23 S rRNA is detected.

In an rnc, rnp strain, spacer tRNAs are linked to 18 S RNA, giving rise to 19 S RNA (Fig. 3, cut 3). Each 19 S molecule (Fig. 2) is initiated with a nucleoside 5' triphosphate and, at its distal end, contains a spacer tRNA that terminates with the mature 3' CCA_{OH} sequence (37). Production of 19 S RNAs therefore requires endonucleolytic cleavage of nascent rRNA transcripts at a site near the 3' end of each spacer tRNA sequence (cut 3 in Fig. 3). In an *rnc, rne, rnp* triple mutant, some 19 S and 25 S-sized species are still produced (Fig. 2). It appears that processing activities, distinct from RNases III, E, or P, do exist that can cut in the rRNA spacer region. At present, we refer to such activities as RNase "F." The various rRNA molecules observed in the different strains are listed in Table I.

C. Efficiency and Order of Processing Steps

Since RNase III⁻ cells are viable, and form normal, functional mature m16, m23, and m5 ribosomal RNAs, the physiological necessity of RNase III could be questioned. An answer may lie in the observation that the doubling time of an RNase-III⁻ cell is longer (at 37°C) than that of an isogenic RNase-III⁺ cell (*15*). This observation could be explained by the lower efficiency of rRNA processing in RNase-III⁻ cells. While in *rnc⁺* cells no uncleaved primary transcripts are detected, in *rnc-105* cells a large proportion of the newly synthesized rRNA transcripts are uncleaved 30 S RNA and partially cleaved 25 S RNA molecules, few if any of which contribute significantly to the pool of mature rRNA species (*16, 17*).

RNase P cleavage of spacer tRNAs is less efficient when p16 sequences are not previously removed by RNase III, as evidenced by the fact that uncleaved 30 S transcripts are detected in RNase-III⁻ RNase-P⁺ strains (see Fig. 2), even though RNase P can cleave tRNA sequences in purified 30 S RNA (*38*). Similarly, the action of the endonuclease at the 3′ end of the spacer tRNAs (RNase "F") is impaired by the presence of p16 sequences linked to spacer tRNA, since, as seen in Fig. 2, relatively more 30 S RNA is found in the RNase-III⁻ RNase-P⁻ strain than in the strain lacking only RNase III. Since the 25 S species is seen in RNase-III⁻ single-mutant strains even though RNase E is active, it can be concluded that the addition of p23 sequences to nascent 9 S transcripts severely impairs the efficiency of p5 excision by RNase E.

This pattern of impaired processing might result from steric hindrance. Indeed, since ribosomal proteins attach to rRNA during transcription (*60*), it is likely that the uncleaved nascent rRNA exists as a ribonucleoprotein particle, which restricts access to the 5 S RNA and tRNA processing sites.

VI. Processing of *Escherichia coli* tRNA

The participation of RNase P in the processing of tRNAs is well established (*32*). However, the participation of RNase III and RNase E

TABLE I

RIBOSOMAL RNA MOLECULES APPEARING IN VARIOUS RNA-PROCESSING MUTANTS[a]

Genotype			Containing 5 S			Containing 16 S					Containing 23 S				Intact transcript 30 S
rnc	me	rnp	5 S	9 S	11 S	16 S	17 S (p16a)[b]	17 S (p16b)[b]	18 S	19 S	23 S	p23a[c]	p23b[c]	25 S	
+	+	+	v			v	v		v		v	v			
−	+	+	v			v	v	v	v		v	v	v	v	v
+	+	−	v			v	v				v	v			
+	−	+		v		v	v				v	v			
−	−	+				v		v	v		v				
−	+	−	v			v		v	v		v	v	v	v	v
+	−	−			v	v		(v)[d]	(v)[d]	v	v		v	v	v
−	−	−				v		(v)[d]	v	v	v		v	v	v

[a] This table shows the rRNA molecules that can be observed (v) in the various strains at elevated temperatures. For further details see the text (Section V) and Figs. 2 and 3. Some of the molecules cannot be clearly observed in Fig. 3, and the reader is advised to consult specific references mentioned in the text: 11 S contains 5 S and trailer tRNAs; 18 S contains 16 S and leader sequences; 19 S contains 16 S, leader sequences, and spacer tRNAs; 25 S contains 23 S and 5 S; 30 S is the whole RNA from the rRNA transcription units, containing leader sequences, 16 S, spacer tRNA, 23 S, 5 S, and trailer tRNAs.

[b] p16a is slightly smaller than p16b, the difference being in the double-stranded stem of the molecule (24 and Fig. 3).

[c] p23a is slightly smaller than p23b (24 and Fig. 3).

[d] Low levels were observed.

in tRNA metabolism has not been investigated. An indication that RNase E could be involved in tRNA metabolism came from the finding of monomeric (61) and multimeric (62) tRNA precursors in an *rne* mutant at the nonpermissive temperature.

A. Participation of RNase III, RNase E, and RNase P in the Processing of tRNA

To illustrate the participation of RNase III, RNase E, and RNase P in tRNA maturation, the effects of *rnc*, *rne*, and *rnp* mutations on tRNA production *in vivo* has been examined (57). Figure 5 summarizes this information, which demonstrates that tRNA maturation is more severely restricted in strains lacking RNase E or RNase E and RNase III, as well as RNase P, compared with the single RNase P mutant.

The level of tRNA that matures is very much diminished in the absence of these enzymes, and larger RNA precursors are accumulated (1). The RNA from the various processing mutants at the 4 S to 5 S size range were separated in two-dimensional polyacrylamide gels (Fig. 5). Figure 5a is a two-dimensional gel pattern of tRNAs from a wild-type strain labeled at 43°C for 1 hour. The tRNAs of the *rnc* strain, displayed in Fig. 5b, are all apparently normal. The *rne* strain, panel 5c, shows a fairly normal pattern, but lacks mature 5 S rRNA and a few tRNAs. The molecules accumulating in the 5 S region contain monomeric tRNA precursors (61). It is noteworthy that the *rnp* strain (Fig. 5d) produces an appreciable amount of mature or almost mature-sized tRNA molecules as compared to wild-type cells. Many of these molecules represent the previously described "small monomeric" tRNA precursors (63, 64), which are produced by endonucleases other than RNase P. The 4 S to 5 S RNAs of the *rnc, rne* strain (panel e) are very similar to those of the single *rne* strain (panel c). Combination of the *rnc* allele with *rnp* does not significantly change the pattern of tRNA accumulation from that of the single *rnp* strain, as seen in Fig. 5f. Most dramatically, however, an *rne, rnp* double mutant (panel g) shows a drastic reduction in mature tRNA species and a number of new 5 S-sized species, when compared with the single *rnp* mutant (Fig. 5d). A further decrease in tRNA maturation is found upon combining all three processing mutations. The *rnp, rnc, rne* triple mutant accumulates few if any mature-size tRNA molecules (Fig. 5h). Again, although little difference was detected between *rnp* and *rnp,rnc* strains, the enhanced deficiency in tRNA maturation observed upon introduction of the *rnc* mutation into an *rnp,rne* strain indicates that RNase III is involved in tRNA maturation in *E. coli* (compare Fig. 5g with Fig. 5h).

Most of the RNA species (16, out of 22 tested) in the 4 S to 5 S

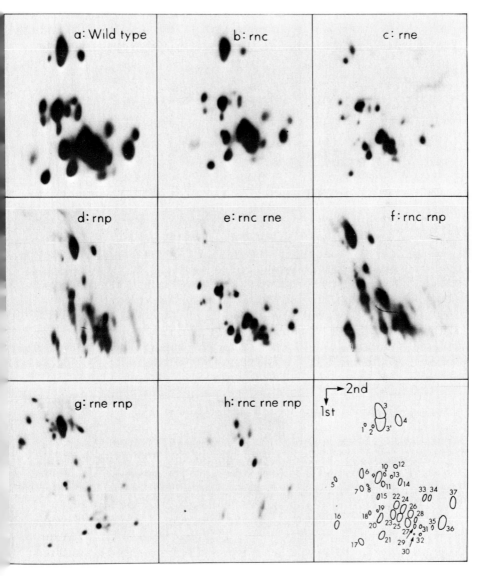

FIG. 5. Transfer RNAs and 5 S rRNA produced in different RNA-processing mutants. Cultures of strains with the indicated genotypes were grown at 30°C, shifted to 43°C, and labeled after 40 min with ³²Pᵢ for 60 min. RNA was fractionated on 10% → 20% two-dimensional polyacrylamide gels (36, 57). Spots 3, 3′, and 4 are 5 S rRNA isomers; the other spots are tRNA—e.g., spot 17 is tRNAᴳˡᵘ (see last panel).

range, which accumulate in an *rnc,rne,rnp* strain at the nonpermissive temperature, are primary transcription products initiated with ATP or GTP (65). The *rnc,rne,rnp* mutant also accumulates large (>6 S) precursors to most cellular tRNAs, which can be processed with a wild-type cell extract to give a pattern of small RNAs indistinguishable from that shown in Fig. 5a (65).

Even though the results alluded to here and shown in Fig. 5 support rather convincingly the notion that RNase E is required for the maturation of tRNA, I consider it more likely that RNase E is not involved directly in tRNA metabolism and that the phenomenon seen in Fig. 5 is a result of interference of the mutant RNase E, in strains containing the mutation *rne-3071*, with another enzyme that normally participates in tRNA processing, most likely RNase F. Such an inhibition can be explained if RNA processing enzymes exist in a complex, or if the mutant RNase E can directly inhibit the activity of the other enzyme (see below). These two mechanisms are not mutually exclusive. The fact that the RNase E cleavage sites in the seven rRNA genes are very conserved (see Fig. 4), and the realization that similar sequences are not found in tRNA precursors that accumulate in the *rne* mutant (61, 62) suggest that indeed the observations in Fig. 5 indicate a very close relationship among the RNA processing enzymes, rather than the involvement of the wild-type RNase E in the maturation of tRNA.

B. Cooperativity of Processing

Our present understanding of the function, efficiency, and order of cleavages of RNase III, E, and P in rRNA processing may be used to assemble a coherent picture of the involvement of these enzymes in tRNA processing. Since most processing of *E. coli* tRNA probably occurs during transcription, the availability of processing sites is governed by the linearity of transcription, as well as by the three-dimensional structure assumed by the newly synthesized sequences. The endonucleolytic cleavages of tRNA transcripts that generate their 5' end are performed by RNase P and another enzyme, a 3' endonuclease(s), which alone or followed by the 3' trimming activity of RNase D (58), or a similar enzyme, produces the mature 3' terminus. In this simple situation, only a 5' endonuclease (RNase P), a 3' endonuclease, and a 3' exonuclease are required to produce mature-sized tRNAs. The endonuclease cuts are not strictly ordered.

An example of strict ordering of endonucleolytic cleavage events is demonstrated in the processing of $tRNA_1^{Ile}$ and $tRNA_{1B}^{Ala}$ from the spacer region of ribosomal RNA transcripts (36–38). In this transcript, endonuclease cleavage at the 3' side of the tRNA$_1^{Ile}$ is a prerequisite for cleavage at the 5' side by RNase P.

Other enzymes also play roles in tRNA processing. RNase III can participate, but is not absolutely required for production of mature tRNAs *in vivo* since RNase-III$^-$ strains are viable (*13–15*). The cellular function of RNase III in tRNA biosynthesis could be to convert large nascent multimeric tRNA transcripts into smaller substrates for which RNase P cleavage is more efficient.

From analysis of tRNA metabolism *in vivo* and *in vitro*, we can conclude that cooperation exists among all the tRNA processing events, and that some but not all of them are ordered. From the available data on tRNA processing, four suggestions can be made: first, that most processing of tRNA occurs during transcription or shortly thereafter; second, that RNase P performs the final 5' maturation of tRNA molecules, and this cleavage cannot be performed by any other enzyme; third, that some transcripts are cleaved near the tRNA 3' termini by RNase "F" or by yet another endonuclease(s); fourth, that (based on genetic evidence) RNase E performs a role *in vivo* compatible with that attributed to "P2" (*66, 67*) activity (or, that the mutant RNase E inhibits RNase "P2" activity, see above), and that "O" activity is performed by RNase III (and is hence a dispensable function). All these endonucleases act synergistically to process mature transfer RNA species from nascent tRNA gene transcripts.

VII. mRNA and the RNA-Processing Enzymes

Considerable attention has been focused on the possibility of processing the host mRNAs. At least one host mRNA appears to be cleaved *in vivo* (*68*), and expression of many genes is altered in cells defective in one or more processing enzymes. However, mutations in the enzymes RNase III, E, or P do not seem to affect the stability of host mRNA (*23, 56*).

Both RNase III and RNase E seem to be required at 43°C for full expression of a significant number of proteins in *E. coli* (*69*). The differential induction of the *lacZ* gene, as well as the amount of β-galactosidase protein, is reduced in *rnc-105* or *rne-3071* strains at 43°C compared to 30°C. In the double *rnc,rne* mutant, this reduction is even more pronounced. Moreover, analysis of total cell protein separated in two-dimensional gels revealed that the synthesis of 21 out of 80 individual proteins examined was markedly decreased in the *rnc,rne,rnp* strain at 43°C, and that this difference is caused mainly by the *rnc* and the *rne* mutations (*69*).

Another interesting and presently unexplained effect of the *rnc-105* mutation is that *rnc-105* strains are nonmotile because they are defective in the production of flagella (*70*). Whether this results from a failure to process a specific mRNA, or simply from the known sensitivity of flagellar production to a variety of physiological perturbations, has not been determined. These results, while not demonstrating mRNA processing, do open up such a possibility. While these intriguing observations could be due to the failure of the mutants to process mRNA, other possibilities, such as effects on synthesis, stability, and utilization of mRNA are not excluded.

Using λ bacteriophage it was found that RNase III introduces cleavages in the "N message" of λ, and in the absence of RNase III, it has been possible to show for the first time that indeed the RNA from the pL promoter is a single large RNA that is cleaved by RNase III (*71*).

VIII. Processing of Bacteriophage T4 tRNA

The analysis of RNA processing described in the foregoing is impaired by the fact that with respect to rRNA there are seven different rRNA gene clusters with a certain amount of heterogeneity among them, and there are numerous tRNA and mRNA molecules. The T4 tRNA system provides a simpler system for analysis of RNA processing.

When T4 infects *E. coli*, host RNA synthesis stops; therefore, in a successful experiment, all the new tRNA-size molecules are derived from T4. Since T4 uses the *E. coli* host enzymes such as RNase P for the processing of its RNA (*72*), we anticipated that it might use other host RNA-processing enzymes as well. There are eight tRNA genes in bacteriophage T4; all are adjacent in the genome and are transcribed from a single promoter (*72*). The same transcription unit contains also two small, relatively stable RNAs of unknown function, Species 1 and 2. Since Species-1 and -2 RNA are conserved among different T-even bacteriophages, it is expected that they are likely to have a function (*73*).

There are also a series of deletions in this region of the T4 genome, and we chose for our work an internal deletion that removes six of the tRNAs and Species-2 RNA. Thus, in this deletion strain, T4Δ27, only the genes for tRNA^{Gln} tRNA^{Leu} and Species-1 RNA (in this order) exist in the tRNA gene cluster. Therefore, when bacteriophage T4Δ27 infects the *E. coli* cell, these three RNAs are major constituents (Fig. 6).

While we were studying T4 tRNA processing, a report appeared showing that when T4Δ27 infects the *E. coli* RNase III⁻ mutant,

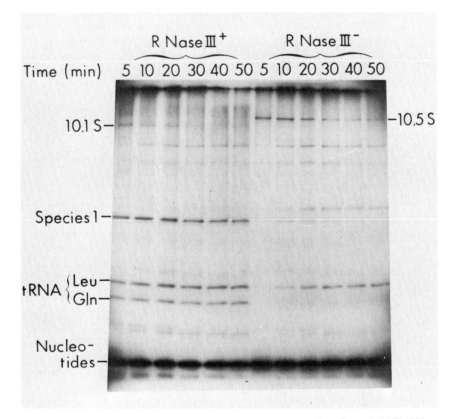

FIG. 6. Small RNA molecules in rnc^+ (N2076, RNase III$^+$) and rnc (N2077, RNase III$^-$) strains after infection with T4Δ27. The cells were grown in Tris-based medium containing 0.6% (w/v) peptone at 37°C. ^{32}P$_i$ (0.2 mCi/ml) was added to the cultures 5 min after infection. Samples were withdrawn at the indicated times (time after labeling) and were treated as described by Gegenheimer *et al.* (*17*). The picture shown here is of an autoradiogram of the 10% portion of the gel. The top fifth of the gel, which consists of 5% (w/v) polyacrylamide, was removed after the gel was dried. The gel contained 7 M urea, and each slot was loaded with about 250,000 cpm. Below the tRNA^{Gln} band there are two smaller RNAs (X1 and X2), the one that migrates slower is referred to as X1. For further details, see the text and Fig. 7.

tRNA^{Gln} appears at very low concentrations, if at all, while the other two molecules, tRNA^{Leu} and Species 1, do accumulate (*74*). This finding was rather puzzling, since tRNA^{Gln} is proximal to the other two RNAs and no precursor was found.

In our studies, when the rnc cell was infected with T4Δ27, we did find a precursor that could be processed to tRNA^{Gln} and tRNA^{Leu}, but we also found that tRNA^{Gln} did not accumulate (*75*). In a more detailed analysis, we compared T4 tRNA metabolism after infection of rnc^+ and rnc isogenic pair with T4Δ27 (see Fig. 6). We found that early in the infection in the rnc^+ strain, a 10.1 S RNA appears that contains all the three RNAs tRNA^{Gln}, tRNA^{Leu}, and Species 1, plus extra nucleotides at the 5' and 3' ends (76). At the 5' end there are only six extra nucleotides, while at the 3' end there are about 80 nucleotides distal to Species 1 (77). The 3' region of this RNA contains a stem and loop structure typical to an RNA terminated independently from the rho termination factor (78–80).

In the rnc mutant a larger RNA, 10.5 S, accumulates, but, like 10.1 S RNA, it is also a transient species. Compared to 10.1 S RNA, it contains extra nucleotides at the 5' end. In vitro, RNase III can process 10.5 S RNA to 10.1 S RNA (76), which accumulates in an rne mutant (77). Extracts of an rnc^+ strain can process 10.5 S to the three RNAs (tRNA^{Gln}, tRNA^{Leu}, and Species 1), while in extracts from an rnc mutant, the level of tRNA^{Gln} is very much reduced (76). However, both extracts can process 10.1 S RNA normally to the three final species. Thus, it became clear that the region at the 5' end of 10.5 S RNA has first to be removed, by RNase III, before the rest of the RNA can be processed further. Indeed, RNase P cannot find its sites either in the 10.5 S or in the 10.1 S RNA (unpublished observations). In the absence of RNase III, this region is removed by nonspecific nucleases that cut into the tRNA^{Gln} region, and therefore the level of tRNA^{Gln} is very much reduced.

This alternative nonspecific degradative pathway is apparently also in operation in the wild-type rnc^+ strain, since even in rnc^+ strains the level of tRNA^{Gln} is somewhat reduced, as compared to the level of tRNA^{Leu} (76). We have found that in general this viewpoint is correct, but it contains a subtle twist. The two tRNAs, tRNA^{Gln} and tRNA^{Leu}, can be isolated in a single dimeric precursor K RNA (81) that appears after infecting an rnp strain with T4Δ27 (72, 77, 81). This RNA contains six extra nucleotides at its 5' end. It also contains two cleavage sites for RNase P (see Fig. 7) at the 5' end of each tRNA. The middle site is processed preferentially. When an rnc rnp cell is infected with T4Δ27, a molecule appears that is like K RNA but is missing four nucleotides at the 5' end (Gurevitz and Apirion, in press). This is because in the absence of RNase III the nonspecific nuclease(s) degrade the 10.5 S RNA to this point, since the tRNA portion of the molecule is rather compact and resists degradation. This RNA, even though it is missing only four nucleotides at its 5' end, is not as good a substrate for RNase P; even though RNase P still can cleave both sites, the efficiency for the first site is even lower than in the K molecule.

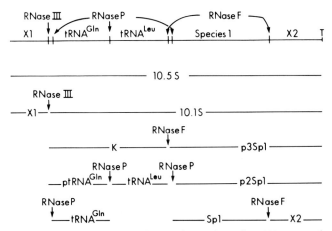

FIG. 7. A schematic processing pathway of RNA from the tRNA gene cluster in the bacteriophage T4Δ27. The precursors 10.5 S and 10.1 S RNA and the final products, Species 1, tRNA^{Leu}, tRNA^{Gln}, X1 and X2 RNAs, can be observed in Fig. 6. For further details, see 76 and 77.

This is apparently of sufficient significance *in vivo* to render this part of the precursor molecule completely sensitive to degradation by nucleases. The tRNA^{Gln} gene does not contain CCA. These nucleotides are added later (33, 72), and in its final conformation tRNA^{Gln} is obviously much more resistant to cellular nucleases than in the precursor form; in the tRNA^{Leu} gene, the CCA is encoded.

While RNase III introduces the first cleavage into the T4 tRNA transcript, converting 10.5 S to 10.1 S RNA, another enzyme(s) has to separate the K portion from Species 1 and finally a cleavage has to take place at the 3′ end of Species 1 (see Fig. 7). We thought that this enzyme could be RNase E because, when T4Δ27 infects an *rne* mutant, the proper intermediates that could result from such cleavage accumulate (10.1 S RNA and p2Sp1) (77). [10.1 S contains the three RNAs, while p2Sp1 contains only Species 1 and the 3′ end (see Fig. 7).] We soon realized that the enzyme that introduces these cleavages is not RNase E, since even in its absence these cleavages can take place, albeit less efficiently, *in vitro* and *in vivo* (77). This led us eventually to the concept of an RNA processing complex (Section IX).

Since the enzyme that cleaves after Species 1 was not RNase E, we used p2Sp1, which is easy to obtain, and searched for an enzyme that can introduce such a cleavage. The activity we call RNase "F" (82) can do just that. This activity can be clearly distinguished from the other three endonucleolytic RNA processing enzymes: RNases III, E, and P (82). This activity introduces a cleavage that results in a 5'-OH and 3'-phosphate (83), while the other three enzymes create a 5'-phosphate and a 3'-OH. A schematic presentation of RNA processing from the tRNA gene cluster in bacteriophage T4Δ27 is presented in Fig. 7.

IX. The Concept of an RNA Processing Complex

It was mentioned in Sections VI and VIII that some of the findings were rather puzzling. For instance, in an *rne* mutant we found tRNA precursors (61, 62), and also after T4 infection of an *rne* mutant we found p2Sp1 (77). In both cases, and definitely in the last case, the precursors did not contain cleavage sites for RNase E. More extraordinary was the finding that while an extract of an *rne*+ strain at the elevated temperature will process 10.1 S RNA to the three RNAs: tRNA^{Gln}, tRNA^{Leu}, and Species-1 RNA, an *rne* extract will do it at 30 °C but not at 43°C; at 43°C the RNase P activity is inhibited and the processing will stop before RNase P action, and the K dimer accumulates (77). These studies were further pursued, and we could show, using 10.1 S RNA as a substrate, that extracts from an *rnc* or from an *rne* mutant could be made to behave like extracts of an RNase P⁻ strain (84).

One appealing concept to explain these results was to assume that the RNA processing enzymes exist in a complex, and therefore a mutation in one of them could affect the activity of the others. This concept of a complex was further supported by the following finding. There are at least two or three genes, mutations in which give rise to *rnp* mutants *rnpA*, *rnpB*, and *rnpC* (35, 85–87). The RNase-P enzyme is composed of a protein and an RNA moiety (88–92). In *rnpB* mutants, the RNA moiety does not accumulate; however, introduction of a plasmid that overproduces this RNA does not complement the *rnpB* defect (87, 93). These findings could be easily explained if the *rnpB* gene specifies a component of the RNA processing complex and therefore a mutation in it would affect the accumulation of the RNA moiety. This concept is very reasonable, since we found that the RNA of RNase P is much less stable in an *rnpB* mutant than in an *rnpA* mutant or in the *rnp*+ strain (G. Dallman and D. Apirion, unpublished observations).

Moreover, using an *rne* mutant we isolated a double mutant *rne,rng* in which, after infection with T4Δ27, only 10.1 S RNA is accumulated see (Fig. 7). In the *rne* mutant (77) there is some processing and maturation of all the three RNAs. We hoped to isolate a mutant defective in RNase "F." However, when we separated the double mutant, the *rng* single mutant behaved somewhat like an *rnp* mutant. In the *rng* mutant after infection with T4Δ27, the K RNA accumulated, but there was also some processing of the tRNA molecules, and extracts of an *rng* mutant contained RNase P activity that could be differentially destroyed (as compared to an *rng*$^+$ strain) by heating the extract (*93a*).

Considering the enzyme RNase P, it seems to me to be a very large RNA (about 130,000 M_r) and a very small protein (about 17,500 M_r). I suspect that in the cell other proteins, including the RNA processing enzymes, are associated, albeit loosely, with this RNP particle (RNase P). The RNA of RNase P in extracts is rather vulnerable to cellular nucleases, and therefore extracts of various mutants that are affected in the complex under certain conditions lose rather easily the RNase P activity. It might be possible to isolate the complex, but it is rather fragile. However, it was possible to cosediment the three RNA processing enzymes in a gravitational field and to some extent in a sucrose gradient (*84*).

X. General Considerations

A. Unity of RNA Processing Mechanisms

The prokaryotic cell, as we have seen, employs a very limited number of nucleolytic activities to accomplish the processing of a variety of RNA transcripts. Indeed, each of the three endoribonucleases of *E. coli*—RNase III, RNase E, and RNase P—plays a role in processing both ribosomal and transfer RNA transcripts. Intracellular parasites, such as the DNA bacteriophages, have evolved so that their RNA transcripts can be processed by host enzymes. Processing of tRNAs and other stable RNAs in T-even and related phages, as well as of messenger RNAs in T3, T7, and λ, is performed by host enzymes (*2, 72*).

B. Function of Polycistronic Transcription and Processing

As Pace originally suggested (*94*) one explanation of precursor-specific sequences in monomeric rRNA precursors is that they are remnants of the recognition sites for the enzymes that generate those precursors. This consideration could be true for tRNA precursors as well. The larger question, however, is the physiological necessity or usefulness of polycistronic transcription of stable RNAs.

Five primary advantages for polycistronic transcription of stable

RNAs can be considered. First, production of equimolar amounts of functionally interdependent molecules, such as ribosomal RNAs, is achieved. Second, cotranscription of rRNAs allows coordinated and orderly sequential assembly of the complex ribonucleoprotein structure of the ribosomal subunits (60). Third, the termini of RNA species are protected during transcription and until the molecule is functional. As an example, endonucleolytic cleavage of rRNA transcripts releases p16 and p23 rRNA precursors (16, 17) whose 5' and 3' termini are paired in a duplex stem resistant to degradative cellular nucleases (24, 95). Since the 3' terminal portion of m16 RNA, for example, must carry out a crucial function in translation, protection of p16 from exonuclease attack is beneficial until the m16 portion, plus ribosomal proteins, can assume the mature, nuclease-resistant (96) conformation of the ribosome, at which time specific maturation endonuclease(s) can safely expose the functional ends. Likewise, precursor tRNAs may be protected from nonspecific degradation—in particular, irreparable excessive removal of 3' terminal sequences—by being present in a long (nascent) transcript until the mature portion of the tRNA has assumed its correct (RNase-resistant) configuration. Fourth, processing of RNA molecules provides the possibility for regulation of stable RNA gene expression, at the posttranscriptional level, by a physiologically controlled balance between productive processing and decay. Processing vs degradation of tRNA precursors has been described and discussed elsewhere (32, 97–99). Five, I suggest that, in order to economize in promoters and terminators for RNAs that are needed in large quantities, they were arranged in groups; this necessitates processing. This idea was suggested by us previously to explain why there are tRNAs cotranscribed with rRNA (52).

One potentially exciting role for precursor-specific sequences could be actively to regulate RNA conformational folding (100). Study of *Bacillus subtilis* p5 rRNA by Pace and co-workers has shown that the first six bases of the precursor are hydrogen-bonded to an immediately adjacent precursor-specific sequence. These latter sequences would otherwise base-pair with an internal region of the m5 portion of the precursor, resulting in an abnormal conformation for the RNA (100). This fact in itself, however, does not explain why any precursor-specific sequences should interact with mature sequences, since isolated m5 rRNA can assume an apparently normal conformation without the aid of precursor-specific sequences. Further work, perhaps with mutants affecting RNA structure, will be required to elucidate the roles of processing and precursor-specific sequences. Similar studies of mutations in mature tRNA sequences have yielded important information on tRNA structure and processing (reviewed in *32, 97–99, 101–104*).

C. Specificity and Efficiency of RNA Processing Reactions

What specific structural elements are recognized by RNA processing enzymes? Since the role of processing events is ultimately to produce mature functional RNA molecules, one could expect that recognition of the mature RNA portion of the precursor transcript would be required. The mature portion contains information indicative not only of the generic species of RNA but also of its "readiness" to be productively processed, as determined by whether or not it has assumed its final and functional configuration. RNase P and *B. subtilis* RNase M5 have been shown to recognize predominantly the mature domain of their respective substrates (*102, 105*). Likewise, maturation of p16 rRNA precursor by RNase(s) M16 appears to require a properly assembled rRNA-protein complex (*7–9, 106*). Since RNase-III cleavage of rRNA transcripts does not generate functional termini, it need not recognize the mature domain; but since it generates base-paired precursor termini, processing by RNase III requires an intact duplex structure.

At present, however, little can be said about such structure–function relationships in processing of phage or host mRNAs. The rationale of processing may well be regulatory, but much more remains to be learned. It is attractive, nonetheless, to imagine that processing enzymes might recognize and cleave a particular configuration, or one of several alternative configurations adopted in a region of an mRNA molecule involved in regulation of its own transcription or translation.

All of the processing endonucleases known thus far—RNases III, E, and P, and *B. subtilis* RNase M5—recognize their substrates only after the 5' and 3' termini are base-paired. The double-stranded nature of these processing substrates may serve the purpose of ensuring that endonuclease cleavages that could otherwise occur during transcription do not take place until transcription of the entire substrate is completed and proper RNA folding has occurred. This also applies to some extent to the yeast enzyme that removes intervening sequences from precursor tRNA molecules. In this case, the substrate for this enzyme contains the aminoacyl stem comprising nucleotides upstream and downstream from the nucleotides excised (*72*).

From these considerations, it can be anticipated that cleavages that produce mature termini cannot be bypassed, whereas other cleavages can be bypassed or performed at slightly different locations by other enzymes. All available experimental evidence supports this view: for example, inactivation of RNase P is a lethal event, since mature tRNA 5' termini are not formed. Inactivation of RNase III is not lethal, however, since nascent rRNA transcripts are cleaved by the remaining enzymes (RNases E, F, and P), and p16b and p23b rRNA precursors, which can be processed successfully to mature m16 and m23 rRNA, are formed. Since inactivation of RNase III does, however, drastically reduce the efficiency of the remaining RNA processing steps, a second point becomes clear: cleavages that do not directly yield mature termini, and those that convert polycistronic transcripts to monocistronic precursors, act in concert with other cleavages to enhance the overall efficiency of an RNA processing pathway. The order of such cleavages is largely determined by the order in which their substrates become available during transcription, in a conformation recognized by the appropriate enzyme.

Another point that should be mentioned is that the transcription machinery of the bacterial cell does not seem to require "feedback" signals from processed RNAs, since transcription of precursors for ribosomal and for transfer RNAs continues unabated in the absence of processing by RNases III, P, and E (see Fig. 2 and 17 and 57).

Bearing these considerations in mind, then, one can offer a general principle governing enzymatic recognition and processing of RNA transcripts. A relatively limited number of processing enzymes, principally endonucleases, acting on a few fundamentally distinctive processing signals, carry out a broad range of distinct, highly specific, and well-ordered processing steps. By their concerted action these enzymes accomplish efficiently the processing of RNA transcripts.

XI. Processing of RNA in Prokaryotic and Eukaryotic Cells: Evolution of Intervening Sequences

A. Prokaryotic and Eukaryotic Cells

It is rather appealing to suggest that the patchy eukaryotic gene is the primitive one and that the prokaryotic uninterrupted gene is the more advanced, or evolved, gene. Indeed, a number of students of this problem prefer this view (111–113). However, the overall complexity of the eukaryotic cell and especially the complex and elaborate nucleus with the ability to go through extremely elaborate cell cycles, mitosis and meiosis, makes the possibility of the prokaryotic cell being a stripped, economy version of a eukaryotic cell rather unappealing.

Moreover, as is discussed below, the absence of a nucleus and the presence of a coupled transcription translation system preclude the possibility of using intervening sequences in genes coding for proteins, since transcription is terminated in such systems in the absence of translation. Therefore it was only with the evolution of the nucleus and the separation of transcription from translation that the transcription machinery had "to learn" how to complete transcripts without terminating them in the absence of protein synthesis. Only with the evolution of these facets of cell biology could intervening sequences have become useful to the cell, since it could have coped with transcription in the absence of protein synthesis, a property that the prokaryotic cell does not have.

If, as is more or less accepted now, prokaryotic-type cells preceded cells with nuclei by a few billion years (*114*), it is unlikely that the genes of these ancient prokaryotic cells contained intervening sequences in a manner similar to that found presently in many eukaryotic genes. Therefore we must come up with an explanation for how the patchy eukaryotic gene evolved from the compact and "elegant" prokaryotic gene.

B. The Guiding Principle

Students of evolution maintain—and one can see the logic of such an argument—that by and large a feature found in an organism could not have been established there unless when it first arose it conferred some selective advantage on the individual. Therefore, I shall try to point out what could have been and still is the immediate advantage to the eukaryotic cell of chopping and splicing its RNA transcripts. The basic idea I would like to develop is that *the excision and splicing affects the three-dimensional structure of the RNA molecule in a way that helps it achieve greater protection from nucleases, and hence stability.*

C. Are Intervening Sequences Unique to Eukaryotic Cells?

We know at present that intervening sequences (or patched up genes) *do exist* in prokaryotic cells. (For a good treatment of this area, see articles in *115*). However, there is a fundamental difference: while in eukaryotic cells this is a standard feature of many genes, in each population of prokaryotic cells some cells contain patched genes that arose by the insertion of extra DNA sequences. This could come from bacteriophages such as mu or from insertion sequences, or from transposons (*115*). Although in the eukaryotic cell an elaborate mechanism

evolved to ensure the proper expression of patched genes, in prokaryotes such a mechanism apparently did not evolve; such genes are
functionally inactive, and are diluted out from the population.

D. The Relevance of Having Separated Transcription from Translation to the Problem of Patched Genes

In the prokaryotic cell, in genes that include inserted DNA, the
following events take place. When transcription starts, soon after
ribosomal initiation sites are formed, ribosomes join the messengers
and translation commences. However, when the inserted DNA is
transcribed, nonsense codons sooner or later are formed and the ribosomes fall off and transcription stops, either dependently or independently of the rho termination factor. [For a detailed discussion of transcription termination in prokaryotes, see 78–80.]

Thus, the presence of an insertion in a gene of a prokaryotic cell
brings about termination of transcription. This is not the case in the
eukaryotic cell, where the nucleus spatially separates transcription
from translation. Since such a situation could have led on the one hand
to premature termination of transcription (78) and on the other hand to
immediate degradation of the transcribed RNA (116), at some point the
eukaryotic cell had to invent a system that would prevent premature
termination of transcription and decay of untranslated RNAs. This
could have been achieved by attaching some protein(s) to the growing

Once the problem of preventing premature termination is solved,
the presence of inserted sequences in the gene poses no difficulties
during transcription; therefore when an occasional insertion took
place, RNA synthesis of all the patched gene could continue unabated.

It should be mentioned here that also in prokaryotic cells the tRNA
and rRNA genes are transcribed without being translated. Therefore
one could expect that insertion of extra sequences in one of these genes
will not lead to termination of transcription and therefore these genes
could potentially contain intervening sequences even in prokaryotic
cells.

E. A Difference between DNA and RNA Relevant to This Discussion

Pro- and eukaryotic cells contain specific enzymes—"nicking-
closing" enzymes (117), DNA topoisomerases (118, 119), etc.—that
can break and seal DNA. Thus it is possible for a cell to twist and turn
DNA molecules in a most astonishing way. On the other hand, such

mechanisms are not known for RNA, and therefore the larger the RNA molecule is, the more difficult it should be for the cell to stitch and shape it into any particular three-dimensional structure.

F. Why Can Eukaryotic Cells, but Not Prokaryotic Cells, Benefit from a Mechanism That Allows a Certain Flexibility in Shaping the Three-Dimensional Structure of an RNA Molecule?

Let us consider the major RNA molecules in a prokaryotic cell. These are the messenger, ribosomal, and transfer RNAs. The mature tRNAs are rather small; achieving their three-dimensional structure should not pose any special problems. There are only three species of rRNA that are remarkably similar among prokaryotes. Since the 5 S RNA is rather small, this leaves us with only two RNA molecules the 16 S and 23 S rRNA that had to "learn" how to achieve a complex three-dimensional structure. The 16 S rRNA of *E. coli* is a very complex structure indeed. It is 1542 nucleotides long and contains a very large amount of secondary structure, but it is free of knots (*120, 121*). Knots undoubtedly would interfere with proper folding, and it is likely that the structure of hnRNA (heterogeneous nuclear RNA) in the nucleus must also be devoid of knots. It is possible to comprehend that the two large rRNA molecules, 16 S and 23 S, could have arrived at their present-day three-dimensional structure during a lengthy evolutionary process, and that once the proper forms were established they were conserved rather carefully throughout the biological kingdom (*121*).

Interestingly, it seems now that in a number of bacteria the 23 S rRNA is actually in two pieces (*122*, and references therein). This might reflect the difficulty of the large 23 S rRNA to attain its necessary three-dimensional structure as a single RNA molecule. This could explain why in mitochondria (*123, 124*) only the large rRNA contains an intervening sequence. If this idea is correct, it also predicts that intervening sequences are unlikely to be found in rRNA genes that code for the RNA of the small ribosomal subunit.

The bulk of the RNA species in the bacterial cell are the mRNAs. Since they do not exist as complete molecules before they have to be used, mRNAs do not require a very elaborate three-dimensional structure; but rather, as soon as a part of the molecule is made, ribosomes are attached to them and protein synthesis starts. Therefore, the prokaryotic mRNA molecule does not require a very elaborate three-dimensional structure.

It is becoming progressively clearer that, in bacteria, mRNA unprotected by ribosomes is vulnerable to destruction by ribonucleases (116, 125). In the eukaryotic cell, on the other hand, mRNA molecules are relatively stable (126–129). They must first be formed, and then transported to the cytoplasm, where they are translated. In other words, there are very many RNA molecules, not just two, as in the prokaryotic cell, that require careful orchestration into appropriate three-dimensional structures.

Since, in the eukaryotic cell, mRNA half-life is measured in hours and days (126, 129) rather than in seconds or minutes, as in the prokaryote (116, 130), it is clear that in the eukaryotic cell there is a great premium on mRNA stability. The particular folding of the mRNA molecule could help, by providing by itself a certain amount of protection from nucleases, or by permitting specific associations with proteins to produce particular RNP particles that might afford better protection from nucleases.

G. How an RNA Molecule Can Be Cut Rather Than Degraded by a Ribonuclease

From the study of processing of RNA in bacteria, it is known that there are enzymes that can introduce specific cuts into RNA molecules (see Sections V, VI, and VIII). RNase III (Fig. 3), RNase E (Fig. 4), and RNase M5 (105) cut RNA molecules at or near stems, to create an open loop and two ends. While the prokaryotic cell is "interested" in the looped part of the processed RNA, the eukaryotic cell is "interested" in the ends. Obviously those inserted sequences that resemble, in their junction region, signals recognizable by a processing enzyme can become successfully established. It is also useful to mention in this context that we already know from studies of RNA processing in E. coli that the specificity of the processing cuts is not affected by the size of the substrate (17, 57), and therefore the size of the intervening sequence could vary without much effect on the processing reaction.

H. Splicing

The last part in the puzzle is how to splice the cut RNA molecule. Here we can fall back on two precedents: the T4-infected E. coli contains an RNA ligase that could ligate "blunt" ends (131), and the DNA ligase can do the same for DNA molecules, under proper conditions (132). Thus, all that is necessary is to bring together these two abilities: the one that can process an RNA molecule, and the other that can ligate an RNA molecule.

In summary, we can see how from the known systems in prokaryotic cells a mechanism could have evolved for inserting sequences into DNA and for slicing and splicing the resultant RNA molecules. Such a process would allow the various RNA molecules to assume three-dimensional structures they could not otherwise have, and these could endow them with the necessary increased stability.

If these arguments are of any value, they make it obvious why chloroplasts (133) and mitochondria (123), which are presumably pro-karyotic in nature, could have used intervening sequences to their advantage in the eukaryotic milieu.

One obvious corollary of these suggestions is that the three-dimensional structure of an mRNA before it is translated is unique and is not coded in its sequence. In other words, if such an RNA is dena-tured, it should not be able to renature to the same original configura-tion. However, one should keep in mind that part of the configuration could result from protein–RNA interactions in the RNP particles; therefore, experimenting with the naked RNA might be insufficient.

It was established that in *Tetrahymena* an intervening sequence in the rRNA is sliced and ligated without the intervention of any enzyme (134). This raises the possibility that the evolution of intervening se-quences in general did not require participation of enzymes and there-fore is completely unrelated to RNA processing in prokaryotic cells.

It is important to point out that, in the case of the intervening sequences in yeast tRNA genes, there are at least two enzymes in-volved in the reaction, one for slicing and the other for ligation (72). Moreover, in wheat germ there is an RNA ligase that is an excellent candidate to participate in RNA processing reactions (135). In addi-tion, the sequences at the exon–intron boundaries in the intervening sequence in the rRNA gene of *Tetrahymena* are different from the canonical sequences found in the exon–intron junctions of numerous genes (113). Therefore, the rRNA gene of *Tetrahymena* could repre-sent a specific case of splicing without enzymes. Moreover, the effi-ciency of this self-splicing reaction is rather low (134), and the cell might contain proteins (enzymes) that facilitate splicing. Furthermore, while the discovery of a self-splicing RNA (134) could indicate that it originated in prebiotic times, it could also, on the other hand, be viewed as a relatively recent development.

In all or many RNA processing cleavages, a good part of the specificity could lie in the substrate. The enzyme could be derived from a nonspecific nuclease, and the specificity could be provided by various limitations on the potential cleavage sites derived from the secondary and/or tertiary structure of the RNA molecule. This could be helped by the evolution of an RNA molecule that contains a relatively sensitive site to cleavage, and this could become the preferential, but not the only, cleavage site. It is known that some of the processing enzymes, especially RNase III, but also RNase P, can cleave a substrate at more than a single site. The preferential cleavage site could be sufficiently destabilized by the structure of the RNA to permit spontaneous cleavage to occur.

Regardless of whether or not intervening sequences are spliced by enzymes, the considerations, discussed here, why they cannot be used in prokaryotic genes because they will interrupt transcription are still valid.

I. Phylogenetic Considerations

Once the insertion–excision–splicing mechanism was established, it enabled "patched" genes to be spread in the population. The establishment of such genes permitted further developments, such as shuffling blocks of polypeptides (*136, 137*) and thus, on a population and phylogenetic, but not ontogenetic basis, increased the amount of genetic variability (*137*).

For example, it has been shown that different forms of immunoglobulin μ chains are translated from different mRNAs (*138, 139*), which could be derived, by excision and splicing, from the same primary RNA transcript (*140, 141*). Such features of the intervening sequences are most likely later developments in the evolution of multicellular organisms, but are not the reasons why intervening sequences became established in the first place.

Thus, I envisage in this scheme the progression of evolution from the "simple" prokaryotic gene to the "patched" eukaryotic gene (which evolved as a consequence of the separation of transcription from translation), to very complex families of patchy genes, which could offer biological advantages to complex organisms.

XII. Conclusions and Suggestions

1. All "stable" RNAs and some messages in *E. coli* are "processed."

2. Most "stable" RNA transcripts are processed by more than a single endonuclease.

3. Most of the processing of rRNA and tRNA occurs during transcription.

4. Transcription of RNA is independent of its processing.

5. The enzymes responsible for most processing of stable RNA transcripts in *E. coli* are four endoribonucleases—RNases III, E, F, and P—and at least one exonuclease, e.g., as RNase D; some, perhaps all, of these enzymes might exist in a complex.

6. A given ribonuclease, by and large, fulfills either a degradative or a processing function.

7. The efficiency but not the specificity of processing cuts is affected by the size of the substrate; multiple cleavages facilitate efficient and accurate processing, but not all the steps are essential.

8. Some processing steps are completely dependent on the occurrence of an earlier step.

9. Processing endonucleases are highly specific, and each performs a unique function. Their recognition sites may be composed of unique combinations of secondary and tertiary structure.

10. In some processing events, the substrate is not "naked" RNA, but RNA in a ribonucleoprotein particle.

11. The order of processing steps is governed primarily by the order in which substrate recognition signals become available. A certain amount of flexibility exists in the order of initial processing events, but the final steps, which generate the mature RNA termini, must be preserved. These final cleavages are performed by enzymes that recognize the "mature" domains of the substrate in its final conformation.

12. The complex eukaryotic gene containing intervening sequences evolved from the simpler prokaryotic gene during or after the evolution of the nucleus.

ACKNOWLEDGMENTS

It is a great pleasure to thank all my co-workers who coauthored with me the papers that provided some of the material for the treatise presented here. I am very proud and gratified to have been associated with these people during the years. While they deserve the credit for the useful information produced in my laboratory, I myself am responsible for any misinterpretations presented here. A special note of appreciation is due my former student Peter Gegenheimer, who worked with me on a number of reviews that influenced the writing of this paper. The experimental work from my laboratory was supported by a Public Health Grant GM19821 from the National Institute of Health.

REFERENCES

1. D. Apirion and P. Gegenheimer, *FEBS Lett.* **125**, 109 (1981).
2. P. Gegenheimer and D. Apirion, *Microbiol. Rev.* **45**, 502 (1981).
3. D. Apirion and P. Gegenheimer, in "RNA Processing." CRC Press, Boca Raton, Florida, 1983.
4. S. C. Weatherford, L. Rosen, L. Gorelic, and D. Apirion, *JBC* **247**, 5404 (1972).
5. G. Corte, D. Schlessinger, D. Longo, and P. Venkov, *JMB* **60**, 325 (1971).
6. A. Yuki, *JMB* **62**, 321 (1971).
7. B. Meyhack, I. Meyhack, and D. Apirion, *FEBS Lett.* **49**, 215 (1974).
8. F. Hayes and M. Vasseur, *EJB* **61**, 433 (1976).
9. A. E. Dahlberg, J. E. Dahlberg, E. Lund, H. Tokimatsu, A. B. Rabson, P. C. Calvert, F. Reynolds, and M. Zahalak, *PNAS* **75**, 3598 (1978).
10. R. Kaplan and D. Apirion, *JBC* **249**, 149 (1974).
11. R. Kaplan and D. Apirion, *JBC* **250**, 1854 (1975).
12. R. Kaplan and D. Apirion, *JBC* **250**, 3174 (1975).
13. P. Kindler, T. U. Keil, and P. H. Hofschneider, *Mol. Gen. Genet.* **126**, 53 (1973).

14. D. Apirion and N. Watson, *Mol. Gen. Genet.* **132**, 89 (1974).
15. D. Apirion and N. Watson, *J. Bact.* **124**, 317 (1975).
16. P. Gegenheimer and D. Apirion, *JBC* **250**, 2407 (1975).
17. P. Gegenheimer, N. Watson, and D. Apirion, *JBC* **252**, 3064 (1977).
18. D. Apirion, J. Neil, and N. Watson, *Mol. Gen. Genet.* **149**, 201 (1976).
19. J. J. Dunn and F. W. Studier, *PNAS* **70**, 3296 (1973).
20. N. Nikolaev, L. Silengo, and D. Schlessinger, *PNAS* **70**, 3361 (1973).
21. D. Apirion, J. Neil, and N. Watson, *Mol. Gen. Genet.* **144**, 185 (1976).
22. H. D. Robertson, R. E. Webster, and N. D. Zinder, *JBC* **243**, (1968).
23. D. Apirion and N. Watson, *Mol. Gen. Genet.* **136**, 317 (1975).
24. P. Gegenheimer and D. Apirion, *NARes* **8**, 1873 (1980).
25. B. K. Ghora and D. Apirion, *JMB* **127**, 507 (1979).
26. P. Gegenheimer, N. Watson, and D. Apirion, *in* "Molecular Mechanisms in the Control of Gene Expression" (D. P. Nierlich, W. J. Rutter, and C. F. Fox, eds.), p. 405. Academic Press, New York, 1976.
27. M. A. Caras, S. C. Bailey, and D. Apirion, *FEBS Lett.* **74**, 283 (1977).
28. S. C. Bailey and D. Apirion, *J. Bact.* **131**, 347 (1977).
29. T. D. Doerr and D. Apirion, *J. Bact.* **135**, 274 (1978).
30. E. Lund, J. E. Dahlberg, L. Lindahl, S. R. Jaskunas, P. P. Dennis, and M. Nomura, *Cell* **7**, 165 (1976).
31. E. Lund and J. E. Dahlberg, *Cell* **11**, 247 (1977).
32. S. Altman, *Cell* **4**, 21 (1975).
33. W. H. McClain, *Acc. Chem. Res.* **10**, 418 (1977).
34. P. Schedl and P. Primakoff, *PNAS* **70**, 2091 (1973).
35. D. Apirion, *Genetics* **94**, 291 (1980).
36. P. Gegenheimer and D. Apirion, *Cell* **15**, 527 (1978).
37. P. Gegenheimer and D. Apirion, *JMB* **143**, 227 (1980).
38. E. Lund, J. E. Dahlberg, and C. Guthrie, *in* "Transfer RNA: Biological Aspects" (D. Söll, J. Abelson, and P. Schimmel, eds.), p. 123. Cold Spring Harbor Laboratory, Cold Spring Harbor, New York, 1980.
39. J. J. Dunn and F. W. Studier, *PNAS* **70**, 1559 (1973).
40. D. Apirion, J. Neil, T. S. Ko, and N. Watson, *Genetics* **90**, 19 (1978).
41. D. Apirion and A. B. Lassar, *JBC* **253**, 1738 (1978).
42. B. K. Ghora and D. Apirion, *JBC* **254**, 1951 (1979).
43. B. K. Ghora and D. Apirion, *Cell* **1015**, 1055 (1978).
44. T. K. Misra and D. Apirion, *JBC* **254**, 11154 (1979).
45. T. K. Misra and D. Apirion, *J. Bact.* **142**, 359 (1980).
46. D. Apirion, *Genetics* **90**, 659 (1978).
47. M. K. Roy, B. Singh, B. K. Ray, and D. Apirion, *EJB* **131**, 119 (1983).
48. C. Yanofsky, *Nature* **289**, 751 (1981).
49. B. Singh and D. Apirion, *BBA* **698**, 252 (1982).
50. E. A. Morgan, T. Ikemura, L. E. Post, and M. Nomura, *in* "Transfer RNA: Biological Aspects" (D. Söll, J. Abelson, and P. Schimmel, eds.), p. 259, Cold Spring Harbor Laboratory, Cold Spring Harbor, New York, 1980.
51. B. K. Ray, B. Singh, M. K. Roy, and D. Apirion, *EJB* **125**, 283 (1982).
52. B. K. Ray and D. Apirion, *JMB* **139**, 329 (1980).
53. A. Ray and D. Apirion, *Gene* **12**, 87 (1980).
54. A. Ray and D. Apirion, *BBRC* **107**, 1361 (1982).
55. K. Goldblum and D. Apirion, *J. Bact.* **146**, 128 (1981).
56. D. Apirion and D. Gitelman, *Mol. Gen. Genet.* **177**, 139 (1980).
57. D. Apirion, B. K. Ghora, G. Plautz, T. K. Misra, and P. Gegenheimer, *in* "Transfer

RNA: Biological Aspects" (D. Söll, J. Abelson, and P. Schimmel, eds.), p. 139, Cold Spring Harbor Laboratory, Cold Spring Harbor, New York, 1980.
58. R. K. Ghosh and M. P. Deutscher, *NARes* **5**, 3831 (1978).
59. R. P. Perry, *ARB* **45**, 605 (1976).
60. C. Cowgill de Narvaez, and H. W. Schaup, *JMB* **134**, 1 (1979).
61. B. K. Ray and D. Apirion, *JMB* **149**, 599 (1981).
62. B. K. Ray and D. Apirion, *EJB* **114**, 517 (1981).
63. T. Ikemura, Y. Shimura, H. Sakano, and H. Ozeki, *JMB* **96**, 69 (1975).
64. H. Sakano and Y. Shimura, *JMB* **123**, 287 (1978).
65. G. Plautz and D. Apirion, *JMB* **149**, 813 (1981).
66. P. Schedl, P. Primakoff, and J. Roberts, *Brookhaven Symp. Biol.* **26**, 53 (1975).
67. P. Schedl, J. Roberts, and P. Primakoff, *Cell* **8**, 581 (1976).
68. G. Barry, C. Squires, and C. L. Squires, *PNAS* **77**, 3331 (1980).
69. D. R. Gitelman and D. Apirion, *BBRC* **96**, 1063 (1980).
70. D. Apirion and N. Watson, *J. Bact.* **133**, 1543 (1978).
71. H. A. Lozeron, P. J. Anevski, and D. Apirion, *JMB* **109**, 359 (1977).
72. J. Abelson, *ARB* **48**, 1035 (1979).
73. G. V. Paddock and J. Abelson, *JBC* **250**, 4207 (1975).
74. W. H. McClain, *BBRC* **86**, 718 (1979).
75. B. Pragai, T. S. Ko, and D. Apirion, *BBRC* **95**, 1431 (1980).
76. B. Pragai and D. Apirion, *JMB* **153**, 619 (1981).
77. B. Pragai and D. Apirion, *JMB* **154**, 465 (1982).
78. S. Adhya and M. Gottesman, *ARB* **47**, 967 (1978).
79. M. Rosenberg and D. Court, *Annu. Rev. Genet.* **13**, 319 (1979).
80. T. Platt, *Cell* **24**, 10 (1981).
81. C. Guthrie, *JMB* **95**, 529 (1975).
82. N. Watson and D. Apirion, *BBRC* **103**, 543 (1981).
83. M. Gurevitz, N. Watson, and D. Apirion, *EJB* **124**, 283 (1982).
84. S. K. Jain, B. Pragai, and D. Apirion, *BBRC* **106**, 768 (1982).
85. H. Ozeki, H. Sakano, S. Yamada, T. Ikemura, and Y. Shimura, *Brookhaven Symp. Biol.* **26**, 89 (1975).
86. D. Apirion and N. Watson, *FEBS Lett.* **110**, 161 (1980).
87. H. Motamedi, K. Lee, L. Nichols, and F. J. Schmidt, *JMB* in press (1982).
88. R. Kole and S. Altman, *PNAS* **76**, 3795 (1979).
89. R. Kole, M. F. Baer, B. C. Stork, and S. Altman, *Cell* **19**, 881 (1980).
90. R. Kole and S. Altman, *Bchem* **20**, 1902 (1981).
91. C. Guthrie and R. Atchison, *in* "Transfer RNA: Biological Aspects (D. Söll, J. N. Abelson, and P. Schimmel, eds.), p. 83. Cold Spring Harbor Laboratory, Cold Spring Harbor, New York, 1980.
92. K. Gardiner and N. R. Pace, *JBC* **255**, 7507 (1980).
93. S. K. Jain, M. Gurevitz, and D. Apirion, *JMB* **162**, 515 (1982).
93a. A. Miczak, J. Ford, M. Marian, and D. Apirion, *BBRC*, in press.
94. N. R. Pace, *Bacteriol. Rev.* **37**, 562 (1973).
95. H. D. Robertson, E. G. Pelle, and W. H. McClain, *in* "Transfer RNA: Biological Aspects (D. Söll, J. N. Abelson, and P. Schimmel, eds.), p. 107. Cold Spring Harbor Laboratory, Cold Spring Harbor, New York, 1980.
96. J. W. Wireman and P. A. Sypherd, *Bchem* **13**, 1215 (1974).
97. J. Smith, This Series **16**, 25 (1976).
98. S. Altman, A. K. M. Bothwell, and B. C. Stark, *Brookhaven Symp. Biol.* **26**, 12 (1975).

99. C. Guthrie, J. G. Seidman, M. M. Comer, R. M. Bock, F. J. Schmidt, B. G. Barrell, and W. H. McClain, *Brookhaven Symp. Biol.* **26**, 106 (1975).
100. D. A. Stahl, T. A. Walker, B. Meyhack, and N. R. Pace, *Cell* **18**, 1133 (1979).
101. G. P. Mazzara, G. Plunkett and W. H. McClain, *in* "Cell Biology: A Comprehensive Treatise" (L. Goldstein and D. M. Prescott, eds.), Vol 3: "Gene Expression: The Production of RNAs," p. 439. Academic Press, New York, 1980.
102. S. Altman, *in* "Biochemistry of Nucleic Acids II" (*Int. Rev. Biochem.*) (B. F. C. Clark, ed.), p. 19. Univ. Park Press, Baltimore, Maryland, 1978.
103. J. D. Smith, *Brookhaven Symp. Biol.* **26**, 1 (1975).
104. V. Daniel, *CRC Crit. Rev. Biochem.* **9**, 253 (1981).
105. B. Meyhack and N. R. Pace, *Bchem* **17**, 5804 (1978).
106. J. Feunteun, R. Rosset, C. Ehresmann, P. Stiegler, and P. Fellner, *NARes* **1**, 141 (1974).
107. F. W. Studier, *J. Bact.* **124**, 307 (1975).
108. M. P. Deutscher and R. H. Hilderman, *J. Bact.* **118**, 621 (1974).
109. J. Foulds, R. H. Hilderman, and M. P. Deutscher, *J. Bact.* **118**, 628 (1974).
110. R. Zaniewski and M. P. Deutscher, *Mol. Gen. Genet.* **185**, 142 (1982).
111. J. E. Darnell, Jr., *Science* **202**, 1257 (1978).
112. W. F. Doolittle, *Nature* **272**, 581 (1978).
113. P. Chambon, *Sci. Am.* **244**, 60 (1981).
114. C. R. Woese, *Sci. Am.* **244**, 98 (1981).
115. A. I. Bukhari, J. A. Shapiro, and S. L. Adhya, Eds. "DNA Insertion Elements, Plasmids, and Episomes," p. 782. Cold Spring Harbor Laboratory, Cold Spring Harbor, New York, 1977.
116. D. Apirion, *Mol. Gen. Genet.* **122**, 313 (1973).
117. J. C. Wang, *JMB* **55**, 523 (1971).
118. N. R. Cozzareli, *Cell* **22**, 327 (1980).
119. K. Mizuuchi, L. M. Fisher, and M. H. O'Dea, *PNAS* **77**, 1847 (1980).
120. C. H. Cantor, P. L. Wollenzien, and J. E. Hearst, *NARes* **8**, 1855 (1980).
121. H. F. Noller and C. R. Woese, *Science* **212**, 403 (1981).
122. M. E. Winkler, *J. Bact.* **139**, 842 (1979).
123. G. Faye, N. Dennebouy, C. Kujawa, *et al.*, *Mol. Gen. Genet.* **168**, 101 (1979).
124. U. Hahn, C. M. Lazarus, H. Lunsdorf, *et al.*, *Cell* **17**, 191 (1979).
125. E. Schneider, M. Blundell, and D. Kennell, *Mol. Gen. Genet.* **160**, 121 (1978).
126. H. Aviv, R. Voloch, R. Bastos, *et al.*, *Cell* **8**, 495 (1976).
127. J. R. Greenberg and R. P. Perry, *BBA* **287**, 361 (1972).
128. O. Meyhaus and R. P. Perry, *Cell* **16**, 139 (1979).
129. R. H. Singer and S. Penman, *JMB* **78**, 321 (1973).
130. M. Blundell, E. Carig, and D. Kennell, *Nature NB* **238**, 46 (1972).
131. R. Silber, V. G. Malathi, and J. Hurwitz, *PNAS* **69**, 3009 (1972).
132. V. Sagramella, *PNAS* **69**, 3389 (1972).
133. J. D. Rochaix and P. Maline, *Cell* **15**, 661 (1978).
134. K. Kruger, P. J. Grabowski, A. J. Zaug, J. Sands, D. E. Gottschling, and T. R. Cech, *Cell* **31**, 147 (1982).
135. M. Konarska, W. Filipowicz, and H. J. Gross, *PNAS* **79**, 1474 (1982).
136. C. C. F. Blake, *Nature* **273**, 367 (1978).
137. W. Gilbert, *Nature* **271**, 501 (1978).
138. F. W. Alt, A. L. M. Bothwell, and M. Knapp, *Cell* **20**, 293 (1980).
139. J. Rogers, P. Early, and C. Carter, *Cell* **20**, 303 (1980).
140. P. Early, M. Rogers, and K. Davis, *Cell* **20**, 313 (1980).
141. D. J. Kemp, A. W. Harris, and J. M. Adams, *PNAS* **77**, 7400 (1980).

Nearest-Neighbor Effects in the Structure and Function of Nucleic Acids

E. Bubienko*
P. Cruz†
J. F. Thomason* and
P. N. Borer‡

*Department of Chemistry,
University of California at Irvine,
Irvine, California*

I. The Nearest Neighbor Approximation

A. Introduction

Nucleic acids do not exist as the completely symmetrical helices often portrayed on the covers of biochemistry texts. The structure is irregular and depends on the sequence of bases; there are also influences of salt and water activity. Three conformational families are widely recognized: right-helical A- and B-forms and the left-handed Z-structure (*1*). Each is considered in this article, although the major focus is on the A-family.

A segment of DNA helix might look something like that in Fig. 1a. An A-family structure is shown for a part of the sequence that controls expression of the gene for β-globin. Experimental studies suggest that

---

* Present address: Department of Pharmaceutical Chemistry, University of California at San Francisco, San Francisco, California.

† Present address: Department of Chemistry, University of California at Berkeley, Berkeley, California.

‡ Present address: Department of Chemistry, Syracuse University, Syracuse, New York.

Progress in Nucleic Acid Research
and Molecular Biology, Vol. 30

42   E. BUBIENKO *et al.*

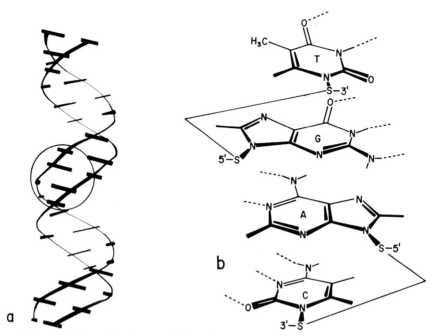

FIG. 1. (a) An A-family DNA helix showing a part of the control region for the
β-globin gene. The sugar–phosphate backbones are indicated by the intertwined vertical strands, and the bases by the short (pyrimidine) and long (purine) bars. The four
bases circled in the center of the sequence form a continuous stack, shown in the detailed perspective in (b).

the four bases circled in Fig. 1a exist as a continuous stack. The arrangement of bases in stacks of two, three, or four depends on the
sequence and can be predicted with rules given in this article. Figure
1b shows molecular details of the 4-stack.

An enzyme such as RNA polymerase may contact a pattern of stacks
along two or three turns of the helix, as well as specific hydrogen-bond
donor or acceptor sites, to initiate synthesis at the proper location. For
instance, the enzyme might use its aromatic amino acids in hydrophobic interactions, such as intercalation between the two purines
(Fig. 1b), or "outercalation"—associating with the ends of stacks. Proteins may also recognize deformations created in the sugar–phosphate
backbone of the molecule by extended stacks of bases.

This article examines the hypothesis, called the RY model, that
these extended stacks occur in special arrangements of purines (R) and
pyrimidines (Y) along the chains. The RY model comes from measurements of the nuclear magnetic resonance (nmr) chemical shifts in

oligoribonucleotides and finds some support in X-ray diffraction studies. The model will evolve into a more comprehensive picture when the nearest-neighbor effects are characterized more thoroughly by further experiments.

Our purpose is to stimulate molecular biologists to think beyond sequence, to consider the arrangement of nearest neighbors. It is largely these neighbor interactions that determine the local three-dimensional shape imparted by the sequence.

B. History

The nearest-neighbor approximation has been applied to the properties of polymer molecules for many years. It states that monomer properties and the interactions between adjacent monomers determine the polymer's properties, e.g., optical absorption, helix-coil equilibrium, conformation. The approximation is often an implicit assumption in studies of the structure and stability of nucleic acids.

Its first use in nucleic-acid chemistry came when it was noticed that the optical rotatory dispersion and ultraviolet absorption of an oligoribonucleotide could be closely approximated by an appropriate sum of monomer and dimer spectra (2–4). This was extended to the optical properties of double-stranded DNA (5, 6) and RNA (7, 8), and the stability of oligoribonucleotide duplexes (9–11). A comprehensive discussion of the approximation (12) introduced the terms first, second, third neighbors, etc., to replace the clumsier terms nearest, next-nearest, next-next-nearest neighbors.

C. Implications

Usually, there are discrepancies between measured properties and those approximated by the first-neighbor method. The importance of second and third neighbors varies with the property being considered. For an interaction varying with distance as r^{-n}, the interaction at the second-neighbor distance, $I_2 = 2^{-n}I_1$, where I_1 is the first-neighbor interaction (see Fig. 2). Circular dichroism in nucleic acids varies roughly as r^{-2} (13), so the second-neighbor effect may be as much as one-fourth of the first-neighbor effect. Hypochromism, shielding in nmr, and free energy of duplex formation are commonly thought to fall as r^{-3}, so ignoring second neighbors in approximate theories may account for a discrepancy of more than one-eighth of the measured effect.

Figure 1b depicts a stack of four bases that may exist in double-stranded nucleic acids. The drawing shows only the positions of the nuclei, but it should be remembered that the electron clouds of adjacent bases are in van der Waals contact. The pi electrons are highly

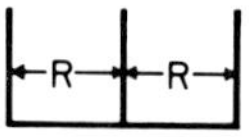

$$I_1 = kR^{-n}$$
$$I_2 = k(2R)^{-n}$$
$$\frac{I_2}{I_1} = 2^{-n}$$

FIG. 2. Description of the effect of distance, R, on some property I, when I follows an R^{-n} law. I_1 gives the first-neighbor effect between adjacent stacked bases (vertical lines), and I_2 the second-neighbor effect between the outer bases.

mobile and respond readily to changes in the electronic distribution of nearby bases. Oscillation of these electrons in the A base will affect the first neighbors G and C most strongly (Fig. 1b). Clearly, there will also be an effect on the second-neighboring T that will be mediated by the G base.

The average distribution of electrons is not symmetrical in the bases; this is usually represented as a permanent dipole moment, which decreases in the order $G = C > U > A$ for the nucleotide bases (14). A more accurate electrostatic picture of this average distribution treats the bases as being composed of partial charges on each atom, which sum to the overall dipole moment for each base. The interactions between these average charge distributions may be attractive or repulsive depending on geometry.

There is also an attraction between this average distribution on one base and the polarizable electrons of its neighbors. However, the principal enthalpic component of the stabilization of nucleic-acid helices is thought to be the London force due to the coordinated oscillation of electrons (15, 16). These last two forces are dependent on the polarizability, which is about 25% larger for purines than for pyrimidines (15). The polarizability reflects the mobility of electrons in response to an electric field.

The attraction due to the London force is generally thought to fall as r^{-6}, but this relation is for isolated point molecules in the gas phase. In solution, the attraction may fall off far more slowly and may even go by an r^{-2} law, as in the case of interacting lipid bilayers (17). Charge fluctuations throughout a system are correlated since each particle simultaneously sends and receives information to and from all other particles (18). Extended stacks such as in Fig. 1b may be stable owing to the correlated motion of electrons throughout the stack; the properties of these stacks may show second- and third-neighbor effects, though the first-neighbor effects should still dominate.

Theoretical evaluation of the energies is critically dependent on the choice of a value for the effective dielectric constant, a divisor in the mathematical representation of the interaction forces. The dielectric constant is 1 for a vacuum, 2.4 for bulk benzene, and 78.5 for bulk water. The effect of a polar solvent is to increase even further the importance of the London force relative to the other forces (15, 19).

Clearly, the London forces are not as orientation-dependent as are the electrostatic forces. Thus, the London contribution would be nearly the same if any of the bases were rotated about the long axis of the 4-stack in Fig. 1b. This suggests that bases in the 4-stack (i) could have different geometric details than those shown here, (ii) could oscillate rather freely about some average structure, and (iii) could be easily deformed upon interaction with other molecules.

D. Applications

Nearest-neighbor effects are useful in understanding the physical properties of nucleic acids. Applications to optical properties (20) and nmr properties (21, 22) have been reviewed. The X-ray diffraction of a deoxy dodecamer helix also shows some interesting nearest-neighbor effects (23). Some of these studies are discussed in the following sections. Certain drugs that interact with nucleic acids show clear nearest-neighbor preferences (24), although we do not consider this topic further.

It is safe to suppose that local elements of structure play a central role in the regulation of genetic expression. In Section II,D we discuss the local structure of several interesting control sequences in the context of the RY model. We do not imply that interactions between distant residues are unimportant; they clearly are involved in maintaining the complex folding of RNA. These interactions are simply not predictable at our current level of understanding.

II. A-Family Structures and the RY Model

A. The A-Family

We discuss three major classes of double helix in this article: the A, B, and Z families, with brief mention of a few others. Each of the families has characteristics that distinguish it from the others, but there are variations within a family that depend on base sequence, tertiary folding, crystal packing, etc. Several reviews document the similarities and differences of the helix forms observed in the solid state (1, 13, 25–27). In this article we adopt a designation such as "A-form" to indicate molecular structures with features in common with the A model derived from X-ray diffraction.

The parameters of A-family helices in current use are derived from X-ray diffraction patterns of fibers of double-stranded DNA (29), RNA

(*30*), and DNA · RNA complexes (*31*). The A-form diffraction pattern was observed by Franklin and Wilkins (*32*), and the original Watson–Crick structure was a variant of the A-family (*27, 33, 34*). The general picture is of Watson–Crick paired bases arranged outside the helix axis, 11 to 12 pairs comprising one full turn of the helix. The surface of a cylinder concentric with the helix axis that intersects the glycosyl nitrogen atoms has a radius of 7.27 Å (A'-RNA), and a cylinder intersecting the phosphorus atoms has a radius of 9.3 Å. The shallow minor groove and deep major groove are apparent in Fig. 3, as is the characteristic tilt of the base-pairs with respect to the helix axis. The bases within a pair are twisted in a propeller-like fashion with a dihedral angle on the order of 10°. The ribose sugars are 3'-*endo*, and intrachain phosphates are separated by about 5.9 Å. [These terms and structural details are further defined in *26* and *27*.]

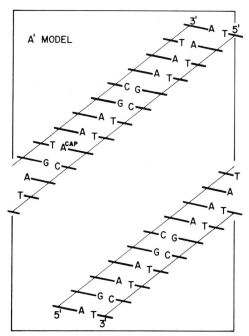

FIG. 3. Base-stacking pattern of a part of the β-globin control region in the A' structure. Heavy lines represent the base planes viewed edge-on. The light lines denote the sugar–phosphorus linkages. Note the regular backbone in the A' model. A photocopy of the page folded such that the left margin overlaps the right produces a cylinder whose dimensions show the helix in proper scale. The cylinder intersects the glycosyl nitrogen atom on each base; this atom is at the intersection of the light and heavy lines. The base designated A[cap] indicates the first base in the mRNA transcript.

The variability within the A-family observed in the solid state implies a certain flexibility in conformation within the general constraints mentioned in the preceding paragraph. Most of the details of this variability have come from single-crystal studies of tRNA (35–38) and complementary oligonucleotides (39–44). Even here the resolution is usually too low to locate light atoms (C, N, O) with a precision better than 0.5 Å; the C—C bond lengths within a base are about 1.4 Å. The later stages of refinement of a crystal structure depend on the crystallographer's intuition to a large extent; it will be interesting to see what develops given the current awareness of irregularity in nucleic-acid conformation.

It is important to realize that the crystal results may not define the solution structure. First is the problem of insufficient resolution discussed in the preceding paragraph. Second, crystals do not form unless each of the molecules has a very similar shape. Thus, in a population of flexible molecules, a minor conformer may be the one to crystallize. Third, the structure must satisfy a crystal-wide free-energy minimum, so packing forces and reduction in water activity may cause distortions in conformation. Fourth, the X-ray structure gives little information on the distribution of motions allowed in the molecule, which may be important in defining its interactions with proteins, etc. (45). Crystal structures are a logical starting point in discovering the conformation in solution, so we make frequent reference to solid-state studies in this article.

Unfortunately, solution methods lack the richness of information available to the crystallographer, although several experiments show that a structure similar to the A-form can exist in water. Circular dichroism studies of DNA in thin films provide a link between the solution and solid states (20, 46). Films prepared under conditions where fiber diffraction shows the A-form pattern have a circular dichroism spectrum like that found with double-stranded RNA dissolved in water. Synthetic oligoribonucleotide duplexes have spectra similar to DNA · RNA complexes with corresponding sequences, though there are some differences (47). The same paper showed that similar spectra could be induced in cognate DNA · DNA sequences by reducing the water activity with ethanol. [B-form fiber diffraction patterns change to the A-form upon decreasing water activity (48).] Nuclear magnetic resonance studies of duplexed RNA oligomers show that the sugars are 3'-endo and that the base overlap belongs to the A-family (49–59). The nmr measurements give information on the local environment of several atoms in each nucleotide residue. This can be used to test and propose alternatives to the crystal structures.

B. Introduction to the RY Model

The RY model is such an alternative where changes in the A-family structure have been used to rationalize the nmr chemical shifts of 65 protons in 13 oligo-RNA duplexes (*49*; P. Cruz *et al.*, unpublished). The model poses intriguing possibilities for the recognition of specific sequences by enzymes. We describe these possibilities here for the first time and offer a set of simple rules for applying the model to other sequences.

1. BASE OVERLAP AND THE HELIX WINDING ANGLE

Figure 4a defines W, the helix winding angle, which is used as the adjustable parameter in fitting the nmr chemical shifts. The left-hand panels of the figure show base overlap in the A'-RNA geometry (*30, 60*) for the three ways purines and pyrimidines can occur in Watson–Crick paired chains. The right-hand panels show corresponding views of overlaps that give a satisfactory fit to all of the nmr data; this set of overlaps is the basis of the RY model. Base overlap changes with W, and comparison of the left and right panels shows how each proton changes position relative to its neighboring rings. The shielding of a

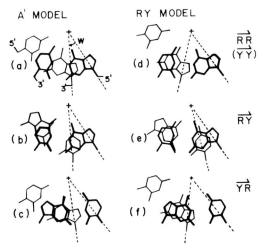

FIG. 4. Comparison of base-pair overlaps between the A' model and the RY model, as viewed along the helix axis. Pairs drawn in heavy outline lie nearest the observer. Panel (a) defines W as the angle successive C-1' atoms make with respect to the helix axis. Views (a) RR, (b) RY, and (c) YR show A'-overlap with $W = 30°$. Corresponding views (d) $W = 50°$, (e) $W = 20°$, and (f) $W = 45°$ show overlaps according to the RY model. The polarity of the chain as shown in (a) holds for each of the panels. Panels a–c were traced from Fig. 2b of Arnott *et al.* (*60*) and are projections of the base-pairs onto a plane approximately perpendicular to the helix axis. (See Fig. 1b for proton positions.)

proton by an adjacent base was approximated by ring-current and local-atomic anisotropies provided as isoshielding contours (61).

Details of the calculation at the first-neighbor level are given in (49); subsequent second-neighbor corrections have not changed our conclusions (P. Cruz et al., unpublished). Our analysis indicates that W values of 50° for RR (and its complement, YY), 20° for RY, and 45° for YR (all ± 10°) fit most of the data within 15% of the largest measured value, and within 25% in the few other cases. Errors arise in the calculation of values for the magnetic anisotropy. We chose A'-RNA (12 bases per turn) as our starting geometry rather than the similarly stacked A-RNA (11 bases per turn) because the base pairs are tilted less radically in the former. This reduces the error in our nmr analysis. The conclusions about base overlap will be very similar for A-RNA.

It is vital to note that the analysis does not directly measure W; varying W is only a systematic way of changing base overlap. It is the overlaps that have meaning and predict stacking patterns in natural sequences. Thus, the overlapping pairs represented in Fig. 4 could lie closer to the helix axis or farther away or skewed in some fashion. A helix axis is an abstraction that helps one visualize these sorts of structures, but it has no meaning from a molecular standpoint.

What must happen to the ribose-phosphate links if base-overlap changes? An analysis of fiber diffraction patterns shows that poly(X) · poly(X), and poly(s^2U) · poly(s^2U), among others, can crystallize in the A-form, maintaining a backbone nearly equivalent to A-DNA (27). In the first case, the base pair is nearly 2 Å broader than a Watson–Crick pair, and in the second it is 1.6 Å smaller. If the backbone can accommodate changes this large, it should allow the base overlaps proposed in the RY model. Poly(C) · pG, a complex of poly(C) with guanosine 5'-monophosphate (27), crystallizes in an A-family structure, although only one of the strands is covalently linked. There is a clear emphasis on base stacking in stabilizing A-family structures.

Figure 4d,e,f shows the extensive overlap of the hydrophobic surfaces of the bases in the RY model. Base-stacking, rather than hydrogen-bonding, provides the major stabilization to nucleic-acid helices. The RY overlaps lead naturally to ideas regarding the enzymatic recognition of specific sequences by their shape. A mechanism for this recognition is now proposed.

2. EXTENDED STACKS

Consider the four ways R (purine) and Y (pyrimidine) can occur along a single chain: RR, YY, YR, and RY, which in double strands are

$$5'\ldots R\ R\ldots Y\ Y\ldots Y\ R\ldots R-Y\ldots 3'$$
$$\hphantom{5'\ldots}/\quad\ \ /\quad\ \ /$$
$$3'\ldots Y\ Y\ldots R\ R\ldots R\ Y\ldots Y-R\ldots 5'$$
$$\hphantom{3'\ldots}1\quad\ \ \ 2\quad\ \ \ 3\quad\ \ \ 4$$

The slashes (/) and dashes (−) connect the bases that are predicted to stack upon each other (the covalent links between bases go from left to right across a line of text). A similar cross-strand stacking interaction occurs in all but the last doublet, where there are two intrastrand stacks.

Only the first, third, and fourth "doublets" of base-pairs are unique; the second is related to the first by a twofold rotation, which implies that the interactions between monomers are the same. The unique doublets can be specified by a shorthand notation where the bases along only one of the strands are written, 5′ to 3′. Thus, in the shorthand,

$$RR = \frac{R\ R}{Y\ Y} = \frac{Y\ Y}{R\ R}, \quad YR = \frac{Y\ R}{R\ Y}, \quad \text{and } RY = \frac{R\ Y}{Y\ R}$$

The simple stacking rules predict extended stacks of up to four bases in certain sequences. For instance,

$$5'\ldots C\ A-C\ A-C\ C\ldots 3'$$
$$\hphantom{5'\ldots}/\quad\ \ \ /\quad\ \ \ /$$
$$3'\ldots G\ T-G\ T-G\ G\ldots 5'$$

has two "3-stacks," $\begin{smallmatrix}A-C\\ /\\ G\end{smallmatrix}$ and $\begin{smallmatrix}C\\ /\\ T-G\end{smallmatrix}$, and a "4-stack," $\begin{smallmatrix}A-C\\ /\\ T-G\end{smallmatrix}$

Figure 1b is a drawing of the 4-stack; the first 3-stack can be visualized by covering the T base in the drawing, and the second 3-stack by covering the C and replacing the A with a C.

A 20-mer from the sequence flanking the 5′ end of the gene for human β-globin (62) illustrates this further.

$$5'\ldots T A-T T G-C T T A-C A-T T T G-C T T C T\ldots\ldots A T G\ldots 3'$$
$$\hphantom{5'\ldots}/\quad /\ /\quad\ /\ /\ /\quad\ \ /\quad\ /\ /\ /\quad\ \ /\ /\ /\ /$$
$$\hphantom{5'\ldots}A T-A A C-G A A T-G T-A A A C-G A A G A$$

The top strand continues into the gene, signified by the ATG "start" codon. Again, the dashes and slashes connect the bases involved in 2-, 3-, and 4-stacks. The same sequence is drawn in Fig. 5 to help visualize the RY model in three dimensions; boxes are drawn around representative extended stacks.

The base designated A^{cap} (upper left in Fig. 5) corresponds to the first base in the mRNA transcript. Perhaps the adjacent 4-stack is im-

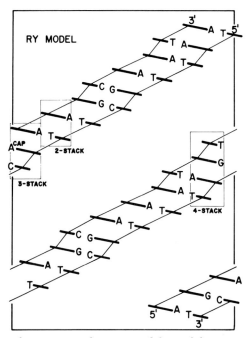

FIG. 5. Base-stacking pattern of a portion of the β-globin control region in the RY model. Note the irregular backbone and improved base overlap, as compared to Fig. 3. Representative examples of a 4-stack, 3-stack, and 2-stack are enclosed in boxes. The arrangement of stacks may be important in the specific interaction of DNA with RNA polymerase. As in Fig. 3, the glycosyl nitrogens lie on the surface of a cylinder made by superimposing the right and left margins.

portant in the specific interaction of RNA polymerase with this DNA segment. Patterns of extended stacks along two or three turns of the helix may determine key aspects of sequence recognition by enzymes. Section II,D elaborates some possibilities along these lines.

A question may occur at this point: Isn't DNA in the B-form? The answer is that the form of DNA in solution or upon association with proteins is not really known. We pose an A-family structure as a legitimate hypothesis for several reasons. First, DNA · RNA complexes in fibers and single crystals have A-family diffraction patterns (27, 27a). An RNA transcript must be associated with a DNA strand while it is being formed. That the A-form may be present during transcription was pointed out in the original fiber diffraction analysis of a DNA · RNA complex (63). Second, most organisms require an RNA primer, thus a DNA · RNA complex, in the replication of their DNA. Third, DNA fibers at low water activity have A-family structures (27), as do three of the published single-crystal structures of oligodeoxynucleotides (43, 44, 75a). Water activity should be reduced in the presence of protein. Fourth, some evolutionists suggest that RNA chains were the carriers of genetic information before DNA existed (64); RNA chains have A-family structures. Nature has a memory of its early successful processes—for instance, in the myoglobin fold preserved in diverse species (65)—so one might argue that basic features on the first successful processes in genetic expression should remain. In other words, if the ancestors of modern enzymes developed to express RNA genes (A-form), then their descendants called upon to perform similar tasks with DNA may induce a conformational change to the A-form.

Before we consider other possibilities with DNA or DNA · RNA sequences (Section II,D), we consider RNA duplexes in the codon anticodon interaction (Section II,B,3) and with dangling unpaired bases (Section II,B,4).

3. The Codon · Anticodon Interaction

The genetic code is written in three-letter "words," called codons, along the mRNA chain, and read by an "adaptor" molecule (tRNA) with three complementary bases in its anticodon. There are 64 (4^3) codons, but only 20 amino acids; several codons specify the same amino acid (redundancy). Table I shows the genetic code. Most of the fourfold redundant codons lie in the left half of the table, whereas in the right half, most are twofold redundant.

a. Two-out-of-Three Reading. A "two-out-of-three" hypothesis for codon reading has been proposed to explain the arrangement of the genetic code (66a–c). The hypothesis supposes that some tRNAs read only the first two codon bases without regard for the third or "wobble" base, while other tRNAs require all three codon bases to translate the code faithfully. In cases where two-out-of-three reading involves mismatched pairing at the wobble position, translational efficiency is usually 1 to 10% compared to standard wobble pairing (66a). Standard pairing in the wobble position allows A · U, G · C, G · U, I · C, I · U, and I · A pairs (67).

Two-out-of-three reading is thought to occur for the fourfold redundant codons, e.g., the Val (GUU, GUC, GUA, GUG) set, where a tRNA with GAC in its anticodon is able to read all four even though there will be G · A and G · G mismatches with the latter two codons. Experiments have shown that two-out-of-three reading occurs in the Val and Ala families, and probably in Gly also (66a, 66c). It is also known that each of the eight families of codons that are fourfold redundant in mitochondria have only one tRNA to read all four codons

TABLE I
THE GENETIC CODE AND STACKS PREDICTED BY THE RY MODEL

YYN				YRN			
UUU	1222 Phe	UCU	1222 Ser	UAU	232 Tyr	UGU	232 Cys
UUC	1222 Phe	UCC	1222 Ser	UAC	232 Tyr	UGC	232 Cys
UUA	1222 Leu	UCA	1222 Ser	UAA	1222 Term	UGA	1222 Term[a]
UUG	1222 Leu	UCG	1222 Ser	UAG	1222 Term	UGG	1222 Trp
CUU	1222 Leu[b]	CCU	1222 Pro	CAU	232 His	CGU	232 Arg
CUC	1222 Leu	CCC	1222 Pro	CAC	232 His	CGC	232 Arg
CUA	1222 Leu	CCA	1222 Pro	CAA	1222 Gln	CGA	1222 Arg
CUG	1222 Leu	CCG	1222 Pro	CAG	1222 Gln	CGG	1222 Arg

RYN				RRN			
AUU	133 Ile	ACU	133 Thr	AAU	232 Asn	AGU	232 Ser
AUC	133 Ile	ACC	133 Thr	AAC	232 Asn	AGC	232 Ser
AUA	133 Ile[c]	ACA	133 Thr	AAA	1222 Lys	AGA	1222 Arg[d]
AUG	133 Met[e]	ACG	133 Thr	AAG	1222 Lys	AGG	1222 Arg
GUU	133 Val	GCU	133 Ala	GAU	232 Asp	GGU	232 Gly
GUC	133 Val	GCC	133 Ala	GAC	232 Asp	GGC	232 Gly
GUA	133 Val	GCA	133 Ala	GAA	1222 Glu	GGA	1222 Gly
GUG	133 Val[f]	GCG	133 Ala	GAG	1222 Glu	GGG	1222 Gly

[a] Trp in mitochondria.
[b] The CUN all code for Thr in yeast mitochondria.
[c] Met in mammalian mitochondria.
[d] AGA and AGG are chain terminators in mammalian mitochondria.
[e] Chain initiator in most genes.
[f] Occasional chain initiator.

(66d–f). These mitochondrial tRNAs have U or a modified U in the wobble position of their anticodons. Some of their codon · anticodon duplexes must have U · U or U · C mispairs; reading must occur by the two-out-of-three mode, since the codons are correctly translated.

b. A Structural Model for Codon · Anticodon Duplexes. The RY model predicts that there will be three distinctly different stacking forms for codon · anticodon duplexes. Figure 6a shows the 133 pattern where the wobble base of the anticodon is unstacked, the next two anticodon bases and the 3'-codon base form a 3-stack, and the two other codon bases form a 3-stack with the purine, R', which always occurs on the 3' side of the anticodon in tRNA. (The number of bases in each of the stacks from left to right are 1, 3, and 3, hence the nomenclature, 133.) Figure 6 panels b and c display the 1222 and 232

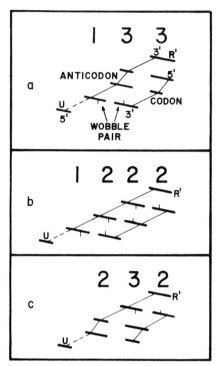

FIG. 6. Stacking patterns for the anticodon · codon duplexes predicted by the RY model: (a) the 133 pattern for RYN codons; (b) the 1222 pattern for YYN, YRR, and RRR codons; and (c) the 232 pattern for YRY and RRY codons. The base marked R′ is a purine usually modified to prevent hydrogen-bonding. The base marked U is invariant in all tRNA. Pyrimidines are denoted by a short heavy line (as with the invariant U) and purines by a longer line (as with R′). A vertical tick in the base shows the extent of a pyrimidine where either R or Y can occupy the same position.

patterns, respectively. Table I shows which stacking pattern is appropriate for each duplex between codon and anticodon.

The models in Fig. 6 offer a simple explanation of many well-known features of the tRNA · mRNA complex (67, 68). R′, a purine often modified in a manner that prevents normal hydrogen bonding, occurs at the 3′ end of the anticodon. We predict for *all* tRNAs that R′ will form a cross-strand stack on the first codon base (see Fig. 6), thus stabilizing the duplex beyond the contribution of three base-pairs. The R′ stack "cements" this end of the duplex, while the U at the 5′ end of the anticodon should never stack. This gives the duplex considerable flexibility at the wobble end. The molecular design incorporates the natural tendency toward stacking of the hydrophobic purines, while uracil, the most hydrophilic of the bases, has a poor stacking ability.

Wobble pairing and two-out-of-three reading are easily understood by examining Fig. 6. In the 133 and 1222 duplexes, the wobble base in the anticodon is not stacked. It should thus be free to align for pairing with nearly any base. The energetic cost of wobble will not be great in 232 duplexes either. The anticodon wobble base is the lower base in the leftmost 2-stack in Fig. 6c; it can move small distances to the left or right and still preserve the 2-stack. Mismatches at the wobble position as in two-out-of-three reading will also not be disruptive of the stacking arrangement.

An early model of tRNA interaction with mRNA and the ribosome (68–70) suggested two conformations for the anticodon, one stacked upon its 3' neighbors (the FH conformation) and the other (hf) stacked upon the 5' neighbors. For both forms, it was proposed that the anticodon bases stack only with each other, and the same for the codon bases. In the RY model, the stacks commingle the bases from the two strands in a sequence-specific manner. This updates our picture of the FH form but does not change the basic concept. The RY model is wholly inconsistent with the hf form; the invariant U at the 5' end should never stack on the anticodon. Furthermore, the structure of yeast tRNA^{Phe} in crystals (35–37) has an abrupt turn in the folding of the chain and a discontinuity in stacking between the invariant U and the wobble base in the anticodon.

The FH and hf forms were intended to rationalize the problem of binding two tRNAs to adjacent codons, which must occur on the ribosome. Figure 7a shows the 133 pattern for tRNA^{Val} with its complementary codons, and Fig. 7b depicts our model of two such tRNAs bound side-by-side along the mRNA. The base R' will interfere sterically with the wobble pair of the preceding codon in the 5' direction. The wobble base of this anticodon is illustrated as being pushed out of the way in Fig. 7b. Thus we see the incoming aminoacyl-tRNA binding its codon and the ribosome in our updated FH form, while the peptidyl-tRNA is held more loosely to its codon without benefit of its disrupted wobble pair (Fig. 7b). Figure 6 panels a and b show that the wobble base on the anticodon side is already unstacked in 133 and 1222 duplexes, so there should be no gain or loss of stacking interactions upon binding the aa-tRNA. When the peptidyl-tRNA is of the 232 form, there will also be no net change in the number of stacking interactions. In this case, a stacking interaction will be lost with the anticodon wobble base (see Fig. 6c), but will be replaced by a new stack with R' of the incoming aa-tRNA.

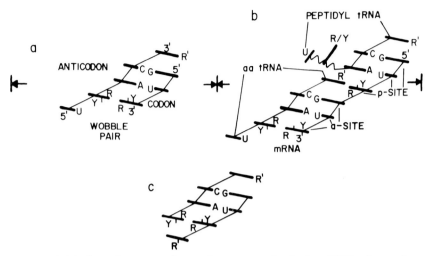

FIG. 7. (a) The codon · anticodon stacking pattern for the four GUN valine codons. Vertical ticks in the wobble-pair bases (bottom base-pair) delimit the pyrimidines; the glycosyl nitrogens are isomorphous whether the wobble base is Y or R. (b) The proposed codon · anticodon interactions for two adjacent tRNA^Val molecules on the ribosome during translation. The invariant U and the wobble base of the tRNA bound at the p-site (already translated) are shown displaced to make room for the stacking of the R' base on the a-site codon. (c) The duplex formed by two complementary tRNAs. The duplex is stabilized by the two R' bases, which form cross-strand stacks. Similar cross-strand stacking is predicted for all other pairs of complementary anticodons. The vertical bars and arrows can be overlapped to produce a cylinder showing the helix form.

c. Redundancy in the Genetic Code. We noted earlier that the codons in Table I are predominantly fourfold redundant in the left half and twofold redundant in the right half. The exceptions to these dominant features are underlined in Table I. The codons are grouped in sets of four, e.g., the UCN (Ser) family or the UAN (Tyr,Term) set; in each set of four, the base, N, increments in the order, U, C, A, G. The predicted stacking pattern changes when N changes from Y to R in the right half of the table, whereas the pattern does not change in the left half. Thus the stacking forms correlate closely with the redundancy in the code. If this correlation is more than fortuitous, we might speculate about its origin and learn something new about stacking from the exceptions. The next four paragraphs consider the exceptions.

AUG codes for methionine, but is also the chain initiation signal for most proteins. It is not very surprising that it should have an exceptional status, a special mechanism allowing this codon to be distinguished from all others under usual circumstances. This mechanism is not perfect, as GUG occasionally initiates a message and AUA codes for Met in mammalian mitochondria. AUG, GUG, and AUA make similarly stacked duplexes with their complements according to the RY model.

The other exceptions are all associated with the 1222 pattern. We think that the relatively poor overlaps between R and Y in each of the 2-stacks may make this configuration more flexible than the others. In the exceptional codons if the wobble pair (Fig. 6b) were moved to the right (this corresponds to a local loosening of the helix, a decrease in winding angle), a 232 configuration would result, and there would be no conflict between stacking pattern and redundancy. This interpretation suggests that CGR, GGR, and UUY sequences in double strands have different conformations from the predictions of the RY model; specifically that the GR and RA doublets in these sequences will have intrastrand base overlaps (RA is the complement of UY).

It is interesting that all of the chain termination signals are also associated with the 1222 pattern, including the AGR's, which are terminators in mammalian mitochondria, but code for Arg in the other known cases. Perhaps this pattern is least reliable in transmitting information.

Throughout this discussion, we have ignored the important influence of "odd" bases in and adjacent to the anticodon. We attempt no exhaustive survey of these effects, but they may contribute to the exceptions under discussion and may require that some aspects of the simple model be revised. Bases with hydrophobic modifications, e.g., alkylated bases and the tricyclic wybutosine in yeast tRNA^{Phe}, should enhance whatever stacking is predicted with adjacent bases. In crystals of tRNA^{Phe}, there is a strong overlap of pseudouridine 39 with m^{5}C 40 (P. Cruz, P. N. Borer, and S. H. Kim, unpublished), the only example where two pyrimidines are known to stack on each other.

d. Origin of the Correlation between Stacking and Coding. Transfer RNAs do not bind their complementary codons with enough specificity to provide the fidelity with which protein sequences are translated from the mRNA in living cells (*70a*). The ribosome must add this additional discriminatory function, although the mechanism remains unknown. Perhaps the ribosome requires a certain stacking geometry as well as correct hydrogen bonding in the codon · anticodon duplex to allow a codon to be translated. If so, there may be ribosomal mutations that affect the translation of the sets of codons with similar stacking forms. For example, a mutation might alter the translational fidelity of all of the 133 codons, but not the others.

The selective pressure to minimize errors in translation is seen as a major factor in establishing the present arrangements of the genetic code. Using this principle, the two-out-of-three hypothesis, the idea that G · C pairs are intrinsically more stable than A · U pairs, and assumptions about single-strand stacking in the anticodon, there is a neat rationalization of the arrangement of the code (*66a–c*). Codons with a high probability of being read in the two-out-of-three manner should end up in fourfold redundant families, because this would effectively suppress translational errors. For example, suppose the CAN codons were easily read by two-out-of-three. Then there would be an unacceptably high error rate of His/Gln substitutions. However, tRNA[Gln] with CUG in the anticodon will translate Gln(CAA) codons (*66a*); this must happen in the two-out-of-three mode, since there is a C · A mismatch in the wobble position. What then prevents tRNA[His] (QUG, where Q is a modified G) from reading the Gln(CAA) and CAG codons by two-out-of-three (*66a*)? We suggest that it has to do with the natural tendency for the stacking patterns of the His and Gln codons to be different.

It is also plausible that the correlation of stacking form and coding redundancy is a remnant from prebiotic evolution, when there may have been a more direct association between the amino acid, the primitive tRNA, and the gene. These prebiotic events occurred within the context of readily available chemical information and chance events. Given the specific chemistry of the bases along with a preferred orientation of base-stacking and hydrogen-bonding, it is possible to imagine ways in which primitive self-replicating systems could synthesize proteins with reasonable fidelity. Nature selected her genetic codes on chemical grounds; our model brings attention to hydrophobic interactions as an important piece of a larger story.

4. DANGLING BASES AT HELIX ENDS

The trinucleotide GCA forms a duplex with a t_m (temperature at which half of the duplexes are "melted out") of 33°C in 1 M NaCl and 7 mM strands, even though there are only two base-pairs (*58*). Under similar conditions, the same t_m is observed for the duplex of UGCA, which has four base-pairs (*58*). By contrast, AGC has a t_m below 0°C (*58*) while AGCU has a t_m of 34°C (*59*). These results are consistent with the base-stacking predicted by the RY model,

```
G–C A        U G–C A        A G–C        A G–C U
/   /          /   /              /   /
A C–G        A C–G U        C–G A        U C–G A
```

The first two duplexes have the same pattern of 3-stacks, while the latter two are very different. The only stacks in AGC are along a single strand, so its instability should not be surprising.

Cross-strand stacks are vital in stabilizing these duplexes between short oligomers. A 3'-dangling purine always leads to such stacks, a fact illustrated by the comparison of GCA and UGCA, and by the discussion of the R' base in stabilizing duplexes of anticodons with complementary codons (Section II,B,3). The duplex between two tRNAs with complementary anticodons is unusually stable in comparison to a duplex between trinucleotides with the same anticodon sequences (71, 71a). It has been observed that this stabilization is primarily enthalpic and is presumably the result of enhanced stacking (71a). A component of the increased binding affinity can be explained with the aid of Fig. 7c. Here there are two R' bases that tie the molecules together with cross-strand stacks. Other aspects of the stabilization of RNA duplexes by dangling residues are clearly important and are considered elsewhere (52, 59; P. Cruz et al., unpublished).

The principles of the RY model might be applied to the thermodynamic parameters characterizing the helix-coil transition in RNA and DNA. However, the problems are formidable. The stacking patterns of four duplexes are shown below along with their free energies relative to the single strands (kilocalories per mole at 25°C) (10).

```
  A A G–C U U          A A–C G–U U
  / /   / /            /   /   /
  U U C–G A A          U U–G C–A A
      –6.0                 –5.1

A A A A A–U U U U U    A A A A–U A–U U U U
/ / / /   / / / /      / / /   /   / / /
U U U U U–A A A A A    U U U U–A U–A A A A
      –5.3                  –6.1
```

The molecules on the left each have two 3-stacks, while those on the right have two 3-stacks plus a 4-stack. In the top two molecules it appears that adding a 4-stack destabilizes the duplex, but the opposite is true with the bottom two. This means that the individual character of the bases in the stacks must be considered, the stacking free energy of 4-stacks with only G's and U's may differ from 4-stacks with only A's and U's. It is also true in the comparisons above that the nature of the 3-stacks is different in the top molecules, and the number of 2-stacks decreases upon adding a 4-stack. There are 10 distinct 4-stacks, 16 distinct 3-stacks, and 7 unique 2-stacks in the context of the RY model.

It seems unreasonable to attempt to divide the current body of ther-modynamic data among 33 distinguishable contributions.

5. Limits on the Model

Figure 5 may be compared with Fig. 3, where the icosamer is drawn in the standard A' configuration. The stacking is less pro-nounced in this regular structure, although it can be seen that the geometry is very similar at the level of neighboring bases. For exam-ple, the 3-stack involving the A^{cap} base is present in both structures, as is the adjacent 4-stack, although these structures are more distorted in the A' model. The RY helix is more tightly wound because the average winding angle is greater than $30°$. However, as discussed in Section II,B,1, our analysis does not define W; rather, it defines base overlaps. Thus, the overall degree of winding must be regarded with caution. With a literal interpretation of the winding angles in the RY model, the icosamer sequence averages 9.5 bases per turn rather than the 12 of A'–RNA or the 11 of A–RNA. We emphasize that the RY model is an oversimplification of sequence effects in A-family structures. It is a useful step toward understanding sequence-dependent variation in local helix structure and should accelerate the evolution of models that lead to a final and accurate description.

As of this writing, there are ten published X-ray diffraction studies of single crystals of duplexed oligonucleotides. Six of these self-complementary molecules adopt the A-form: the dinucleoside monophosphates G–C (*39, 40*) and A-U (*41, 42*), the tetranucleotide d(¹C–C–G–G) (¹C is 5-iodocytosine) (*75*), the octanucleotides d(G–G–T–A–T–A–C–C) (this structure is not fully refined), (*43*) and d(G–G–C–C–G–G–C–C) (*75a*), and the RNA–DNA hybrid decanucleo-tide r(G–C–G)–d(T–A–T–A–C–G–C) (*27a*). A seventh molecule, d(pA–T–A–T) (*72*) adopts the A-form at the A–T doublets but has a unique conformation at the T–A doublets. Two molecules have been found in the left-handed Z-form, d(C–G–C–G) (*152a, 154a*) and d(C–G–C–G–C–G) (*152–154*); only d(C–G–C–G–A–A–T–T–C–G–C–G) (*23, 45, 101–103, 106*) has a structure resembling the B-form.

Base overlaps at the R-Y doublets strongly resemble Fig. 4e in all the A-form molecules. Thus the pair of intrastrand overlaps in R-Y doublets appear to be a standard feature of A-family structures, in both the solution and solid states.

An unusual conformation is observed in single crystals of U-A (*73, 74*), and at the T–A doublet in d(pA–T–A–T) (*72*), that allows one molecule to hydrogen-bond with two other molecules. These crystal lattices have an extended network with a 1 : 1 stoichiometry. Aside from

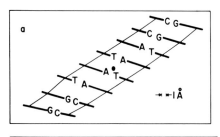

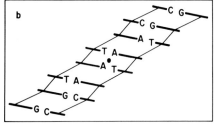

FIG. 8. Comparison of (a) base overlaps in single crystals of d(GGTATACC) and (b) overlaps predicted for this sequence by the RY model. The molecule has a dyad axis perpendicular to the vertical-helix axis intersecting the central oval. The two 4-stacks in the center of the molecule are apparent in both representations, although they are more defined in the RY model, while the 3-stacks at the ends are not seen in the X-ray model. The terminal G is predicted by the RY model to be unstacked, but is partially stacked on the adjacent G in the crystal structure.

seeing an interesting way to pack a crystal, we learn that there is little tendency to form intrastrand stacks at T–A and U–A doublets.

Figure 8 shows that the base overlaps in single crystals of self-complementary d(G–G–T–A–T–A–C–C) (43) in comparison with the RY model for the octamer duplex. The crystal study agrees quite favorably with the RY model in the central six base-pairs, where the two sets of 4-stacks are apparent in both Figs. 8a and 8b. The 3-stacks at the ends are less favored in the X-ray model, and, rather than being unstacked, the terminal G stacks partially on the second G. The interstrand overlap proposed for R–R doublets in the RY-model is not very strong (see Fig. 4d), so the helix may be especially flexible here.

Four-stacks are also apparent in the X-ray structure of r(G–C–G)–d(T–A–T–A–C–G–C) (27a) which has an alternating sequence of purines and pyrimidines. In d(G–G–C–C–G–G–C–C) (75a), the G–G doublets show weak overlaps between the purines, the G–C overlaps have strong intrastrand overlaps, and the C–G doublet has considerable interstrand contact between the six-membered rings of the guanines.

Molecules of d(¹C–C–G–G) (75) pack end-to-end through strong stacks between the ^{1}C of one duplex and the terminal G of its neighbor duplex. These end-stacks may explain why there is no overlap of any of the bases in the end doublets. The central C–G doublet shows a stronger overlap of the six-membered guanine rings than in the case of d(G–G–C–C–G–G–C–C).

The nmr and X-ray studies on oligomers agree that there are strong intrastrand overlaps in R–Y doublets, and a strong interstrand overlap in Y–R doublets (at least for the six-membered rings of the purines) (76). 4-stacks occur only in combinations of these two doublets,

$$
\begin{array}{ccc}
\text{R–Y} & \text{R–Y} & \\
/ & / & / \\
\text{Y–R} & \text{Y–R} &
\end{array}
$$

so it appears that 4-stacks are a feature of A-family structures. By the same logic, certain 3-stacks and 2-stacks must occur:

$$
\begin{array}{cc}
\text{Y R–Y} & \text{Y R} \\
/ & / \\
\text{R Y–R} & \text{R Y}
\end{array}
$$

The other 3-stacks and 2-stacks in the RY model are in doubt because of the uncertainty regarding the R–R doublet between the X-ray and nmr studies. The X-ray interpretation predicts $\begin{array}{c}\text{R–R}\\\text{Y Y}\end{array}$, while the nmr shielding is consistent with $\begin{array}{c}\text{R R}\\/\\\text{Y Y}\end{array}$. Further experiments are needed to decide the point. However, only the nmr prediction is consistent with the stability of duplexed AGCU over AGC (Section II,B,4). The X-ray results predict only intrastrand stacks, whereas the RY model predicts cross-strand stacks that should hold the duplex together.

A study of single crystals of yeast tRNA^{Phe} analyzed local helix parameters around each nucleotide (77). The parameters include the helix turn angle (analogous to W) that would be obtained if the torsional angles in a single nucleotide were continued to generate a long helix. In this procedure, turn angles are derived that disagree widely even within base-pairs. It appears that this method is not very useful in describing base overlaps.

A study of single crystals of yeast tRNA^{Phe}, A–U, and G–C indicated an absence of correlation between base-pair sequence and RNA conformation in helical regions (78). The authors looked for a correlation between sequence and two parameters related to base overlap: the on-plane rotation angle, R, and the on-plane sliding distance, S [see (78)]. Values of R did not correlate for identical doublets in different helices; neither did values of S. However, R and S can change in a concerted fashion to produce very similar overlaps. For example, the sodium salts of A–U and G–C have $R = 27°$ and $29°$, and $S = 3.3$ Å and 2.8 Å, respectively, values that are not well correlated in this study. Yet the X-ray overlaps are very similar to Fig. 4e.

S.-H. Kim (personal communication) has kindly provided us an additional angular parameter that, in addition to R and S, allows unique overlaps to be drawn by hand. Although the overlaps are slightly different from one doublet to the next, those within the RY group are intermediate between Figs. 4b and 4e. Those within the YR group are similar to the A′ overlaps in Fig. 4b, but with less overlap. The RR overlaps show the greatest variation. Again, these are similar to the A′ picture (Fig. 4a), but with a greater intrastrand overlap of adjacent purines, and no overlap of pyrimidines. Contrary to the statements expressed in (78), we see a rather strong correlation of RNA structure with sequence in helical domains of tRNA. The RR and YR overlaps differ substantially from the ones we propose from our nmr analysis.

Theoretical calculations of magnetic shielding are rather crude in the current state of the art. However, our calculations for A-family geometries must simultaneously satisfy six to eight measured shielding values for each overlap. Until results of independent measurements are known, it is prudent to regard the overlaps and their predictions of extended stacks with some sketpicism. Experiments to determine interproton distances by nuclear Overhauser enhancements or using lathanidyne-shift reagents offer a potential for these critical measurements.

C. Using the RY Model

1. Rules for Predicting Extended Stacks

The steps in predicting the arrangement of extended stacks in a sequence are as follows:

   i. Underline the 5′ . . . R Y . . . 3′ doublets along one of the strands (AC, AT, GC, and GT);

   ii. Place a numeral "4" between contiguous underlines to indicate a 4-stack;

   iii. Place a numeral "3" at the remaining ends of underlines to indicate a 3-stack;

   iv. Place a numeral "2" between bases not underlined to denote a 2-stack.

The icosamer introduced in Section II,B,2 serves as an example:

$$\underset{3\rule{1em}{0.4pt}3\ \ 3\rule{1em}{0.4pt}3\ \ 2\ \ 3\rule{1.2em}{0.4pt}4\rule{1em}{0.4pt}3\ \ 2\ \ 3\rule{1em}{0.4pt}3\ \ 2\ \ 2\ \ 2}{\text{T A T T G C T T A C A T T T G C T T C T}}$$

This notation should be compared with Fig. 5 and the previous (Section II,B,2) representation (as follows) using dashes and slashes:

```
T A–T T G–C T T A–C A–T T T G–C T T C T
 /   / /   / / /   /   / / /   / / / /
A T–A A C–G A A T–G T–A A A C–G A A G A
```

Notice that 3-stacks occur in groups of two or more and surround 4-stacks. Although not shown in this sequence, 4-stacks can be adjacent, but a 3-stack must occur at each end of such groups. There is only one kind of 4-stack with two R's sandwiched between Y's. In a 3-stack, the middle base is also R, with Y at one end and R or Y at the other, whereas 2-stacks include R and Y, or two R's (but not two Y's).

2. USING A GRID TO SHOW BASE OVERLAP

Drawings like Figs. 3 and 5–8 can be made very simply by means of the grid in Fig. 9. We recommend the use of a photocopy of the grid

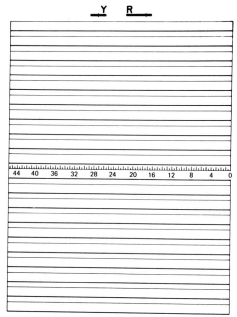

FIG. 9. Grid used as a tool for the construction of overlap models such as Figs. 3 and 5–8. The horizontal axis is marked in angstrom units. See text (Section II,C,2) for details on its use.

to plot positions of the bases according to the parameters in Table I and the following six rules.

i. Plot one strand (5′ to 3′) along the heavy lines in the grid; the first dot goes on the upper heavy line at zero on the horizontal axis (right side). Each dot represents the location of a glycosyl nitrogen atom.

ii. Place the second dot on the next heavy line at the axis position appropriate for that nearest-neighbor doublet (use the appropriate increment in Table II).

iii. Plot the third dot on the third heavy line, etc. The horizontal positions are determined by adding the increment for the current doublet to the previous total. Subtract 45.68 Å when the total exceeds this amount.

iv. Place dots for the complementary bases along the light horizontal lines in order from the top; generate their horizontal coordinate by adding 9.52 Å to the coordinate of their complementary base (subtract 45.68 Å when the total exceeds this amount).

v. Connect the dots along each strand with a light line to represent the covalent linkage.

vi. Connect the dots for each base-pair with a light pencil line. Use the template base-pair shown at the top of the grid to draw each pair along the pencil lines in the proper orientation (the vertical ticks in the template bases should lie on the dots).

When the vertical lines on the grid (or better, a photocopy made on a transparent acetate sheet of the finished drawing without the horizontal grid lines) are superimposed, the resulting cylinder gives a three-

TABLE II
GRID PARAMETERS FOR THE RY MODEL AND A′-RNA[a]

Doublet	W	Increment (A)
R–Y	20°	2.54
Y–R	45°	5.71
R–R (or Y–Y)	50°	6.35
A′–RNA	30°	3.81

[a] The grid is made from the coordinates of A′–RNA (30): 3.00 Å rise per residue, 7.27 Å radius to glycosyl nitrogen, 75° angle between radii from the helix axis to the glycosyl nitrogens of paired bases. When the vertical lines on the grid are superimposed, the resulting cylinder gives a three-dimensional perspective of the double helix. The glycosyl nitrogen atoms lie on the surface of this cylinder, and the stacks of bases are inside. The increments in the table are arc lengths along the circumference (45.68 Å) of the cylinder.

E. BUBIENKO *et al.*

dimensional perspective of the double helix. The glycosyl nitrogen atoms lie on the surface of this cylinder, and the stacks of bases are inside.

3. EXTENDED STACKS IN RANDOM SEQUENCES

In predicting extended stacks, the RY model assumes only two distinguishable items, R and Y; therefore such stacks should occur frequently along any sequence. Table III gives the random probability of finding stacks of various lengths. Another way of expressing these data is that, for each 16 base-pairs (32 bases) within a longer sequence, 4 bases should be part of 4-stacks, 18 bases in 3-stacks, and 10 bases in 2-stacks in the average of many segments. A 3-stack should be the most commonly encountered element along an A-form helix.

D. Application of the RY Model to Some Sequences

We here point out some regularities in the arrangement of purines and pyrimidines that require examination, and we use the RY model to attempt to rationalize these features. Known sequences are now approaching 10^6 nucleotides, so we do not attempt an exhaustive coverage. The simple rules in Section II,C allow others to examine their sequences for patterns of extended stacks. Molecular biologists can build models similar to Figs. 3 and 5–8 without the necessity of using a computer. These visual aids should be useful in proposing methods by which enzymes interact with specific sequences. In all this, we realize that the RY hypothesis is based on simple approximations that require more experimental testing, and is only a part of a full description of the way nucleic-acid structure depends on sequence.

1. DIRECT AND INVERTED REPEATS

Direct repeats are sequences repeated along the same strand. For example,

$$\underset{2}{C}\,\underset{3}{G}\,\underset{}{A}\,\underset{}{C}\!\!-\!\!\!\underset{3}{C}\,\underset{2}{G}\,\underset{3}{A}\,\underset{}{C}\!\!-\!\!\!\underset{3}{C}\,\underset{2}{G}\,\underset{3}{A}\,\underset{}{C}\!\!-\!\!\!\underset{3}{C}\,\underset{2}{G}\,\underset{3}{A}\,\underset{}{C}\!\!-\!\!\!$$

C G A C C G A C C G A C C G A C
 2 3——3 2 3——3 2 3——3 2 3——

TABLE III
RANDOM PROBABILITIES OF EXTENDED STACKS

	2-stacks	3-stacks	4-stacks
Probability[a]	0.15625	0.1875	0.03125
SD[b]	0.01060	0.00526	0.00460

[a] Normalized per nucleotide.

[b] Standard deviation based on 50 randomly generated chains of 1000 nucleotides each.

repeats the tetramer CGAC several times as well as the stacking pattern. Direct repeats are common elements in intergenic regions, for instance, in the replication origins of *Escherichia coli* and lambda phage (79), and in highly reiterated DNA, as in centromeric and satellite DNA (13). The stacking arrangement may be important in the function of these sequences.

Inverted repeats are sequences written along one of the strands, with that sequence repeated in the same 5'–3' polarity along the other strand. These sequences are called palindromes and often have interrupted homology, as in

```
       *   *   *   *
  A–T T A– C  G A A–C  G–T  A G–C A A
  /   / /    / / /   /    / /   / / /
  T–A A T–G  C T T–G  C–A  T C–G T T
                *   *   *   *
```

where the repeating portions are set off by asterisks. The stacking patterns will be the same, but inverted, within each half of the palindrome. Notice that the symmetry in the stacking patterns can extend beyond the palindromic sequence, as it does in this example. Again, it is possible that enzymes recognize features of such unique stacking patterns in their interactions with specific sequences. Such regions can also form "hairpin" and "cruciform" structures (79, 80–82).

2. Escherichia coli LACTOSE REPRESSOR

The *lac* repressor protein binds specifically to about 20 base-pairs of *E. coli* DNA that do not code for protein. This *lac* operator region is just upstream (5') from genes involved in lactose metabolism; when repressor is bound, the genes are not expressed. The sequence is

$$T \underset{3-\!\!-3}{GTG} G \underset{3-\!\!-3}{AA} T \underset{3-\!\!-3}{TGT} G \underset{3-\!\!-3}{AGC} G* \underset{3-\!\!-3}{GAT} A \underset{3-\!\!-3}{AC} A \underset{3-\!\!-3}{ATT}$$

(In this sequence and hereafter, we do not denote 2-stacks.) On a random basis, such a 26-mer should have 29 bases in 3-stacks (42 present), 16 bases in 2-stacks (8 present), and 7 bases in 4-stacks (none present). The partial inverted repeat symmetry in sequence around the asterisk has long been known (83). It can be seen that this near-symmetry also expresses itself in the arrangement of 3-stacks. Perhaps the repressor recognizes aspects of the stacking patterns on associating with the operator.

Two results indicate that the operator may undergo a B-to-A transition upon association with the *lac* repressor. First, when the repressor binds, it unwinds its operator by 40° to 90° (79, 84). Most of the binding contacts are thought to be contained in a segment of 17 to 21 base-pairs (*79, 85, 86*). Thus, there is roughly 2° to 5° unwinding per base-pair, in the right direction for going from B-DNA with $W = 36°$ to A-DNA with $W = 33°$. Second, while repressor binds specifically to operator DNA, it also will bind less strongly to nonoperator sequences. The circular dichroism spectra of poly(dA-dT), calf-thymus DNA, and lambda DNA show changes consistent with a change in geometry toward the A-form upon repressor binding (*79, 87, 88*).

3. LAMBDA REPRESSORS

Phage lambda repressor (cI) and *cro* proteins bind to six 17-pair segments of lambda DNA in regulating the lytic and lysogenic cycles of phage infection (*79, 89, 89a–d*). The relative positions of these segments are shown at the top of Table IV. Each of the binding sites has a different affinity for the *cro* and cI proteins, and there are apparently protein–protein interactions between repressors bound at adjacent sites. These factors make it difficult to draw simple conclusions regarding the influence of structure and binding affinity on the overall regulatory process. A detailed model for the interaction of *cro* with its binding sites has been developed from the crystal structure of the protein and energy refinement of a complex with B-DNA (*89a*). The model is visually appealing, and the reduction in binding affinity of *cro* for mutated operator sites fits with the predicted loss of specific hydrogen bonds. However, as yet there is no direct evidence for the proposed structure. It seems prudent to consider alternatives, including an RY model structure.

One strand of each of the six operator sequences is given in Table IV, with the R–Y doublets underlined. There is a partial inverted repeat symmetry in the double strands, e.g., in the rightward operator site O_R3,

```
                  *     *  *  *  *
T A T C C C T T  G C G G T  G A T A
A T A G G G A A  C G C C A  C T A T
*  *  *  *     *
```

where the repeated bases are marked with asterisks. Also shown in Table IV are several mutated operators, their relative binding affinities for *cro* (*89a*), and the effect these base substitutions have on the pattern of R–Y doublets. Consider first the wild-type sequences. The last nine bases of the O_R3, O_R1, O_L3, and O_L1 sites are identical, but it is also seen that the stacking throughout O_R3 is the same as in O_R1, and similarly, O_L3 and O_L1 have identical patterns. The O_L2 and O_R2 sites, located in the center of the left and right operators, respectively, have a very different array of R–Y doublets from the other four sites.

TABLE IV
REPRESSOR BINDING SITES IN LAMBDA DNA[a]

Leftward operator   Rightward operator
...O_L1..O_L2..O_L3...cI gene ...O_R3..O_R2..O_R1...cro gene...

Site	Mutant[b]	Sequence	Affinity relative to O_R3
O_R3	wt	T A T C C C T T G C G G T G A T A	1
	*c10	G	0.1
	c12	C	0.3
	*r3	T	<1
	r2	A	<1
	r1	A	?
	v3C	C	0.1
O_R1	wt	T A C C T C T G G C G G T G A T A	0.1
	vR18	G	?
	*vs326	A	0.03
	*v3	A	?
	*vs387	T	<0.1
	*vC1	C	0.03
O_L3	wt	A A C C A T C T G C G G T G A T A	0.1
O_L1	wt	T A C C A C T G G C G G T G A T A	0.5
	v101	G	?
	*v2	T	?
	v003	A	?
O_L2	wt	T A T C T C T G G C G G T G T T G	0.5
	*v305	A	?
O_R2	wt	T A A C A C C G T G C G T G T T G	0.1
	v3C	G	0.01
	*vi or vH	A	?
	*virC23	A A	0.003
	*vN or vC34	T	0.1

[a] From Ohlendorf et al. (89a).

[b] The unmodified (wild-type) sequences are designated by wt. Mutants marked by an asterisk (*) should have differences in helical winding over the cro site compared with the wild type site.

What do these similarities and differences predict for the three-dimensional shape of these operator sites? The sites at each end of the cluster of right operator sequences should have a nearly identical shape. The same can be said of the sites at the ends of the leftward cluster, though the addition of one more R–Y doublet should produce a less tightly wound helix than in the rightward cluster. In the context of the RY model, the replacement of an R–R doublet by an R–Y doublet should decrease the winding by $50° - 20° = 30°$. The first four sites listed in Table IV should have only 3-stacks and 2-stacks. As for the central sites in each operator, we predict a substantially different form. 28 of the 34 bases in O_R2 should be in extended stacks, 16 in 4-stacks and 12 in 3-stacks. Again, a literal interpretation of the RY model would suggest that these central sites would be less tightly wound than the others. The mutant sequences, r3, vs326, v3, v305, virC23, and vC34 either add or delete in R–Y doublet compared with their wild-type sites; thus the RY model predicts a different helical winding over much of the length of the site. The other mutants marked with asterisks in Table IV should produce localized changes in the mutant helix. There should be only small alterations in the relative position of atoms separated by three or more nucleotides because these mutants do not add or delete an R–Y doublet, rather they only move the R–Y doublet one base to the left or right compared to the wild type.

The relative affinities of the mutant operator sites for *cro* show that recognition of individual bases by hydrogen-bonding and hydrophobic interaction is essential in determining the binding constant. For instance, the v3C mutant binds *cro* ten times less well than the O_R3 wild type (see Table IV) even though the stacking form is predicted to be the same for both. That the shape of the helix, as influenced by the arrangement of purines and pyrimidines, contributes significantly to the binding remains plausible but unproved.

4. *E. coli* RNA POLYMERASE

RNA polymerase opens the DNA strands at appropriate promoter sites. How does it recognize these sites, and how does it open the strands? A study of polymerase unwinding suggests that 17 ± 1 base-pairs are opened throughout the catalytic cycle of initiation and elongation of the RNA chain (90). In a study of polymerase binding, some of its contacts with promoters were located (91). The classic strong promoter A3 from phage T7 and another strong promoter, the *lac* UV5 from *E. coli*, were used; strong promoters do not require other protein cofactors for fidelity in promotion of synthesis. The latter study showed the open region ending at about the second base from the right in each sequence:

```
                    *                                                    *
T7 A3    G–T A A A–C A–C  G G–T A–C G A–T G–T A–C C A–C A–T  G
         /   / / /   /    / /   /   / /   /   /   / /   /    /
         C–A T T T–G T–G  C C–A T–G C T–A C–A T–G G T–G T–A  C


                    *                                                    *
lac UV5  T T C C G G–C T  C G–T A–T A A–T G–T G–T G G A A–T  T
         / / / / / /  / / /   /   / /   /   /   / / / /   / /
         A A G G C C–G A  G C–A T–A T T–A C–A C–A C C T T–A  A
```

A 17-base-pair segment between the asterisks represents the probable unpaired region in the initiation complex (90, 91). Note how few interstrand stacks are predicted in the T7 A3 promoter, and, necessarily, how many intrastrand stacks. It should be easy to separate the strands, and, once separated, they should be rather stable owing to the number of good stacking interactions that remain. Toward the right of the lac UV5 sequence there are four interstrand stacks in a row (in the GGAA sequence). Three of these are of the presumably weak 2-stacks with R on Y, so they may also be easily broken. In the single strands, it is known that purine stretches have a tendency to self-stack (13); this promoter is probably quite stable in the open form also. Table V contrasts the distribution of stacks we would expect in this 17-mer on a random basis with what is found. These are clearly very special sequences.

5. CONTROL SEQUENCES FOR β-GLOBIN GENES

Figure 10 shows ten sequences from the 5′-flanking regions of β-globin genes from various organisms. There is considerable homology throughout this set, and the rate of mutation from some ancestral sequence can be related to the time elapsed since the species diverged from this common ancestor (62). It is thus reasonable that there should

TABLE V
COMPARISON OF RY-STACKING PATTERNS

Sequence	Number of bases expected (found)		
	2-stacks	3-stacks	4-stacks
T7 A3	11 (0)	19 (18)	4 (16)
lac UV5	11 (4)	19 (17)	4 (12)

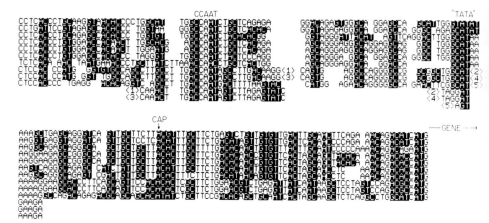

FIG. 10. Control regions of ten different mammalian globin genes, arranged to optimize homology in RY locations. The lower set of ten sequences are continuations of the upper ten. RY sequences are displayed in white on black for emphasis. Blank areas show gaps introduced to improve the alignment, corresponding to deleted sequences. Similarly, long sequence insertions are indicated by numbers in angle brackets ⟨#⟩, with the inserted sequences shown at the figure bottom. The genes are (from the top): mouse beta^{min}, mouse beta^{maj}, rabbit beta, goat beta^A, goat beta^C, human beta, human delta, human ^{A}gamma, human ^{G}gamma, and human epsilon. The arrangement is similar to that in (62). CAP represents the first base in the mRNA transcript.

be gaps in aligning some of the sequences where deletion mutations have occurred; there are also remnants of insertions.

We have adjusted the sequences for optimum alignment of what appear to be conserved "rivers" of R–Y neighbor doublets. We notice several features of this comparison. (i) It is especially easy to align the "rivers" in the region downstream (to the right) from the "cap" base, where the RNA transcript begins. This may have something to do with there being a clear RNA · DNA complex here during transcription, or some event in the processing of the transcript. (ii) Some rivers carefully preserve the identity of the bases while others seem only to require an R–Y doublet around which 3-stacks and 4-stacks can be built. (iii) There is a strong conservation of RY sequences in and around the long-recognized control elements in the "TATA", "CCAAT", and "cap" sites. This conservation extends into the 5'-flanking sequences of many other genes (P. N. Borer et al., unpublished). (iv) We have allowed some of the rivers to bend one base to the left or right. It seems reasonable that when an enzyme finds a stack in more or less the right position, it can twist the flexible DNA molecule into the proper orientation. (v) Such RY rivers may be useful as markers in aligning related sequences for determining their evolutionary relationship. Since the alignment in Fig. 10 decreases the optimal homology discussed in (62), we suppose that the members of the β-globin gene family must be more divergent than was previously thought, and the evolutionary time scale should be adjusted backward. (vi) Though not presented here, there are also RY rivers apparent in the introns, at the intron–exon junctions, and in the 3′-flanking sequences of the β-globin genes collected in (62) (P. N. Borer *et al.*, unpublished).

6. CAUTION

The predictions of the RY model for these sequences that control genetic expression, while attractive, do not prove the model. What has been shown is that it displays intriguing patterns of nearest-neighbor relationships. Another set of rules, incorporating parts of those given in Sections II,B,2 and II,C,1, or recognizing features of individual bases, would also lead to intriguing patterns. In Section II,B,5, we indicated that the helix might be especially flexible around R–R doublets. This is probably the first amendment that should be made to the RY rules. The RY hypothesis is based on experimental and theoretical considerations. We plan experiments to test the rules and hope that this article will stimulate others to do the same.

III. B-DNA

This section treats first-neighbor effects in the three-dimensional structure of B-form DNA. A survey of research concerning B-DNA structure is given elsewhere (1, 26, 27, 79, 92–95).

It is likely that the sequence dependence of structure in RNA duplexes will be discovered before that in DNA, since RNA duplexes have so far crystallized only in the A-form. DNA, however, has been crystallized in the A, B, C, D, E, and Z forms (1, 26, 27). A similar situation holds in solution studies of DNA duplexes. Substantial "premelting transitions" are observed in nmr studies of oligo-DNA (22, 96) that indicate changes in helix parameters with temperature. This premelting also occurs in long DNA as judged by circular dichroism (20, 79, 97). Similar premelting transitions have not been seen in duplexed RNA oligomers (51–59). This premelting behavior may indicate that base-stacking forces are weaker in the B-form than in the A-structures.

A. X-Ray Diffraction Studies

The most commonly used structural model for DNA is the B form, observed in high-humidity fibers (26, 33, 34, 60, 98–100). A structure similar to B-DNA has been shown to exist in single crystals by X-ray diffraction (*23, 45, 101–103, 106*).

The B-DNA model from fiber diffraction has about ten base-pairs per turn, 4.6 Å between the helix axis and the glycosyl nitrogens, and 8.9 Å from the axis to the phosphorus atoms (*30*). The sugar pucker is C2'-*endo* and intrachain phosphorus atoms are separated by 7.0 Å. The base planes are nearly perpendicular to the helix axis. The angle between the helix axis and the 1' carbon atoms of successive nucleosides on the same strand defines the winding angle, W, which is 36° in the fiber model (Fig. 11). The major and minor grooves are of about equal depth. Figure 11 shows the base overlap for RR, RY, and YR first-neighbor interactions in the standard B-form geometry. The bases lie much closer to the helix axis than in A-family structures, and thus variation in W of ±10° does not change the base overlaps significantly.

1. FIBER X-RAY DIFFRACTION PATTERNS

Only average properties are derivable from X-ray diffraction of fibers of naturally occurring DNA, even with semicrystalline fibers and extensive refinement. The B-DNA configuration is such an aver-

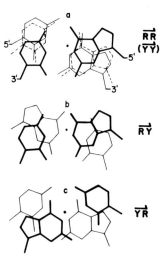

FIG. 11. B-DNA base overlap as viewed along the helix axis for sequences (a) RR, (b) RY, and (c) YR using the coordinates of Arnott and Hukins (*29*). Pairs drawn in heavy outline lie nearest the observer. The helix axis is represented by the dot between the bases of each base-pair, and the winding angle, W, is defined as the angle successive C1' atoms make with respect to the helix axis. The dashed-outline base-pair in (a) indicates the location the far pair would occupy in the case of the most extreme deviation from B-structure, according to the analysis of Kabsch *et al.* (*140*).

age conformation (60, 104). Microheterogeneities in the rise and winding angle between successive base-pairs due to sequence effects cannot be seen.

X-Ray diffraction analysis of fibers with regularly repeating sequences makes it possible to observe some local geometries. This is the case with the helical form of the alternating copolymer poly-[d(A-T)]. An "alternating B" structure, which retains many B-DNA features, has been proposed (105). In one of the differences, the base overlaps for the alternating structure are significantly improved over those of B-DNA [Fig. 2 in (105)].

2. SINGLE-CRYSTAL X-RAY DIFFRACTION STUDIES

The crystal structure of the self-complementary dodecamer d(CGCGAATTCGCG) has been solved at 17°C (23, 101, 106). It forms a right-handed B-family structure with a gradual 19° bend in the helix axis over the course of the entire duplex. Examination of this structure reveals that it is not highly regular; there are local variations in the helix parameters, such as twist, tilt, roll, base overlap, which are more strongly influenced by base sequence than by other forces (23, 106).

Since the helix axis has a gradual bend, there are two sets of parameters that characterize the structure of this dodecamer. Use of a "best overall helix axis" as a reference yields "global" properties, while use of a "local" helix axis, defined by two adjacent base-pairs as a reference, results in "local" features. The local helix twists or winding angles span 30–50° (average 37.3°) with a corresponding range of 8–12 base-pairs per turn (9.65 average). The standard values for B-DNA structure occur only once. Global considerations yield ranges of 30–41° for W and of 9–12 for the number of base pairs per turn. Averages of the global values are 35.8° and 10.1 bases per turn. These agree with the analogous B-DNA fiber values of 36° and 10. Variations in the local parameters lead to different types of DNA structures in the helix. There are localized regions with A-, B-, and D-like base overlaps (23).

More recently, single crystals of the same dodecamer at −257°C have been analyzed by X-ray diffraction (45). The geometry is very similar at 17°C and −257°C, although there are some structural differences. The global averages are still 10.1 base pairs per turn, and W = 35.9° with local variations from 28° to 40°. A nonuniform distribution of atomic positions is observed in the structure, with the largest displacements at the phosphates and the smallest at the bases; a similar result is found at 17°C. Hence, these displacements are due to static disorder rather than to thermal factors. The implication is that the dynamic motions, which produce local fluctuations in winding angle and helix unwinding in solution, are not accessible in the crystal, even at room temperature (45).

Changes in W also signify changes in base overlap. Detailed examination of the base stacking in the dodecamer reveals that, in certain cases, interstrand and intrastrand overlaps increase relative to those of standard B-DNA, while stacking decreases for others (23). Presently, a clear relationship between sequence and geometry cannot be proposed; however, certain correlations have been made (23). When more single-crystal structures with varying sequences are known, a correspondence between sequence and structure and its biological significance may become possible.

Another important result of the crystal study on the dodecamer is the specific hydration of the molecule (26, 102). It has been suggested that this helps to stabilize the B-structure, thus explaining why reduction in water activity facilitates the B-to-A transition (A-form DNA is less heavily hydrated in crystals and solution) (26).

B. Solution Nuclear-Magnetic-Resonance Studies

1. OLIGODEOXYNUCLEOTIDE STRUCTURES

DNA structure in solution clearly depends on sequence. Perhaps the best evidence comes from the ^{31}P-nmr of the duplex of the dodecamer d(CGCGAATTCGCG) (22), where seven of the eleven ^{31}P signals occur as distinct peaks in the spectrum. This implies a considerable range in configuration about the phosphorus atom.

High-resolution nmr has been used to probe the structure of double-stranded oligodeoxyribonucleotides (22, 96, 107–125). In the cases where individual resonance assignments have been made, the nmr data on complementary DNA sequences in solution are qualitatively consistent with B-form geometry (22, 96, 111–117, 125). For the comparison between the experimentally observed and the calculated shielding, the computed parameters were based on ring-current contributions alone (111, 113, 115, 120) or ring-current and local atomic contributions (22, 114, 117, 118, 125), and used standard DNA geometries derived from X-ray diffraction.

The duplex of the decamer d(CCAAGCTTGG) in solution was extensively characterized by nmr (125). In the comparison between experiment and theory, the ring-current and local anisotropies were used individually and as a sum for A-, A'-, and B-form geometries. The most consistent result is given by the sum of the effects in a B-DNA structure; however, significant deviations were noted.

A similar evaluation has been performed for the duplex of the dodecamer d(CGCGAATTCGCG) (22). The calculated parameters also include monomer corrections (49, 126) in addition to all the previously mentioned contributions. The computed values were based on the d(CGCGAATTCGCG) crystal structure (106). The correlation between calculated and experimental shifts is good, with some significant deviations. Other DNA geometries were not tested.

We have been unsuccessful in using the winding angle in B-DNA as an adjustable parameter to produce quantitative agreement with measured nmr shieldings (49). There are two major problems. (i) The overlap changes much less by altering W by 10° to 20° than with A-forms (see Fig. 11a). A method must be developed that systematically eliminates unreasonable overlaps, perhaps using sliding motions of neighboring base-pairs to fit the measured nmr shielding. (ii) There is reason to doubt that a single first-neighbor overlap can accurately describe the structure of a doublet. The "premelting transitions" in chemical shift are sometimes 10% to 20% of the largest measured effect (22, 96).

2. TELESTABILITY

The "telestability" model for gene regulation proposes that a protein that binds to one segment of a DNA helix can influence the properties of a nearby region. This model was suggested by studies on block deoxynucleotide polymers, e.g., $d(C_{15}-A_{15}) \cdot d(T_{15}-G_{15})$ (94, 127–129). The nearest-neighbor model (130) could not be made consistent with all the details of the observed helix-coil transitions (129). Interactions with more distant neighbors must be invoked to explain the details, although first-neighbor considerations make generally correct predictions of t_m values.

Nuclear magnetic resonance studies on the deoxynucleotide block polymer $d(C_{15}-A_{15}) \cdot d(T_{15}-G_{15})$ indicated that the conformation of the main $A \cdot T$ helix is unchanged when joined with the $G \cdot C$ helix (115). The $G \cdot C$ helix induced a structural perturbation extending only 3 or 4 base-pairs into the $A \cdot T$ region. This study showed that most of the telestabilization of the $A \cdot T$ helix is a result of changes in dynamic properties, rather than a change in conformation. In addition, nmr spectra of the duplex $(dG)_n \cdot (rC_{11}-dC_{16})$ demonstrates that two contiguous conformations can coexist along a nucleic-acid helix with minimal disruption at the covalent ribose–deoxyribose linkage (116). Whatever its importance in genetic regulation, there does not appear to be a large interaction between the equilibrium structures of distant regions.

C. Helical Repeat

The helical periodicity of DNA in nucleosomes has been determined by partial nuclease hydrolysis experiments to be 10.4 ± 0.1 base-pairs per turn (*131, 132*), while the periodicity in solution has been evaluated by the electrophoretic band-shift method (*133–135*) and by nuclease hydrolysis of DNA adsorbed to surfaces (*136–138*) to be 10.6 ± 0.1 base-pairs per turn for both methods (*139*).

The ten first-neighbor winding angles for B-DNA were derived from the band-shift method, nuclease hydrolysis of adsorbed DNA, and the crystallographic data on the B-DNA dodecamer d(CGCGAATTCGCG) (*140*). The resulting winding angles are different from the classical B-DNA value of 36°, ranging from 28° to 40°. The most extreme deviation is shown with the dashed outline in Fig. 11a, where the helix axis is not varied from the B-DNA structure. These studies provide the contribution of an individual first-neighbor doublet to the overall winding in a long helix. Many geometries other than those in Fig. 11 can provide this contribution; the correct geometry will probably have the base-pairs displaced different distances from the helix axis.

D. Other Studies

The classic B-DNA geometry was derived from highly hydrated fibers (*26, 33, 34, 60, 98–100*). Circular dichroism studies of oriented and unoriented DNA films at high humidities yield circular dichroism spectra similar to those in solution. This suggests that the solution and film structures are similar (*20, 46, 141*). Also the preferred sites for nuclease hydrolysis of d(CGCGAATTCGCG) are between adjacent bases related by large winding angles in the crystal structure (*142*). Some of the other measured properties of DNA in solution suggest that there are significant differences between the solid-state and solution structures.

It has been reported that bundles of about seven parallel DNA molecules are present in the solutions from which fibers are drawn, and that these bundles exhibit physical properties expected for B-DNA as observed in fibers (*143*). On the other hand, monomeric DNA shows properties inconsistent with the fiber structure (*143*). This suggests that packing forces in the solid state play a large role in determining the helix parameters, and it argues for caution in applying the diffraction results to the structure of DNA and RNA in solution.

The X-ray diffraction models of B-DNA indicate that the base planes are nearly perpendicular to the helix axis. Birefringence data are consistent with this feature (*144*). However, linear electric dichroism indicates a tilt of at least 17° out of the plane perpendicular to the helix axis (145), which is closer to the A-DNA value of 20° (92).

The spacing per residue in solution has been determined by a variety of methods. Light-scattering data give a value of 3.25 Å for DNA in dilute solution while low-angle X-ray scattering yields a range of 2.7–3.25 Å (146). Measurements of rotational and translational friction coefficients show a 3.34 Å value (147).

The ratio of contour lengths of A- to B-form molecules should be about 0.8, according to fiber diffraction results (29, 30). This ratio is 0.79 in electron micrographs of double-stranded RNA and DNA obtained from phage G4 (148). Here, the absolute contour length varied from one experiment to the next, but the ratio was constant. Phage ϕX174 duplex DNA was found, by the same method, to have absolute contour lengths 15% shorter than predicted from B-DNA fiber studies (149). In this study, no variation in length was seen in duplicate experiments. On the other hand, RNA · DNA complexes with the same sequence had contour lengths in close agreement with data on A-DNA fibers. In both studies, it is not clear whether the contour length is changed by spreading the molecules on an electron-microscope grid, or if spreading differentially affects the lengths of DNA · DNA, RNA · DNA, or RNA · RNA complexes.

The experimental circular dichroism spectra of sequenced DNA restriction fragments (150) have been compared to calculated spectra based on the nearest-neighbor approximation (5, 6). There is a lack of quantitative agreement that suggests either (i) that second- and third-neighbor interactions contribute extensively to the spectra or (ii) that first-neighbor doublets have different configurations in different sequences. A combination of the two explanations is probably closer to the truth.

In conclusion, the structure of B-DNA in the solid state and in solution shows a wide variability, and there is no clear correlation of the solution and crystal forms.

IV. Z-DNA

A. X-Ray Diffraction Studies

The last of the known major families of DNA structures is the left-handed Z-form (1, 26, 79, 151). Z-DNA is distinguished from the other families by a radically different set of characteristics. Some heterogeneity in structure is also noted within the Z-family.

1. SINGLE-CRYSTAL X-RAY DIFFRACTION STUDIES

The parameters that characterize Z-DNA helices are derived from single-crystal structures of alternating C and G residues (*152–154a*). The Z-form of DNA is a left-handed double helix with 12 bases per turn. For a given strand, the repeat unit is a dinucleotide, so there are six dinucleotide units per turn. The distance from the helix axis to the phosphorus atom is 7.3 Å for C and 6.3 Å for G, and to the glycosyl nitrogen it is 2.7 Å for C and 7.0 Å for G. For G and C residues, respectively, the glycosylic torsion angles are *syn* and *anti*, and the sugar pucker is C3′-*endo* and C2′-*endo*. The sugar–phosphate backbone goes through a zigzag course; the Z designation arose from this feature. There is a minor groove that extends almost to the helix axis, and the major groove is nearly absent. The base-pairs are situated off the helix axis at the periphery (Fig. 12). In a way, this is analogous to A-form DNA, except that the base-pairs are displaced to the opposite side of the helix axis in Z-DNA as compared to A-DNA.

Examination of the details of base-stacking for the duplex of d(CGCGCG) reveals several interesting observations (Fig. 12). The following notation is used for a half-turn of a Z-DNA helix including the base-stacking:

```
            1  2   3   4   5  6
     5'...C  G – C  G – C  G ...3'
            ·  \       \       \
            G  C – G  C – G  C
            *  *   *   *   *  *
```

The sugar of C(1) overlaps with the six-membered ring of G(2) on the same strand (Fig. 12a). G(2) overlaps with C(3) on the same strand (Fig. 12b). C(3) overlaps with C(4*) on the opposite strand (Fig. 12c). C(4*) overlaps with G(5*) on the same strand (Fig. 12d). G(5*) overlaps with the sugar of C(6*) (Fig. 12e). The final result is that there are 6-stacks composed of a 4-stack base core that is capped on each end with a C sugar. There are six 6-stacks per turn of the helix. The individual steps in the 6-stacks involve rather weak overlaps of the bases, which makes them of dubious value in explaining nearest-neighbor properties in Z-DNA. It is possible that the overlaps are stronger in solution than in the crystal. Certainly the bases involved in one of these stacks all lie along the same face of the helix and are available for recognition by an enzyme.

2. FIBER X-RAY DIFFRACTION STUDIES

The idea of a left-handed double helix is not new. X-Ray and circular dichroism studies on oriented fibers of d(I–C)$_n$ were explained in 1970 as a left-handed double helix (*155*).

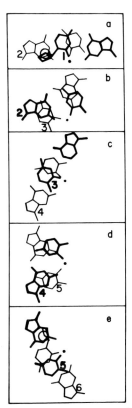

FIG. 12. Base overlaps for a half-turn of Z-DNA helix. The bases along one strand are numbered 1–6 (near the glycosyl nitrogen atom); their complementary bases are denoted by (*) in the text. (a) The stacking of the C(1) sugar (with ring oxygen circled) on G(2). (b) The intrastrand stack between G(2) and C(3). (c) The interstrand stack of C(3) on C(4)*. (d) The intrastrand stack of C(4)* on G(5)*. (e) The stacking of G(5)* on the C(6)* sugar. The dot represents the helix axis in each case.

A number of fiber X-ray diffraction studies have been interpreted in terms of the Z-form (*104, 138, 156*). Under appropriate conditions, fibers of d(G–C)$_n$ (*138, 156*), of d(G–m^{5}C)$_n$ (*138*), of d(A–C)$_n$ · d(G–T)$_n$ (*156*), and of d(A–s^{4}T)$_n$ (*156*) give X-ray diffraction patterns that are consistent with a left-handed polymer model, Z-DNA.

B. Solution Nuclear-Magnetic-Resonance Studies

A variety of ^{1}H and ^{31}P nmr experiments on molecules of d(G–C)$_n$ of varying lengths under the appropriate Z-DNA solution conditions have been performed (*157–162*). The ^{1}H nmr studies indicate that G and C do not have the same glycosylic torsion angles and sugar puckers. The ^{31}P nmr studies show that there are two phosphorus resonances of approximately equal intensity, which indicates an alternating conformation of the phosphodiester linkage. Using theoretically computed magnetic shielding constants, including contributions from local magnetic anisotropy and ring current effects, it was shown that under the appropriate conditions the experimentally observed nmr shift data for d(G–C)$_n$ are consistent with a Z structure (*159, 160*). Even though the nmr results agree with a Z-form DNA structure, they do not prove that Z-DNA is actually present in solution. ^{1}H and ^{31}P nmr studies show that d(A–T)$_n$ adopts a high-salt form that is different from that of d(G–C)$_n$, although they both have two ^{31}P signals consistent with a regularly alternating phosphodiester backbone (*157, 163*).

A series of dinucleoside monophosphate analogs of r(C–G) containing an 8-bromoguanine (br^{8}G) residue have been studied (*164*). The br^{8}G residues are constrained to a *syn* glycosyl conformation as found in Z-DNA. In 0.1 M NaCl, r(C–br^{8}G) forms a duplex. The ^{1}H nmr data for this duplex are consistent with a left-handed helical structure similar to that of Z-DNA. The interpretation of the data shows an interstrand CC 2-stack. Under the same solution conditions, dC–rbr^{8}G does not form a duplex.

C. Other Studies

Alternating DNA polymers under conditions of high salt or intermediate levels of alcohol show a "high-salt" structural form. The original investigations indicated that at high salt concentrations (*165*), or intermediate levels of ethanol (*166*), d(G–C)$_n$ undergoes changes in its circular dichroism and ultraviolet absorbance spectra relative to the low-salt form. Inversion of the circular dichroism spectrum is diagnostic of the cooperative transition from the low-salt conformation to the high-salt conformation. This "Pohl–Jovin transition" is an intramolecular rearrangement that does not require strand separation (*158*). This transition can also be induced at low ionic strength by alcohol and certain cations (*165, 167*). Other properties such as ^{3}H-exchange (*168*), laser Raman scattering (*169*), vacuum ultraviolet circular dichroism (*170*), transient electric dichroism (*171*), and Raman spectroscopy (*172*) have been used to measure this transition in d(G–C)$_n$. A variety of modified d(G–C)$_n$ species also exhibit Z-form structures at lower ionic strengths (*138, 173–175*). d(G–C)$_n$ with 100% methylation of the guanine or cytosine residues is fully converted to Z-DNA at physiological salt conditions (*138, 175*). Methylation should increase the hydrophobic association of bases, perhaps in the 6-stacks suggested in Section IV,A,1.

Laser Raman spectroscopy of d(G–C), in solution at high salt (4 M

NaCl) and of the crystallized hexamer d(CGCGCG) clearly indicates that the solution and crystal structure are similar (176). Calculation of the rise per base-pair from rotational relaxation-time data (171) gives a best-fit value of 3.7 Å with 12 base pairs per turn, which is in accord with crystallographic and fiber diffraction measurements (152–153, 156). The helical repeat as determined by partial nuclease hydrolysis of $d(G-C)_n$ adsorbed onto a solid support is 13 ± 1 under Z-form solution conditions (138), which is in agreement with the above.

A minimum number of repeating $d(C-G)$ units is necessary to exhibit Z-form properties in high-salt solution. At 0.1 M and 4 M NaCl concentrations, 10^{-5}–10^{-2} M oligomer strand concentrations, and 0–90°C temperatures, the dimer $d(C-G)$ does not form a duplex of any sort (162). The tetramer $d(C-G)_2$ forms a Z-structure in 4 M NaCl and 3×10^{-4} M strand concentration (162). One study (177) did not indicate a Z-form duplex at 5 M NaCl; however, the strand concentration was not specified. The hexamer $d(C-G)_3$ at high-salt conditions (>4 M NaCl) and $>1.5 \times 10^{-5}$ M strand concentration forms a Z-structure. This dependence of stability on chain length may be explained using the stacking interactions mentioned earlier (Section IV,A,1); $d(C-G)_3$ can form a full 6-stack with three interstrand stacks while $d(C-G)_2$ has only two interstrand stacks and cannot form a 6-stack.

In other studies on oligomers, the repeating Y–R decamer, $d(C-G)_5$, forms a Z-form duplex at high-salt conditions, whereas the R–Y decamers $d(G-C)_5$, d(GCGCATGCGC), and d(GTGCATGCAC) do not (178). An examination of the stacking patterns shows that an R–Y oligomer should have one less Z-form interstrand stack than a Y–R oligomer of the same length. There seems to be a delicate balance between B- and Z-forms so this may be the explanation. From circular dichroism spectroscopy, the dodecamer d(ATATATCGCGCG) is not in the Z-form (177). The flanking $d(A-T)$ units destabilize Z-structure formation, possibly by disrupting the stacking pattern. On the other hand, we speculate that d(TATATACGCGCG) may show Z-form properties, since the pattern of 6-stacks can remain intact. Also, adjoining Z and B conformations in DNA restriction fragments exhibit short junction conformations different from Z- and B-forms (172, 179).

$d(A-C)_n \cdot d(G-T)_n$ is induced by high salt or ethanol to a conformational form that is consistent with a Z-like form, as evidenced by circular dichroism (180, 181); however, more investigation is required on this point. The polymer adopts the Z-form in fibers (see Section IV,A,2). The generalization that alternating polymers go into Z-form is not warranted at this time, especially in light of the nmr studies on $d(A-T)_n$ (Section IV,B) (163).

Progress is being made with *in vitro* and *in vivo* research concerning the occurrence of potential Z-DNA-forming sequences and their
possible role in biological systems (*80, 167, 179, 182–188*). Stretches
of d(G-C)$_n$ inserted in bacterial plasmids (*80, 186*) are frequently de-
lted if *n* is greater than about 20, but are copied faithfully with a
smaller *n*. These stretches adopt a Z-form when the plasmids have
substantial negative superhelix densities, but have a standard helix in
relaxed plasmids. The d(G-C)$_n$-containing plasmids are 6–12 turns
less supercoiled when isolated from *E. coli* hosts than are their unmodified counterparts.

The *in vivo* significance of these results is not yet clear, though
Z-compatible structures could regulate torsional stress over long regions of DNA. They also offer the potential for specific recognition by
their shape, although the requirement for a strictly alternating RY sequence drastically limits their potential for carrying information. It is
clear that there are potential Z-forming sequences dispersed throughout many genomes (*185, 187, 188*).

It is doubly intriguing that sequences compatible with Z-DNA are
exactly those that should form long stretches of extended stacks in
A-DNA according to the RY model. There may be a competition here, a
sort of regulatory switch, e.g., with (i) the sequences existing in the
Z-form representing the "off" state with supercoils relaxed, and (ii) the
sequences held in the RY-form by an activator protein being the "on"
state with high superhelix density. The free energy from this supercoiling would then be available to drive some of the processes in gene
expression.

V. Summary

Three widely used models for the form of duplexed nucleic acids
have been considered: the A-, B-, and Z-structures. Interactions between adjacent base-pairs are thought to provide the main stabilization
against denaturation to the single strands. The arrangement of
nearest-neighbors was discussed in the context of each of the models.
We have described a variant of the A-form, called the RY model, in
which neighbor-pair overlaps lead to extended stacks of up to four
bases parallel to the helix axis. These extended stacks involve bases
from both strands and have consequences in local stability and recognition by enzymes. The A-structure accommodates a wide chemical
variation in the nature of the bases and sugar–phosphate backbones;
base overlaps appear to be stronger than in the other two forms. RNA
duplexes have been found only in the A-form. Less is known about

base overlap in the B-form in solution, but the plasticity of DNA structure suggests rather weak interactions between neighbor pairs. Even less is known about the stacking of adjacent pairs in the Z-form, but it is proposed that extended stacks are also important here. The A-form may represent the conformation of DNA in its actively expressed form. B-DNA may be a form useful for storage rather than expression of genetic content, although enzymes may also use its special plasticity in "induced-fit" interactions. The left-handed Z-form exists only in specific sequences and is in a delicate balance with the right-handed B-form, easily shifted by solution conditions. Z-DNA may be especially important in regulating torsional stress in supercoiled DNA.

ACKNOWLEDGMENTS

This work was supported in part by National Institutes of Health Grant GM 24494; E. B. was supported by Training Grant GM 07311 (NIH). We are grateful to L.-S. Kan, D. H. Turner, and S.-H. Kim for providing unpublished information, to I. Tinoco, Jr. for advice and assistance, and to K. Moldave, C. S. McLaughlin, and R. C. Warner for helpful discussions.

REFERENCES

1. S. B. Zimmerman, *ARB* **51**, 395 (1982).
2. C. R. Cantor and I. Tinoco, Jr., *JMB* **13**, 65 (1965).
3. M. M. Warshaw and I. Tinoco, Jr., *JMB* **13**, 54 (1965).
4. D. M. Gray, I. Tinoco, Jr., and M. J. Chamberlin, *Biopolymers* **11**, 1235 (1972).
5. F. S. Allen, D. M. Gray, G. P. Roberts, and I. Tinoco, Jr., *Biopolymers* **11**, 853 (1973).
6. D. M. Gray, F. D. Hamilton, and M. R. Vaughan, *Biopolymers* **17**, 85 (1978).
7. D. M. Gray, J.-J. Liu, R. L. Ratliff, and F. S. Allen, *Biopolymers* **20**, 1337 (1981).
8. P. N. Borer, O. C. Uhlenbeck, B. Dengler, and I. Tinco, Jr., *JMB* **80**, 759 (1973).
9. I. Tinoco, Jr., P. N. Borer, B., Dengler, M. D. Levine, O. C. Uhlenbeck, D. M. Crothers, and J. Gralla, *Nature NB* **246**, 40 (1973).
10. P. N. Borer, B. Dengler, I. Tinoco, Jr., and O. C. Ulenbeck, *JMB* **86**, 843 (1974).
11. J. Ninio, *Biochimie* **61**, 1133 (1979).
12. D. M. Gray and I. Tinoco, Jr., *Biopolymers* **9**, 223 (1970).
13. C. R. Cantor and P. R. Schimmel, "Biophysical Chemistry." Freeman, San Francisco, California, 1980.
14. A. Pullman, *Jerusalem Symp. Quantum Chem. Biochem.* **2**, 1970.
15. H. deVoe and I. Tinoco, Jr., *JMB* **4**, 500 (1962).
16. A. Pullman and B. Pullman, *Adv. Quantum Chem.* **4**, 267 (1968).
17. B. P. Rand, *Annu. Rev. Biophys. Bioeng.* **10**, 277 (1981).
18. V. A. Parsegian, *Annu. Rev. Biophys. Bioeng.* **2**, 221 (1973).
19. B. Pullman, P. Claverie, and J. Caillet, *PNAS* **55**, 904 (1966).
20. I. Tinoco, Jr., C. Bustamante, and M. F. Maestre, *Annu. Rev. Biophys. Bioeng.* **9**, 107 (1980).
21. D. R. Kearns, *Annu. Rev. Biophys. Bioeng.* **6**, 477 (1977).
22. D. J. Patel, A. Pardi, and K. Itakura, *Science* **216**, 581 (1982).

23. R. E. Dickerson and H. R. Drew, *JMB* **149**, 761 (1981).
24. H. M. Berman and P. R. Young, *Annu. Rev. Biophys. Bioeng.* **10**, 87 (1981).
25. C. R. Cantor, *Cell* **25**, 293 (1981).
26. R. E. Dickerson, H. R. Drew, B. N. Conner, R. M. Wing, A. V. Fratini, and M. L. Kopka, *Science* **216**, 475 (1982).
27. R. Chandrasekaran, S. Arnott, A. Banerjee, S. Campbell-Smith, A. G. W. Leslie, and L. Puigjaner, *in* "Fiber Diffraction Methods" (K. Corwin and H. Gardner, eds.), p. 483, *Am. Chem. Soc. Symp.* Ser. **141**, 1980.
27a. A. H.-J. Wang, S. Fujii, J. H. van Boom, G. A. van der Marel, S. A. A. van Boekel, and A. Rich, *Nature* **299**, 601 (1982).
28. A. Rich, G. J. Quigley, and A. H.-J. Wang, *in* "Nucleic Acid Geometry and Dynamics" (R. H. Sarma, ed.), p. 273. Pergamon, Oxford, 1980.
29. S. Arnott and D. W. L. Hukins, *BBRC* **47**, 1504 (1972).
30. S. Arnott and D. W. L. Hukins, *BBRC* **48**, 1392 (1972).
31. E. J. O'Brien and A. W. MacEwan, *JMB* **48**, 243 (1970).
32. R. E. Franklin and R. G. Gosling, *Acta Crystallogr.* **6**, 673 (1953).
33. J. D. Watson and F. H. C. Crick, *Nature* **171**, 737 (1953).
34. J. D. Watson and F. H. C. Crick, *Nature* **171**, 964 (1953).
35. S. R. Holbrook, J. L. Sussman, R. W. Warrant, and S.-H. Kim, *JMB* **123**, 631 (1978).
36. C. D. Stout, H. Mizuno, S. T. Rao, P. Swaminathan, J. Rubin, T. Brennan, and M. Sundaralingam, *Acta Crystallogr. Sect. B* **34**, 1529 (1978).
37. B. Hingerty, R. S. Brown, and A. Jack, *JMB* **124**, 523 (1978).
38. S.-H. Kim, *in* "Transfer RNA: Structure, Properties, and Recognition" (P. R. Schimmel, D. Söll, and J. N. Abelson, eds.), p. 83. Cold Spring Harbor Laboratory, Cold Spring Harbor, New York, 1979.
39. R. O. Day, N. C. Seeman, J. M. Rosenberg, and A. Rich, *PNAS* **70**, 849 (1973).
40. N. C. Seeman, J. M. Rosenberg, F. L. Suddath, J. J. P. Kim, and A. Rich, *JMB* **104**, 109 (1976).
41. J. M. Rosenberg, N. C. Seeman, J. J. P. Kim, F. L. Suddath, H. B. Nicholas, and A. Rich, *Nature* **243**, 150 (1973).
42. J. M. Rosenberg, N. C. Seeman, R. O. Day, and A. Rich, *JMB* **104**, (1976).
43. Z. Shakked, D. Rabinovich, W. B. T. Cruse, E. Egert, O. Kennard, G. Sala, S. A. Salisbury, and M. A. Viswamitra, *Proc. R. Soc. London Ser. B* **213**, 479 (1981).
44. B. N. Conner, T. Takano, S. Tanaka, K. Itakura, and R. E. Dickerson, *Nature* **295**, 294 (1982).
45. H. R. Drew, S. Samson, and R. E. Dickerson, *PNAS* **79**, 4040 (1982).
46. M. J. Tunis-Schneider and M. F. Maestre, *JMB* **52**, 521 (1970).
47. D. M. Gray and R. L. Ratliff, *Biopolymers* **14**, 487 (1975).
48. R. E. Dickerson, *Nature* **286**, 567 (1980).
49. P. Cruz, E. Bubienko, and P. N. Borer, *Nature* **298**, 198 (1982).
50. E. Bubienko, M. A. Uniack, and P. N. Borer, *Bchem* **20**, 6987 (1981).
51. P. N. Borer, L.-S. Kan, and P. O. P. Ts'o, *Bchem* **14**, 4847 (1975).
52. M. Petersheim and D. H. Turner, *Bchem* **22**, 269 (1982).
53. D. B. Arter, G. C. Walker, O. C. Uhlenbeck, and P. G. Schmidt, *BBRC* **61**, 1089 (1974).
54. D. W. Hughes, R. A. Bell, T. E. England, and T. Neilson, *Can. J. Chem.* **56**, 2243 (1978).
55. P. J. Romaniuk, T. Neilson, D. W. Hughes, and R. A. Bell, *Can. J. Chem.* **56**, 2249 (1978).
56. P. J. Romaniuk, D. W. Hughes, R. J. Gregoire, T. Neilson, and R. A. Bell, *JACS* **100**, 3971 (1978).

57. P. J. Romaniuk, D. W. Hughes, R. J. Gregoire, R. A. Bell, and T. Neilson, *Bchem* **18**, 5109 (1979).

58. D. Alkema, R. A. Bell, P. A. Hader, and T. J. Neilson, *JACS* **103**, 2866 (1981).

59. T. Neilson, P. J. Romaniuk, D. Alkema, D. W. Hughes, J. R. Everett, and R. A. Bell, *Nucleic Acids Symp. Ser.* **7**, 293 (1980).

60. S. Arnott, D. W. L. Hukins, S. D. Dover, W. Fuller, and A. R. Hodgson, *JMB* **81**, 107 (1973).

61. C. Giessner-Pretre and B. Pullman, *BBRC* **70**, 578 (1976).

62. A. Efstratiadis, J. W. Posakony, T. Maniatis, R. M. Lawn, C. O'Connell, R. A. Spritz, J. K. DeRiel, B. G. Forget, S. M. Weissman, J. L. Slightom, A. E. Bleche, O. Smithies, F. E. Baralle, C. C. Shoulders, and N. J. Proudfoot, *Cell* **21**, 653 (1980).

63. S. Arnott, W. Fuller, A. Hodgson, and I. Prutton, *Nature* **220**, 561 (1968).

64. F. H. C. Crick, "Life Itself: Its Origin and Nature." Simon & Schuster, New York, 1982.

65. R. E. Dickerson and I. Geis, "The Structure and Action of Proteins." Harper & Row, New York, 1969.

66a. F. Lustig, P. Elias, T. Axberg, T. Samuelsson, I. Tittawella, and U. Lagerkvist, *JBC* **256**, 2635 (1981).

66b. U. Lagerkvist, *Am. Sci.* **68**, 192 (1980).

66c. U. Lagerkvist, *PNAS* **75**, 1759 (1978).

66d. B. G. Barrell, S. Anderson, A. T. Bankier, M. H. L. de Bruijn, E. Chen, A. R. Coulson, J. Drouin, I. C. Eperon, D. P. Nierlich, B. A. Roe, F. Sanger, P. H. Schreier, A. J. H. Smith, R. Staden, and I. G. Young, *PNAS* **77**, 3164 (1980).

66e. S. G. Bonitz, R. Berlani, G. Coruzzi, M. Li, G. Macino, F. G. Nobrega, M. P. Nobrega, B. E. Thalenfeld, and A. Zagoloff, *PNAS* **77**, 3167 (1980).

66f. J. E. Heckman, J. Sarnoff, B. Alzner-de Weerd, S. Yin, and U. L. RajBhandary, *PNAS* **77**, 3159 (1980).

67. F. H. C. Crick, *JMB* **19**, 548 (1966).

68. R. J. Cedergren, D. Sankoff, B. LaRue, and H. Grosjean, *CRC Crit. Rev. Biochem.* **11**, 35 (1981).

69. W. Fuller and A. Hodgson, *Nature* **215**, 817 (1967).

70. C. Woese, *Nature* **226**, 817 (1970).

70a. T. Ruusala, M. Ehrenberg, and C. G. Kurland, *EMBO J.* **1**, 741 (1982).

71. H. Grosjean, S. deHenau, and D. M. Crothers, *PNAS* **75**, 610 (1978).

71a. H. Grosjean, D. G. Söll, and D. M. Crothers, *JMB* **103**, 499 (1980).

72. M. A. Viswamitra, Z. Shakked, P. G. Jones, G. M. Sheldrick, S. A. Salisbury, and O. Kennard, *Biopolymers* **21**, 513 (1982).

73. J. Rubin, T. Brennan, and M. Sundralingam, *Bchem* **11**, 3112 (1972).

74. J. L. Sussman, N. C. Seeman, S-H. Kim, and H. M. Berman, *JMB* **66**, 404 (1972).

75. B. N. Conner, T. Takano, S. Tanaka, K. Itakura, and R. E. Dickerson, *Nature* **295**, 294 (1982).

75a. A. H.-J. Wang, S. Fujii, J. H. van Boom, and A. Rich, *PNAS* **79**, 3968 (1982).

76. A. Rich, N. C. Seeman, and J. M. Rosenberg, *in* "Nucleic Acid–Protein Recognition" (H. G. Vogel, ed.), p. 361. Academic Press, New York, 1977.

77. B. Hingerty, *Biopolymers* **18**, 1901 (1979).

78. S. R. Holbrook, J. L. Sussman, and S.-H. Kim, *Science* **212**, 1275 (1981).

79. R. D. Wells, T. C. Goodman, W. Hillen, G. T. Horn, R. D. Klein, J. E. Larson, U. R. Muller, S. K. Neuendorf, N. Panavotatos, and S. M. Stirdivant, This series **24**, 167 (1980).

80. C. K. Singleton and R. D. Wells, *JBC* **257**, 6292 (1982).

81. N. Panayotatos and R. D. Wells, *Nature* **289**, 466 (1982).

82. D. M. J. Lilley, PNAS 77, 6468 (1980).
83. M. H. Caruthers, Acc. Chem. Res. 13, 155 (1980).
84. J. C. Wang, M. D. Barkley, and S. Bourgeois, Nature 251, 247 (1974).
85. C. P. Bahl, R. Wu, J. Stavinsky, and S. Narang, PNAS 74, 966 (1977).
86. D. V. Goeddel, D. G. Yansura, and M. H. Caruthers, PNAS 74, 3292 (1977).
87. J.-C. Maurizot, M. Charlier, and C. Helene, BBRC 60, 951 (1974).
88. A. P. Butler, A. Revzin, and P. H. von Hippel, Bchem 16, 4757 (1977).
89. M. Ptashne, A. Jeffrey, A. D. Johnson, R. Maurer, B. J. Meyer, C. O. Pabo, T. M. Roberts, and R. T. Sauer, Cell 19, 1 (1980).
89a. D. H. Ohlendorf, W. F. Anderson, R. G. Fisher, Y. Takeda, and B. W. Matthews, Nature 298, 718 (1982).
89b. W. F. Anderson, D. H. Ohlendorf, Y. Takeda, and B. W. Matthews, Nature 290, 754 (1981).
89c. R. T. Sauer, R. R. Yocum, R. F. Doolittle, M. Lewis, and C. O. Pabo, Nature 298, 447 (1982).
89d. A. D. Johnson, B. J. Meyer, and M. Ptashne, PNAS 76, 5061 (1979).
90. H. B. Gamper and J. E. Hearst, Cell 29, 81 (1982).
91. U. Siebenlist, R. B. Simpson, and W. Gilbert, Cell 20, 269 (1980).
92. E. Palecek, This Series 18, 151 (1976).
93. M. T. Record, Jr., S. J. Mazur, P. Melancon, J-H. Roe, S. L. Shaner, and L. Unger, ARB 50, 997 (1981).
94. R. D. Wells, R. W. Blakesley, S. C. Hardies, G. T. Horn, J. E. Larson, E. Selsing, J. F. Burd, H. W. Chan, J. B. Dodgson, K. F. Jensen, I. F. Nes, and R. M. Wartell, CRC Crit. Rev. Biochem. 4, 305 (1977).
95. S. Arnott, Life Sci. Res. Rep. 4, 209 (1976).
96. D. J. Patel, S. A. Kozlowski, L. A. Marky, C. Broka, J. A. Rice, K. Itakura, and K. J. Breslauer, Bchem 21, 428 (1982).
97. A. Chan, R. Kilkuskie, and S. Hanlon, Bchem 18, 84 (1979).
98. F. H. C. Crick and J. D. Watson, Proc. R. Soc. London Ser. A 223, 80 (1954).
99. R. Langridge, H. R. Wilson, C. W. Hooper, M. H. F. Wilkins, and L. D. Hamilton, JMB 2, 19 (1960).
100. R. Langridge, D. A. Marvin, W. E. Seeds, H. R. Wilson, C. W. Hooper, M. H. F. Wilkins, and L. D. Hamilton, JMB 2, 38 (1960).
101. R. Wing, H. Drew, T. Takano, C. Broka, S. Tanaka, K. Itakura, and R. E. Dickerson, Nature 287, 755 (1980).
102. H. R. Drew and R. E. Dickerson, JMB 151, 535 (1981).
103. R. E. Dickerson and H. R. Drew, PNAS 78, 7318 (1981).
104. A. G. W. Leslie, S. Arnott, R. Chandrasekaran, and R. L. Ratliff, JMB 143, 49 (1980).
105. A. Klug, A. Jack, M. A. Viswamitra, O. Kennard, Z. Shakked, and T. A. Steitz, JMB 131, 669 (1979).
106. H. R. Drew, R. M. Wing, T. Takano, C. Broka, S. Tanaka, K. Itakura, and R. E. Dickerson, PNAS 78, 2179 (1981).
107. A. D. Cross and D. M. Crothers, Bchem 10, 4015 (1971).
108. D. M. Crothers, C. W. Hilbers, and R. G. Shulman, PNAS 70, 2899 (1973).
109. D. J. Patel, Bchem 13, 2396 (1974).
110. D. J. Patel and A. E. Tonelli, PNAS 71, 1945 (1974).
111. D. J. Patel and A. E. Tonelli, Bchem 14, 3990 (1975).
112. N. R. Kallenbach, W. E. Daniel, Jr., and M. A. Kaminker, Bchem 15, 1218 (1976).
113. D. J. Patel, Biopolymers 15, 533 (1976).
114. D. J. Patel, Biopolymers 16, 1635 (1977).

115. T. A. Early, D. R. Kearns, J. F. Burd, J. E. Larson, and R. D. Wells, *Bchem* **16**, 541 (1977).
116. E. Selsing, R. D. Wells, T. A. Early, and D. R. Kearns, *Nature* **275**, 249 (1978).
117. D. J. Patel and L. L. Canuel, *EJB* **96**, 267 (1979).
118. D. J. Patel, *Biopolymers* **18**, 553 (1979).
119. P. S. Miller, D. M. Cheng, N. Dreon, K. Jayaraman, L.-S. Kan, E. E. Luetzinger, S. M. Pulford, and P. O. P. Tso, *Bchem* **19**, 4688 (1980).
120. A. Pardi, F. H. Martin, and I. Tinoco, Jr., *Bchem* **20**, 3986 (1981).
121. D. M. Cheng, L.-S. Kan, E. E. Luetzinger, K. Jayaraman, P. S. Miller, and P. O. P. Ts'o, *Bchem* **21**, 621 (1982).
122. D. J. Patel, S. A. Kozlowski, L. A. Marky, J. A. Rice, C. Broka, J. Dallas, K. Itakura, and K. J. Breslauer, *Bchem.* **21**, 437 (1982).
123. D. J. Patel, S. A. Kozlowski, L. A. Marky, J. A. Rice, C. Broka, K. Itakura, and K. J. Breslauer, *Bchem* **21**, 445 (1982).
124. D. J. Patel, S. A. Kozloski, L. A. Marky, J. A. Rice, C. Broka, K. Itakura, and D. J. Breslauer, *Bchem* **21**, 451 (1982).
125. L.-S. Kan, D. M. Cheng, K. Jayaraman, E. E. Leutzinger, P. S. Miller, and P. O. P. Tso, *Bchem* **21**, 6723 (1983).
126. C. K. Mitra, M. H. Sarma, and R. H. Sarma, *Bchem* **20**, 2036 (1981).
127. J. F. Burd, J. E. Larson, and R. D. Wells, *JBC* **250**, 6002 (1975).
128. J. F. Burd, R. M. Wartell, and R. D. Wells, *JBC* **250**, 5109 (1975).
129. R. M. Wartell and J. F. Burd, *Biopolymers* **15**, 1461 (1976).
120. D. M. Crothers, *Acc. Chem. Res.* **2**, 225 (1969).
131. L. E. Lutter, *NARes* **6**, 41 (1979).
132. A. Prunell, R. D. Kornberg, L. Lutter, A. Klug, M. Levitt, and F. H. C. Crick, *Science* **204**, 855 (1979).
133. J. C. Wang, *PNAS* **76**, 200 (1979).
134. L. J. Peck and J. C. Wang, *Nature* **292**, 375 (1981).
135. F. Strauss, C. Gaillard, and A. Prunell, *EJB* **118**, 215 (1981).
136. D. Rhodes and A. Klug, *Nature* **286**, 573 (1980).
137. D. Rhodes and A. Klug, *Nature* **292**, 378 (1981).
138. M. Behe, S. Zimmerman, and G. Felsenfeld, *Nature* **293**, 233 (1981).
139. J. C. Wang, *Cell* **29**, 724 (1982).
140. W. Kabsch, C. Sander, and E. N. Trifonov, *NARes* **10**, 1097 (1981).
141. M. F. Maestre, *JMB* **52**, 543 (1970).
142. G. P. Lomonossoff, P. J. G. Butler, and A. Klug, *JMB* **149**, 745 (1981).
143. M. Mandelkern, N. Dattagupta, and D. M. Crothers, *PNAS* **78**, 4294 (1981).
144. M. F. Maestre and R. Kilkson, *Biophys. J.* **5**, 275 (1965).
145. M. Hogan, N. Dattagupta, and D. M. Crothers, *PNAS* **75**, 195 (1978).
146. H. Eisenberg and G. Cohen, *JMB* **37**, 355 (1968).
147. M. Mandelkern, J. G. Elias, D. Eden, and D. M. Crothers, *JMB* **152**, 153 (1981).
148. C. A. Holm, S. G. Oliver, A. M. Newman, L. E. Holland, C. S. McLaughlin, E. K. Wagner, and R. C. Warner, *JBC* **253**, 8332 (1978).
149. J. D. Griffith, *Science* **201**, 525 (1978).
150. W. Hillen, T. C. Goodman, and R. D. Wells, *NARes* **9**, 3029 (1981).
151. D. R. Davies and S. Zimmerman, *Nature* **283**, 11 (1980).
152. A. H.-J. Wang, G. J. Quigley, F. J. Kolpak, J. L. Crawford, J. H. van Boom, G. van der Marel, and A. Rich, *Nature* **282**, 680 (1979).
152a. H. Drew, T. Takano, S. Tanaka, K. Itakura, and R. E. Dickerson, *Nature* **286**, 567 (1980).

153. J. L. Crawford, F. J. Kolpak, A. H.-J. Wang, G. J. Quigley, J. H. van Boom, G. van der Marel, and A. Rich, *PNAS* **77**, 4016 (1980).

154. A. H.-J. Wang, G. J. Quigley, F. J. Kolpak, G. van der Marel, J. H. van Boom, and A. Rich, *Science* **211**, 171 (1980).

154a. H. R. Drew and R. E. Dickerson, *JMB* **152**, 723 (1981).

155. Y. Mitsui, R. Langridge, B. E. Shortle, C. R. Cantor, R. C. Grant, M. Kodama, and R. D. Wells, *Nature* **228**, 1166 (1970).

156. S. Arnott, R. Chandrasekaran, D. L. Birdsall, A. G. W. Leslie, and R. L. Ratliff, *Nature* **283**, 743 (1980).

157. D. J. Patel, L. L. Canuel, and F. M. Pohl, *PNAS* **76**, 2508 (1979).

158. R. T. Simpson and H. Shindo, *NARes* **8**, 2093 (1980).

159. C. K. Mitra, M. H. Sarma, and R. H. Sarma, *Bchem* **20**, 2036 (1981).

160. C. K. Mitra, M. H. Sarma, and R. H. Sarma, *JACS* **103**, 6727 (1981).

161. J. S. Cohen, J. B. Wooten, and C. L. Chatterjee, *Bchem* **20**, 3049 (1981).

162. S. Uesugi, T. Shida, and M. Ikehara, *Chem. Pharm. Bull.* **29**, 3573 (1981).

163. J. Kypr, M. Vorlickova, M. Budesinsky, and V. Sklenar, *BBRC* **99**, 1257 (1981).

164. S. Uesugi, T. Shida, and M. Ikehara, *Bchem* **21**, 3400 (1982).

165. F. M. Pohl and T. M. Jovin, *JMB* **67**, 375 (1972).

166. F. M. Pohl, *Nature* **260**, 365 (1976).

167. W. Zacharias, J. E. Larson, J. Klysik, S. M. Stirdivant, and R. D. Wells, *JBC* **257**, 2775 (1982).

168. J. Ramstein and M. Leng, *Nature* **288**, 413 (1980).

169. F. M. Pohl, A. Ranade, and M. Stockburger, *BBA* **335**, 85 (1973).

170. J. C. Sutherland, K. P. Griffin, P. C. Keck, and P. Z. Takacs, *PNAS* **78**, 4801 (1981).

171. H. M. Wu, N. Dattagupta, and D. M. Crothers, *PNAS* **78**, 6808 (1981).

172. R. M. Wartell, J. Klysik, W. Hillen, and R. D. Wells, *PNAS* **79**, 2549 (1982).

173. E. Sage and M. Leng, *PNAS* **77**, 4597 (1980).

174. M. Behe and G. Felsenfeld, *PNAS* **78**, 1619 (1981).

175. A. Moller, A. Nordheim, S. R. Nichols, and A. Rich, *PNAS* **78**, 4777 (1981).

176. T. J. Thamann, R. C. Lord, A. H. J. Wang, and A. Rich, *NARes* **9**, 5443 (1981).

177. F. Quadrifoglio, G. Manzini, M. Vasser, K. Dinkelspiel, and R. Crea, *NARes* **9**, 2195 (1981).

178. W. Leupin, P. A. Mirau, W. A. Denny, and D. R. Kearns, *Magn. Reson. Biol. Syst., Proc. Int. Conf. 10th* (1982).

179. S. M. Stirdivant, J. Klysik, and R. D. Wells, *JBC* **257**, 10159 (1982).

180. C. Zimmer, S. Tymen, C. Marck, and W. Guschlbauer, *NARes* **10**, 1081 (1982).

181. M. Vorlickova, J. Kypr, S. Stokrova, and J. Sponar, *NARes* **10**, 1071 (1982).

182. E. M. Lafer, A. Moller, A. Nordheim, B. D. Stollar, and A. Rich, *PNAS* **78**, 3546 (1981).

183. B. Malfoy and M. Leng, *FEBS Lett.* **132**, 45 (1981).

184. A. Nordheim, M. L. Pardue, E. M. Lafer, A. Moller, B. D. Stollar, and A. Rich, *Nature* **294**, 417 (1981).

185. J. Klysik, S. M. Stirdivant, J. E. Larson, P. A. Hart, and R. D. Wells, *Nature* **290**, 672 (1981).

186. J. Klysik, S. M. Stirdivant, and R. D. Wells, *JBC* **257**, 10152 (1982).

187. H. Hamada and T. Kakunaga, *Nature* **298**, 396 (1982).

188. R. D. Wells, J. J. Miglietta, J. Klysik, J. E. Larson, S. M. Stirdivant, and W. Zacharias, *JBC* **257**, 10166 (1982).

The Elongation Factor EF-Tu
and Its Two Encoding Genes

L. Bosch
B. Kraal
P. H. Van der Meide
F. J. Duisterwinkel, and
J. M. Van Noort

Department of Biochemistry,
State University of Leiden,
Leiden, The Netherlands

The polypeptide chain elongation factor EF-Tu is an important protein that fulfills essential functions in protein biosynthesis (*1, 2*) and in bacteriophage RNA replication (*3*). It is a protein of moderate size (M_r 43,000) that can interact with a great number of reaction partners of both low and high molecular weight. Its primary structure has been determined (*4, 5*), and considerable progress has been made in the elucidation of its three-dimensional structure by means of X-ray diffraction (*6–9*). Notable is its abundance in the cell (*10–15*). Depending on the growth conditions, the intracellular EF-Tu in *Escherichia coli* can amount to 5–10% of the total bacterial protein. It thus exceeds the other elongation factors and the ribosomes by a factor of about ten. This high abundance and a reported peripheral association with the inner membrane of *E. coli* (*11, 16*) have led to speculations about a possible structural role of EF-Tu in the bacterium (*17–20*). A regulatory function in ribosomal RNA synthesis has also been suggested (*21*).

91

Progress in Nucleic Acid Research
and Molecular Biology, Vol. 30

This multifunctional character of EF-Tu and its capacity to interact with so many ligands makes this protein an ideal object for studies of the relationship of function to structure.

In *E. coli*, two unlinked genes code for EF-Tu (22) (see Fig. 1). These genes, designated *tufA* and *tufB*, are remarkably similar in nucleotide sequence. Differences have been found only at 13 positions (23, 24). The corresponding gene products, EF-TuA and EF-TuB, are identical except for the C-terminal amino-acid residue (4, 5). No functional difference between the two proteins has been reported (25, 26).

The considerable amount of structural information regarding EF-Tu and its encoding genes and the construction of plasmids harboring these genes (15, 23, 24, 27–33) have opened new avenues toward an understanding of EF-Tu function at the molecular level. Structural alterations in the polypeptide chain have been brought about by mutagenesis (34–36); the functional consequences will be reviewed in this chapter.

The availability of *E. coli* mutants, specifically altered in *tufA* or *tufB* or in both, also enabled the study of the regulation of the expression of these genes (15, 30, 37, 38). These studies have led to the conclusion that the expression of *tufA* and *tufB* is coordinately regulated, but that two distinct mechanisms control the expression of the two genes. They have also indicated that EF-Tu itself is involved in the regulation of the expression of *tufB*, but not in that of *tufA*. The evidence supporting the hypothesis that EF-Tu acts as an autogenous repressor inhibiting *tufB* expression is discussed in this essay.

We have not sought to review all of the current knowledge concerning EF-Tu. Rather we have restricted ourselves to a discussion of some recent insights that emerge from an integration of genetic, biochemical, and biophysical studies of this interesting protein. The reader is referred to more complete reviews (1–3, 39, 40).

I. The Genes Encoding EF-Tu

A. Organization of *tufA* and *tufB*

The two genes encoding EF-Tu are rather distantly located on the linkage map of *E. coli* (22). Gene *tufA* lies at 73 minutes, in the so-called *str* region, while *tufB* lies at 88 minutes, in the *rif* region (41).

tufA is the last gene in a transcriptional unit with three other genes coding for EF-G (*fus*) and the two ribosomal proteins S12 and S7 (*rpsL* and *rpsG*, respectively), which are cotranscribed in the direction *rpsL*, *rpsG*, *fus*, and *tufA* (42). (Fig. 1). Although EF-G and the

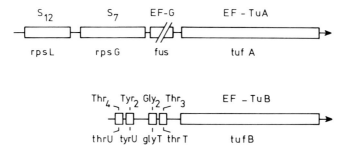

FIG. 1. The *str* operon and the tRNA-*tufB* operon.

ribosomal proteins (S12 and S7) are expressed in about equimolar amounts, the rate of expression of *tufA* is much higher (*15, 43*). Genetic manipulations of the *str* region reveal that the four genes are under the control of a common promoter (*22, 44*). This suggests that some kind of signal responsible for the increased expression of *tufA* must be located near the *tufA* gene. Such a signal might account for an increased rate of translation of the distal part of the primary transcript from the *str* operon (*45*). However, a number of investigations (*30, 32, 33*) point to the existence of a secondary promoter for EF-TuA expression, which is thought to be located within the coding region for EF-G. This promoter is approximately 30% as active as the major *Pstr* (*46*) and might significantly contribute to the rate of EF-TuA synthesis.

The other locus on the genetic map of *E. coli* that codes for EF-Tu is the *tufB* gene. Detailed structural analysis of a transducing phage carrying the *tufB* gene of *E. coli* (λ*rif*d18) has shown that four tRNA structural genes immediately precede *tufB* (*24*). The intergenic region between *tufB* and the four tRNA genes includes only 110 base-pairs (*47, 48*). Results of *in vivo* and *in vitro* transcription studies (*31, 49*) indicate that the cluster of four tRNA genes and *tufB* (*thrU, tyrU, glyT, thrT,* and *tufB,* in this order) are included in the same transcription unit. The major promoter is located directly upstream of the *thrU* gene and closely resembles a computer-generated model (*50*). The same holds true for the −35 region of this promoter. It has been demonstrated that complexes can be formed between restriction fragments containing this presumptive promoter and RNA polymerase (*60*). A weak promoter located 32 bases upstream of *tufB* has been suggested, and indeed some promoter activity has been found in this region *in vivo* (*31*). Genetic and biochemical evidence locates the terminator 34 bases downstream of *tufB* (*24, 49, 51*). Inspection of the DNA sequence of the intergenic region between *thrT* and *tufB* reveals a terminator-like sequence (*52, 53*) that overlaps a region possibly in-

volved in processing of the five-gene transcript (49, 54). The physiological significance of a potential uncoupling of tRNA from tufB transcription remains to be determined. The presence of large amounts of
the full 1800 base-pair transcript in cell extracts of E. coli argues
against effective termination at this intergenic site (49).

B. Conservation and Duplication of tuf Genes in Prokaryotes

Duplication of tuf genes also occurs in prokaryotes other than E.
coli K12, e.g., in E. coli B and the related strain Salmonella
typhimurium (55). The functional necessity of this duplication is not
clear. Inactivation of the tufB gene in E. coli inhibits growth only
slightly (38). In addition, certain prokaryotes contain only one tuf gene
(56). These observations are difficult to reconcile with the idea that the
tufB product is responsible for an essential function.

The two tuf genes of E. coli have diverged little (23, 24). DNA
hybridization experiments show that twelve unrelated bacterial
genomes harbor genes that contain sequences homologous to that part
of the E. coli tuf gene encoding the COOH-terminal half of EF-Tu
(57). Even the strictly anaerobic purple sulfur photosynthetic bacterium Chromatium vinosum displays a certain degree of homology in
the distal part of the tuf gene. Heterologous hybridization between the
E. coli tuf gene DNA and DNA from Chlamydomonas reinhardtii
indicates that the latter DNA contains a gene showing extensive homology with the E. coli tuf gene (58). Cloning of the chloroplast tuf gene
in E. coli resistant to kirromycin changed the phenotype to sensitivity,
demonstrating that the chloroplast tuf product can substitute EF-Tu
during protein synthesis in E. coli (59). Immunological cross-reactivity
between EF-Tu of E. coli and different Streptomyces species indicates
that the factors contain structural similarities (60, 61). Furthermore, a
fully active hybrid Qβ replicase can be formed by substituting E. coli
EF-Tu by the analogous factors of Bacillus subtilis or Caulobacter
crescentus (62, 63). Taken together, these findings imply a strong
selective pressure operating on certain tuf gene sequences in the prokaryotic kingdom.

C. Mutants of E. coli with Altered tuf Genes

Initially two obstacles seemed to be unsurmountable in the isolation and characterization of mutants with an altered EF-Tu: the existence of two EF-Tu encoding genes and, until 1974, the lack of any
antibiotic with a target site on EF-Tu. Nonetheless a few attempts
were reported in the years before 1977 (64, 65), but the E. coli mutants

described as temperature-sensitive and altered in EF-Tu were poorly characterized, and no definite information concerning the genetic alteration(s) was reported. In 1976 it was demonstrated (66) that the mutant strain HAK88, reported to carry a temperature-sensitive EF-Ts (67), harbored two EF-Tu species differing in isoelectric point by 0.1 pH unit. It was a product of tufB, that was slightly more acidic than wild-type EF-Tu. No apparent difference in function was found.

The discovery of a new class of antibiotics that affect the function of EF-Tu in protein synthesis, i.e., mocimycin, also called kirromycin (68–70), and the antibiotic X5108 or aurodox (71–73) [cf. Fig. 2; for a review, see (39)] greatly facilitated the isolation of mutants with an altered EF-Tu. Of major importance in this context were the studies showing that kirromycin inhibits protein synthesis by specifically binding to EF-Tu, thus preventing the release of EF-Tu from the ribosome (39, 74–81). Immobilization by the antibiotic of one ribosome on a polysome blocks the movement of all the ribosomes in its trail. Consequently, in bacterial cells, the wild-type allele sensitive to kirromycin is dominant over the mutated allele that confers resistance to kirromycin (35, 36), and phenotypic expression of resistance requires alteration of both tufA and tufB.

About 1977, two groups reported the isolation of kirromycin-resistant strains derived from E. coli K12 (35, 36). Mutagenesis with N-methyl-N'-nitro-N-nitrosoguanidine of the strain D22, which has an increased membrane permeability for kirromycin, yielded the kirromycin-resistant mutant D2216. Both genetic and biochemical experiments indicated that one of the tuf genes of D2216 is inactive (35, 82) and that the kirromycin-resistant EF-Tu (EF-TuD2216) thus is a homogeneous single-gene product. At the same time, another mutant (LBE2012), harboring a kirromycin-resistant tufA and a recessive tufB, was reported (34, 36, 38, 83).

Table I presents a number of mutant strains illustrating the dominance of sensitivity over resistance. All strains with a kirromycin-resistant phenotype are derived from the strain LBE2012, and thus harbor the same tufA gene coding for an EF-Tu with a strongly reduced affinity for the antibiotic (15, 84). In some strains, the tufB gene

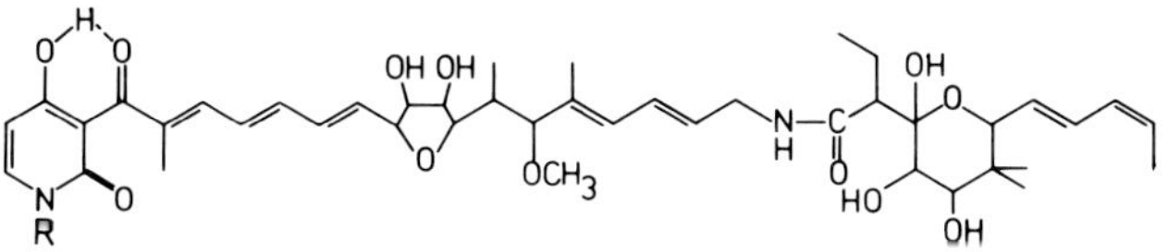

FIG. 2. Structure of mocimycin, also called kirromycin (R = H) and aurodox (R = CH₃) (68, 69, 72, 73).

TABLE I

Escherichia coli K12 MUTANTS ALTERED IN *tufA* AND/OR *tufB*

Strain[a]	EF-Tu symbols[b]	Genotype	Suppression	Phenotype[c]
LBE1001	AsBs	Wild type	–	Kir^s
LBE2012	ArBo	*tufA, tufB, xyl*	–	Kir^r
LBE2035	Ar	*tufA, tufBam60, cysam, galam, his, mal, lam, fus*	–	Kir^r
LBE2039	ArBs	*tufA, tufBam60, cysam, galam, his, mal, lam, fus, sup*	+	Kir^s
LBE2051	ArBs	$\Delta proB$-*lac, thi*(209), *supE, fus, tufA, tufBts*	–	Kir^s at 32°C
	Ar		–	Kir^r at 39°C
LBE2045	Ar	*cys-am, gal-am, his, mal, lam, fus, rpoB, tufA, tufB*::(*Mu*)	–	Kir^r, Rif^r
LBE2050	As	*cys-am, gal-am, hisA, mal, lam, rpoB, tufB*::(*Mu*), *rpsL*	–	Kir^s, Rif^r
LBE2020	AsBo	*tufB, rpoB*	–	Rif^r
LBE2021	ArBo	*tufA, tuf^{ts}, rpoB*		Kir^r, Rif^r
LBE12020	AsBo	*tufB, rpoB, recA$_{56}$*		Kir^s, Rif^r, UV^s
PM505	As	*tufB*::(*Mu*), *rpoB*		Kir^s, Rif^r
PM455	Ar	*tufA, tufB*::(*Mu*), *rpoB*		Kir^r, Rif^r
PM816	ArBs	*fus, tufA*		Kir^s

[a] Further details concerning these strains have been reported (15, 34).

[b] The designations As, Ar, Bs, and Bo refer, respectively, to a wild-type *tufA* product, a kirromycin-resistant *tufA* product, a wild-type *tufB* product, and an altered *tufB* product; the products have been described (83–85).

[c] Kir^r is kirromycin resistance; Rif^r is rifampicin resistance; UV^s is ultraviolet sensitivity; and Kir^s is kirromycin sensitivity.

is inactivated by an amber mutation (LBE2035) or by an insertion of DNA from bacteriophage Mu (LBE2045). Suppression of the amber mutation in LBE2039 yields a *tufB* product that is functional in protein synthesis. In the presence of the antibiotic, this product immobilizes the ribosome and protein synthesis stops. Suppression of the amber mutation thus renders LBE2039 cells sensitive to kirromycin. In LBE2051, *tufB* codes for a temperature-sensitive EF-Tu. At the permissive temperature, the cells are sensitive to kirromycin; at the nonpermissive one they are resistant (36, 83).

The nature of the mutations in the two *tuf* genes of LBE2012, the mutant strain first isolated in this series, was not directly clear. Transduction experiments (34) demonstrated that both genes had been altered. Replacement of *tufB* by the wild-type gene, followed by inactivation of the latter as described above, clearly demonstrated that *tufA* of LBE2012 codes for a kirromycin-resistant EF-Tu, but the nature of the *tufB* mutation remained obscure. When *tufA* of LBE2012 was replaced by wild-type *tufA*, subsequent treatment with the bacteriophage Mu did not yield kirromycin-resistant strains with Mu DNA inserted in the latter gene. This made it less likely that *tufB* of LBE2012 is also kirromycin-resistant unless one assumes that inactivation of *tufA* eliminates an essential gene. The possibility was entertained for a while that *tufB* coded for a product inactive in protein synthesis. This product was designated EF-TuBo; the product of the kirromycin-resistant *tufA* was called EF-TuAr (see Table III). Later it appeared (84, 85) that the mutation of *tufB* in LBE2012 is recessive to that of the kirromycin-resistant *tufA* of this strain because EF-TuBo does not immobilize the ribosome upon binding of the antibiotic (85).

Dominance of sensitivity over resistance can also be demonstrated by *in vitro* experiments (34, 35). Addition of increasing amounts of sensitive EF-Tu to a poly(U)-translating system containing resistant EF-Tu and the antibiotic resulted in progressive inhibition of poly-(Phe) synthesis. One sensitive EF-Tu molecule in the presence of 5–10 resistant ones causes more than 80% reduction in synthetic activity.

The data of Table I show that one *tuf* gene (*tufA*) in *E. coli* is sufficient for growth. It has been speculated (31) that *tufB* might be required for certain rare growth conditions, such as a rapid shift to fast growth. In accordance with such an assumption are the growth rates of wild-type cells from LBE1001 and cells from PM505 (compare Table II). In a relatively rich medium (Casamino acids), cells lacking an active *tufB* gene fail to grow as fast as their wild-type counterparts, whereas in poorer media both types of cells show virtually the same generation times.

Gausing (86, 87) described a *tufA*-defective strain of *E. coli* possessing a functional *tufA* gene that is not linked to the major *Pstr* promoter. The activity of this gene is reduced to about 10%. The growth rate of this strain is significantly decreased.

Of interest in this context is the report that *Bacillus subtilis* harbors only one gene coding for EF-Tu (56). This conclusion was based on a characterization of kirromycin-resistant mutations, which showed that these mutations map in the same chromosomal region as other mutations affecting EF-G and EF-Tu. In isoelectric-focusing gels, the mutant EF-Tu migrated as a single band. Earlier observations (88) con-

TABLE II

GROWTH RATES OF DIFFERENT STRAINS OF *Escherichia coli* K12 ALTERED IN
tufA AND/OR *tufB*[a]

Strain	EF-Tu[b] symbols	LC[c]	Generation times (doublings/hour) Casamino acids	Glucose	Rhamnose	Acetate
LBE1001	AsBs	ND[d]	2.30	0.99	0.68	0.24
LBE2020	AsBo	2.25	1.50	0.89	0.52	0.30
LBE2021	ArBo	1.95	1.16	0.63	0.43	NG[d]
PM505	As	ND	1.85	0.92	0.65	0.30
PM455	Ar	2.11	1.37	0.88	0.48	NG
PM816	ArBs	1.98	1.39	0.89	0.63	0.36

[a] For experimental details, see Van der Meide *et al.* (*38*).
[b] See Table I.
[c] LC is a "rich" medium (defined in *15*).
[d] ND, not done; NG, no growth possible.

cerning a temperature-sensitive mutation (ts-5) of *B. subtilis* affecting
EF-Tu *in vitro* are in agreement with the above conclusion.

Finally it may be mentioned that *Lactobacillus brevis, Halobac-
terium cutirubrum,* and *Streptoverticillium mobaraense,* which are
naturally insensitive to kirromycin, produce an EF-Tu resistant to the
antibiotic (*89*). Also EF-Tu from *Bacillus stearothermophilus* has a
low affinity for kirromycin (*90*). On the other hand, the kirromycin-
producing *Streptomyces ramocissimus* is inhibited by its own product
during fermentation. This is due to the binding of the antibiotic to
EF-Tu, which occurs in a 1 : 1 ratio and is at least as effective as the
binding to *E. coli* EF-Tu in inhibiting poly(U) translation and in en-
hancing GDP exchange with (EF-Tu) · GDP (*61*).

II. Structure and Function of EF-Tu from *E. coli* Mutants

Although bacterial cells harboring two active *tuf* genes produce
two EF-Tu species that, because of their great structural similarity, are
difficult to separate, single-gene products can be isolated from cells in
which one of the *tuf* genes is inactive. Attempts to inactivate *tufA* have
not yet been successful. The *tufA*-defective *E. coli* strain described by
Gausing still produces about 10% of the EF-TuA of the parental strain
(*86*).

A number of EF-Tu preparations, representing either a mixture of
two different EF-Tu species or a homogeneous protein derived from

tufA only, have thus become available. They display interesting properties in protein synthesis and phage RNA replication that have deepened our insight into the mechanisms underlying these processes. In some cases, these properties could also be related to structural alterations caused by mutagenesis.

A. Mutant EF-Tu Species Derived from *tufA*

Two EF-Tu species have been described (*35, 36, 82–84, 86, 91*) that have a greatly reduced affinity for kirromycin: EF-TuAr and EF-TuD2216 isolated from the kirromycin-resistant strains LBE2045 (see Table I) and D2216, respectively. Both are single-gene products derived from *tufA* (see below). The low affinity for the antibiotic became apparent indirectly by a lack of response to the addition of the antibiotic in a number of assays like [^{3}H]GDP exchange with (EF-Tu) · GDP (*82, 83*), *in vitro* translation of poly(U) and aminoacyl-tRNA binding to mRNA · ribosome complexes (*35, 83, 85*), protection by kirromycin against heat denaturation (*82*), kirromycin-induced GTPase activity of EF-Tu (*91*), and probing conformational changes by measuring the rate of limited proteolysis of EF-Tu by trypsin (*84*).

Direct measurement of the binding of [^{14}C]kirromycin to (EF-TuAr) · GDP at 0°C yielded a binding constant of 0.6 × 10^3 M^{-1}. The corresponding value for wild-type (EF-Tu) · GDP is 1.3 × 10^6 M^{-1} (*92*). EF-TuD2216 appeared to be at least three times more resistant to the antibiotic than EF-TuAr when the antibiotic concentrations causing a 50% inhibition of poly(U) translation were compared (*93*).

Figure 3 illustrates the effect of increasing concentrations of kirromycin on *in vitro* translation of poly(U) mediated by mutant and wild-type EF-Tu (*83*). At 2.5 μg of kirromycin per milliliter, polypeptide synthesis mediated by wild-type EF-Tu is completely blocked whereas that mediated by EF-TuAr is not diminished and, for unknown reasons, is even somewhat increased.

In order to study the functioning of mutant EF-Tu as a subunit of Qβ replicase, advantage has been taken of a procedure that allows the replacement of endogeneous EF-Tu by EF-TuAr (*94*). The enzyme thus obtained is defective; it is rapidly inactivated in the reaction mixture, even at temperatures as low as 20°C. It shows virtually no activity in the standard poly(C)-dependent poly(G)-polymerase reaction, although it is active in the presence of Mn^{2+}, which reduces template specificity. The mutant Qβ replicase also transcribes QβRNA. The results imply that EF-Tu is involved in the maintenance of enzyme structure, which in turn is implicated in template specificity (*95*).

The two mutant EF-Tu species (EF-TuAr and EF-TuD2216) and

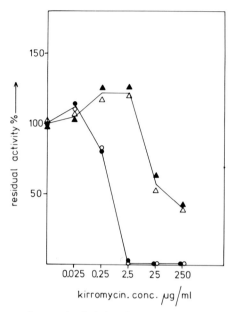

FIG. 3. In vitro translation of poly(U) with increasing concentrations of kirromycin and with EF-Tu from LBE2012 (△), from LBE2045 (▲), from LBE2050 (●) and wild-type EF-Tu from LBE1001 (○). For experimental details, see Van der Meide et al. (83). Translation occurred with ribosomes from wild-type cells and EF-Tu from strains as indicated.

wild-type EF-Tu differ not only in their interaction with kirromycin but also in that with GTP (93) and aminoacyl-tRNA (96). As illustrated in Table III, the enhanced affinity for GTP is expressed only in a decreased rate of dissociation of the binary complex (EF-Tu) · GTP (93). The rates of protein–nucleotide association are the same for all three EF-Tu species. Interestingly, the EF-Tu from Lactobacillus brevis, which is naturally resistant to kirromycin, also displays an affinity for GTP considerably higher than that of E. coli EF-Tu (89). It has been pointed out (97) that wild-type EF-Tu is highly affected by $[NH_4^+]$ in its interaction with GTP. The GTPase center of the molecule is activated in the presence of increasing monovalent cation concentrations (Table III). This is also the case for EF-TuAr and EF-TuD2216.

The relative affinities of mutant and wild-type (EF-Tu) · GTP for aminoacyl-tRNA have been studied qualitatively by analyzing ternary complexes (15), and more quantitatively by assaying the protection that (EF-Tu) · GTP provides against hydrolysis of the aminoacyl-tRNA (96). Both methods show that the mutant species of (EF-Tu) · GTP bind aminoacyl-tRNA less efficiently than wild-type (EF-Tu) · GTP.

TABLE III
DEPENDENCE OF THE NH_4^+ CONCENTRATION OF THE APPARENT RATE CONSTANTS
OF THE GTPASE (A), THE DISSOCIATION (B), AND THE ASSOCIATION (C) REACTIONS
OF THE BINARY COMPLEX OF GTP WITH VARIOUS SPECIES OF EF-Tu[a]

	Rate constants			Ratio of rate constants	
[NH$_4^+$]	Wild-type EF-Tu	EF-TuAr	EF-TuD2216	EF-TuAr Wild-type EF-Tu	EF-TuD2216 Wild-type EF-Tu
A. GTPase: (EF-Tu) · GTP → (EF-Tu) · GDP + P$_i$; rate constants in (10^{-4} min^{-1}); 37°C					
0	14	14	73	1.00	5.36
40	49	55	222	1.12	4.51
200	172	207	703	1.20	4.08
400	220	425	997	1.93	4.53
B. Dissociation: (EF-Tu) · *GTP + GTP → (EF-Tu) · GTP + *GTP; rate constants in (10^{-4} sec^{-1}); 5°C					
0	187	147	38.5	0.78	0.21
50	154	115	18.2	0.75	0.12
400	27.1	17.5	3.1	0.64	0.11
800	13.7	10.6	1.9	0.77	0.14
C. Association: EF-Tu + *GTP → (EF-Tu) · *GTP; rate constants (10^{-4} m^{-1} sec^{-1}); 5°C					
50	2	2	2	1.00	1.00

[a] For experimental details, see text (Section II,A) and Swart et al. (93).

These interesting differences raise the question of how to relate them to differences in structure. "Fingerprint" mapping of EF-TuD2216 showed that only one tryptic peptide was shifted in position, and no shadow of the original parental polypeptide was detectable. This led to the conclusion that EF-TuD2216 is a homogeneous protein (35) derived from one single gene. Analysis of the COOH-terminal structure of this mutant EF-Tu species and that of EF-TuAr identified glycine instead of serine as the terminal amino-acid residue in both proteins (98). This means that both are tufA products. Amino-acid sequencing of individual tryptic peptides demonstrated that the alanine at position 375 of wild-type EF-Tu is replaced by threonine in EF-TuAr and by valine in EF-TuD2216 (98, 99). Position 375 may be considered to be the only site of mutation of EF-TuAr on the basis of the frequency of spontaneous mutations of tufA (36). In the case of EF-TuD2216, less certainty exists considering the type of mutagenesis applied (35). In accordance with the assumption is that both mutant EF-Tu species display behavioral shifts in the same direction (see Table III).

It is of great interest that crystallographic data indicate that Ala-375

102   L. BOSCH *et al.*

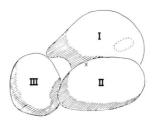

FIG. 4. A simplified drawing of the overall shapes of the domains of (EF-Tu) · GDP
at low resolution. The position of GDP is shown by the region encircled by a dashed line
Domains I, II, and III are described in the text. X marks the putative position of the
mutation conferring kirromycin resistance (9; also personal communication by B. F. C.
Clark, T. F. M. La Cour, and J. Nyborg).

is located in a region profoundly involved in the allosteric control of
the EF-Tu molecule. This is illustrated in Fig. 4, which is a simplified
drawing of the overall shape of EF-Tu based on X-ray diffraction at low
resolution (8, 9). Three domains can be recognized.

Domain I, the "tight" domain (9), is highly structured and comprises 180 amino acids of the protein chain ranging from Ile-60 to
Glu-240. It contains the GDP binding-site indicated by a region encircled by a dashed line in Fig. 4. Although some ambiguities in the
interpretation of the crystallographic data still exist (8, 9), it has been
possible to trace the folding of the polypeptide chain in the tight domain. This folding (Fig. 5) is consistent with information obtained by
other means. Figure 5 shows a five-stranded parallel β-sheet that has
been extended by a sixth antiparallel strand. The β-strands are connected by six α-helices via loops that are rather short, except in one
case. The β-sheet forms a central hydrophobic core with a relatively
large left-handed twist. Surrounding this core, the α-helices provide
an efficient interface to the solvent. The whole arrangement appears
very compact. It belongs to the class of α/β structures, an arrangement
found in other nucleotide-binding proteins, such as dehydrogenases
and kinases (100).

Domain II is below the tight domain and is referred to as the
"loose" domain. It contains about 100 residues, which form a number
of β-strands but no α-helices. The loose domain is in contact with
helices I and II of the tight domain. At the present resolution, the only
covalent connection between domains I and II appears to be via the
strand 44–58, whereas the rest of the contacts are due to hydrophobic
forces and salt bridges (9).

Domain III is still ill-defined. The electron density is difficult to

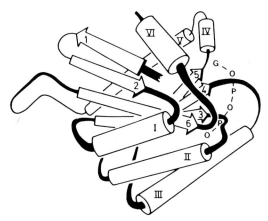

FIG. 5. Secondary structural elements found in the "tight" domain of Fig. 4. The directions of flat arrows depicting β-strands are from N-terminal to C-terminal ends. Cylinders represent α-helices. Since the central β-sheet is parallel, all the C-terminal ends of the β-strands are found at one edge of the sheet. The position of the GDP binding position is also given in schematic form (9).

trace. This domain, the "floppy" domain, may reflect a flexible part of the protein structure in the absence of aminoacyl-tRNA.

A preliminary interpretation of the electron density near the C-terminal end of the polypeptide chain locates residue 375 in the cleft formed between domains I and II, not far from and below the strand 44–58 (9). This seems to be a strategic position. It is not unreasonable to assume that substitution of Ala-375 by threonine or valine alters the positions of domains I and II relative to each other. As discussed above, the substitution affects not only the interaction with the antibiotic kirromycin, but also that with GTP and aminoacyl-tRNA. The guanine of GDP (and presumably that of GTP as well) is bound in a pocket lined with hydrophobic side-chains above and below the plane of the base (8) (Fig. 5). There appears to be no stacking interaction between the guanine and any aromatic amino-acid side-chain. The ribose ring is partly buried, but with the 2',3' cis-vicinal diol exposed to the solvent. The α- and β-phosphates are H-bonded to side-chain residues and backbone amide groups belonging to α-helix VI, and to the loop between this helix and β-strand 6. Studies with GDP analogs and various metal ions indicated that the β-phosphate is bound to the protein via two H-bridges and a Mg^{2+} ion (101, 102). The expected position of the γ-phosphate in GTP is at the end of the cleft formed by strands 1 and 2 and helices I and II. Hydrolysis of GTP proceeds with inversion of configuration at the cleaved γ-phosphate, implying that there is not a phosphoenzyme intermediate (*103*).

In the light of these structural data, it is conceivable that alteration of the interaction between domains I and II as a result of substitution of Ala-375 by either Thr or Val may have consequences for the position of α-helices I and II and thus for the binding and cleavage of GTP. It has been suggested (*8*) that the region at the end of the cleft formed by strands 1 and 2 and helices I and II (the expected position of the γ-phosphate of GTP) is important in the control of the action of the protein, specifically with respect to binding aminoacyl-tRNA when GTP is bound and releasing aminoacyl-tRNA when GTP becomes hydrolyzed upon contact with the ribosome. Table III clearly shows changes in affinity of EF-Tu toward GTP upon perturbation of the allosteric site around Ala-375. These changes are more pronounced when Ala-375 (R $=$ —CH$_3$) is replaced by Val

$$(R = -CH \underset{\displaystyle CH_3}{\overset{\displaystyle CH_3}{<}}) \text{ than by Thr } (R = -CH \underset{\displaystyle OH}{\overset{\displaystyle CH_3}{<}})$$

In the former case, the binding constant for GTP is increased to such an extent that the γ-phosphate is hydrolyzed in the absence of any effector and of NH_4^+ ions. Under the latter conditions, the effect of the replacement of Ala-375 by Thr on the GTPase center is not detectable, but is progressively revealed by raising $[NH_4^+]$ (*93*). On the other hand, substitution of Ala by Val activates the GTPase center at all $[NH_4^+]$ to about the same extent (compare Table III, lanes 5 and 6).

Studies with 3'-terminal fragments of aminoacyl-tRNA (e.g., CpA-Phe or A-Phe) provide further evidence for the importance of the above-mentioned region at the end of the cleft between helices I and II and strands 1 and 2. In a way similar to that of intact aminoacyl-tRNA, these analogs protect Cys-81 (at the end of strand 2) against modification with N-tosyl-L-phenylalanylchloromethane, which locates the 3' terminus of tRNA in the ternary complex with (EF-Tu) · GTP (*104*). Complex formation with ϵ-N-bromoacetyllysyl-tRNA yielded a cross-link in the same region, namely with His-66 (*8*) on strand 1 at the top of the cleft. Binding of the above-mentioned 3'-aminoacyl-tRNA fragments also stimulates the uncoupled GTPase reaction in the presence of kirromycin or ribosomes (*105, 106*). It is therefore gratifying to observe that both the affinity for GTP and that for aminoacyl-tRNA change when amino-acid substitutions occur in the allosteric site around position 375.

That the latter site is involved in the interaction between domains I and II is further suggested by conformational changes (107) affecting the accessibility of Arg-44, Lys-56, and Arg-58 for trypsin. These residues are located at the strand 44–58 connecting domains I and II (9). They are the only sites accessible to trypsin under mild conditions. Addition of kirromycin to (EF-Tu) · GDP or replacement of GDP by GTP increases the rate of cleavage by trypsin significantly, and to about the same extent (84, 107). These data suggest that the antibiotic converts the conformation of (EF-Tu) · GDP into an (EF-Tu) · GTP-like conformation. It seems that this is accompanied by a positional shift of the connection between the two domains.

Up to now, nothing is known about the binding site for kirromycin except that it and GTP do not compete for the same site (39). Kirromycin increases the binding affinity of EF-Tu for GTP (78) and greatly amplifies the effect of increasing $[NH_4^+]$ on the interaction between EF-Tu and GTP (97, 108). By changing the conformation of (EF-Tu) · GDP into an (EF-Tu) · GTP-like conformation, the antibiotic opens up a binding site for aminoacyl-tRNA. Accordingly, an [(EF-Tu) · GDP · (aminoacyl-tRNA) · kirromycin] complex that can be bound to the ribosome · mRNA complex can be formed (75, 76) (see also below; Fig. 7). It has been shown that kirromycin induces a second tRNA-binding site on both (EF-Tu) · GDP and (EF-Tu) · GTP (109). This conclusion is based on modifications of EF-Tu with sulfydryl agents like $TosPheCH_2Cl$ and MalNEt. In the presence of a nucleotide and Mg^{2+}, one unique target site for either agent is exposed on EF-Tu, i.e., Cys-81 located on the loop connecting helix I and strand 2 (Fig. 5). Kirromycin protects (EF-Tu) · GDP and (EF-Tu) · GTP against modification by $TosPheCH_2Cl$. However, addition of aminoacyl-tRNA again exposes Cys-81 on the [(EF-Tu) · GDP · kirromycin] complex. As illustrated in Fig. 6, labeling with $TosPheCH_2Cl$ rises until the aminoacyl-tRNA reaches a concentration of about 20 μM. Interestingly, the labeling drops again when the aminoacyl-tRNA level is raised beyond 20 μM and is completely abolished at a concentration of about 300 μM. In contrast, addition of non-aminoacylated tRNA or N-acetylaminoacyl-tRNA causes a continuous rise in the labeling over the entire concentration range of tRNA studied. These data have been taken to indicate that kirromycin opens up not one but two binding sites for aminoacyl-tRNA. Binding of the latter to one site (site II) of the [(EF-Tu) · GDP · kirromycin] complex again exposes Cys-81, whereas binding to the other (site I) blocks the reaction with the modifying agent. Site II can be filled by all three species of tRNA: uncharged, aminoacylated, and N-acetylaminoacylated

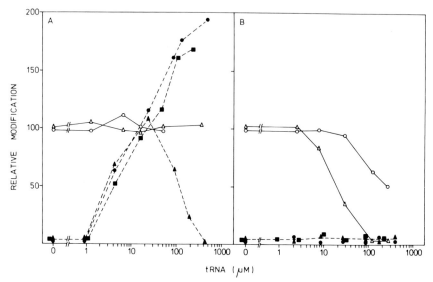

FIG. 6. The effects of uncharged tRNA (circles), aminoacyl-tRNA (triangles) or
N-acetylaminoacyl-tRNA (squares) upon the modification of (EF-Tu) · GDP (A) and
(EF-Tu) · GTP(B) by [^{14}C]TosPheCH$_2$Cl. The modification was performed in the absence (open symbols) or presence (filled symbols) of 180 μM kirromycin. For further
details see the text and (*109*).

tRNA. On the other hand, the data of Fig. 6 reveal only interaction of
aminoacyl-tRNA with site I. It is the antibiotic effector that opens up
the two tRNA binding sites, since none of the three tRNA species
affects the labeling of (EF-Tu) · GDP in the absence of kirromycin.

The modification data obtained with [^{3}H]MaINEt, although different in the details of aminoacyl-tRNA dependence, fully support the
conclusions drawn from TosPheCH$_2$Cl labeling. They also disclose an
additional tRNA binding site on (EF-Tu) · GTP, a site that cannot be
established using the latter labeling technique.

Site I, unable to interact with *N*-acetylaminoacyl-tRNA either in
the presence or the absence of the antibiotic, is assumed to be the
classical binding site for aminoacyl-tRNA. The presence of the additional site II on EF-Tu may have important implications. It means that
in the presence of kirromycin (EF-Tu) · GTP can bind two tRNA molecules simultaneously, one bearing an aminoacyl and the other a peptidyl moiety. On the ribosome, this may account for a stable complex of
EF-Tu with tRNAs at the A- and P-sites. The stability of this complex
will even be enhanced when hydrolysis of GTP occurs, as site II on
[(EF-Tu) · GDP · kirromycin] has a higher affinity for peptidyl-tRNA
than site II on [(EF-Tu) · GTP · kirromycin] (*109*). This explains the

tenacity with which [(EF-Tu) · GDP · kirromycin] binds to the ribosome because EF-Tu becomes anchored both to aminoacyl- and peptidyl-tRNA.

Both the antibiotic and the ribosome can trigger the intrinsic GTPase activity of EF-Tu. This indicates that in a way kirromycin mimics the ribosome in its action on (EF-Tu) · GTP. The possibility may be envisaged, therefore, that site II is also opened upon binding of the ternary complex [(EF-Tu) · GTP · aminoacyl-tRNA)] to the ribosome · mRNA complex, enabling EF-Tu to interact both with aminoacyl-tRNA in the A-site and with peptidyl-tRNA in the P-site. This could explain why the (EF-Tu) · GTP-dependent binding of aminoacyl-tRNA to the A-site can occur only when the P-site is occupied either by non-aminoacylated tRNA or by peptidyl-tRNA (110, 111). Furthermore, it could account for the finding that, in the presence of $2'(3')$-O-L-phenylalanyladenosine, GTP hydrolysis on the (EF-Tu) · ribosome complex is stimulated by N-acetylphenylalanyl-tRNA prebound to the ribosome (112).

Experiments (113) indicate that the 3′ terminus of non-aminoacylated tRNA can be cross-linked to the [(EF-Tu) · GDP · kirromycin] complex. In these experiments, the vicinal 2′- and 3′-OH groups of the terminal adenosine were oxidized by periodate, and the tRNA terminus was cross-linked to the protein with [^{3}H]borohydride. After degradation of the tRNA moiety and peptide mapping of the labeled EF-Tu, Lys-208 was identified as the major and Lys-357 as the minor labeled amino-acid residue. Lys-208 is located on the loop connecting α-helix V and β-strand 6 (8, 9). When the cross-linking of uncharged tRNA is performed with [(EF-Tu) · GTP · kirromycin], an additional peptide, containing Lys-237, becomes labeled. In conclusion, these cross-linking experiments, although still preliminary in nature, are in agreement with the existence of an extra tRNA binding site of the EF-Tu protein inducible by kirromycin. In the next section, we discuss a point mutation of *tufB* that makes this extra site defective.

B. Mutant EF-Tu Derived from *tufB*

EF-Tu isolated from the kirromycin-resistant strain LBE2012 (see Table I) and purified to apparent homogeneity as judged by dodecyl sulfate polyacrylamide gel electrophoresis, consists of two proteins differing in isoelectric point (83). The two proteins are indistinguishable immunologically with antibodies raised against wild-type EF-Tu. When studied by isoelectric focusing (compare Fig. 7), one protein comigrates with wild-type EF-Tu and with EF-Tu isolated from the

108

L. BOSCH *et al.*

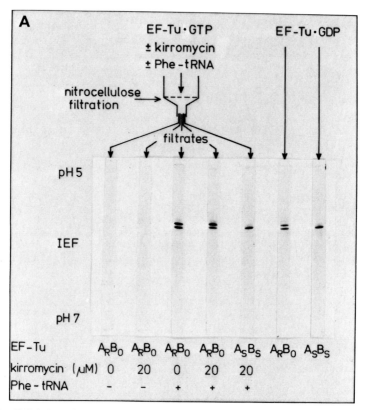

Fig. 7. (A) Complex formation of (EF-TuAr) · GTP and (EF-TuBo) · GTP with Phe-tRNA[Phe] in the absence and in the presence of kirromycin. (B) Complex formation of (EF-TuAr) · GDP and (EF-TuBo) · GDP with Phe-tRNA[Phe] in the presence of kirromycin. For experimental details, see the text and (85).

kirromycin-resistant strains LBE2035 and LBE2045, lacking an active *tufB* gene. This identifies this protein as a *tufA* product. The other product displays a shift in isoelectric point of 0.1 pH unit to the acidic side and thus is identified as a *tufB* product. This has been confirmed with transduction experiments. The two EF-Tu proteins from LBE2012 have been designated EF-TuAr and EF-TuBo, respectively (see also Section II,C). The corresponding wild-type proteins, which are kirromycin-sensitive, have been designated EF-TuAs and EF-TuBs. A difference in isoelectric point has also been reported for the *tufA* and *tufB* products of the innocuous mutant HAK88 (66).

EF-TuBo binds kirromycin. This could be concluded from nu-

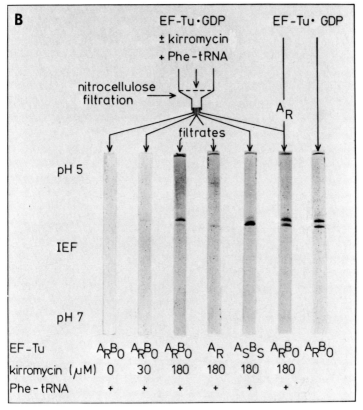

FIG. 7B.

cleotide exchange between EF-Tu-bound and free nucleotide in reaction mixtures containing (EF-TuAr) · GDP and (EF-TuBo) · GDP in almost equimolar amounts (83). The same conclusion was reached by probing conformational changes (84). Kirromycin added to the above mixture of mutant EF-Tu species becomes protein-bound. However, this binding does not immobilize the ribosomes on the mRNA, which can be concluded from the experiment illustrated in Fig. 3, where poly(U) translation was studied at EF-Tu concentrations that are not rate limiting. Under these conditions, polyphenylalanine synthesis with EF-TuAr alone and that with the above mixture of EF-TuAr and EF-TuBo respond in identical fashion to the addition of increasing amounts of kirromycin. In an *in vitro* experiment, wild-type EF-Tu added to a fivefold excess of the mixture of EF-TuAr and EF-TuBo blocked almost all ribosomes upon binding of the antibiotic (34, 35).

The failure of (EF-TuBo) · GDP to immobilize the ribosomes upon binding of kirromycin explains the recessive nature of the tufB mutation with respect to the kirromycin-resistant tufA. Initially it was assumed that EF-TuBo is inactive in protein synthesis and does not interact with the ribosome either in the presence or the absence of kirromycin. This turned out not to be true, however, when the above mixture was submitted to fractionation on DEAE-Sephadex A50, and fractions strongly enriched in EF-TuBo were obtained (84). These fractions, when studied at rate-limiting concentrations, were fully active to sustain poly(U) translation, but became defective in this respect after binding kirromycin.

In further attempts to define the primary site of polypeptide synthesis inhibition resulting from the interaction of kirromycin with EF-TuBo, it was found that the latter is able to form a stable complex with EF-Ts either in the presence or the absence of kirromycin (85). The experiment illustrated in Fig. 7A demonstrates that complex formation between (EF-TuBo) · GTP and Phe-tRNA^{Phe} occurs also in the presence of the antibiotic. In this experiment, (EF-TuAr) · GDP and (EF-TuBo) · GDP were incubated at 0°C for 5 min with phosphoenolpyruvate, pyruvate kinase, and Phe-tRNA^{Phe} in the presence and the absence of kirromycin. The reaction mixture was then filtered over nitrocellulose, and the EF-Tu in the filtrates was analyzed by isoelectric focusing (IEF). Under these conditions, ternary complexes of (EF-Tu) · GTP and aminoacyl-tRNA pass through the filter, but (EF-Tu) · GTP is retained (compare lanes 1, 2, and 3). When kirromycin is included in the reaction mixture, ternary complexes containing either mutant EF-Tu species can thus be detected in the filtrates (lane 4). Ternary complexes containing (EF-TuBo) · GTP readily bind to poly(U)-programmed ribosomes in the presence of the antibiotic (85) and fully resemble their wild-type (EF-Tu)-containing counterparts.

Since kirromycin binding to (EF-Tu) · GDP induces an [(EF-Tu) · GTP]-like conformation (107), it eliminates the need for GTP during enzymic binding of aminoacyl-tRNA to the ribosomes (75, 76). Figure 8A illustrates such a binding for Phe-tRNA^{Phe} mediated by increasing amounts of (EF-TuAs) · GDP. Omission of kirromycin reduces the binding to the level seen with (EF-TuAr) · GDP (Fig. 8C). Since the latter species of (EF-Tu) · GDP does not bind the antibiotic, it fails in mediating Phe-tRNA^{Phe} binding to the ribosome. Most significantly, Fig. 8B shows that such a kirromycin-dependent binding

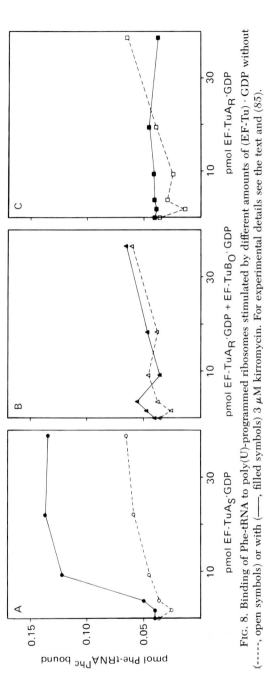

FIG. 8. Binding of Phe-tRNA to poly(U)-programmed ribosomes stimulated by different amounts of (EF-Tu) · GDP without (----, open symbols) or with (——, filled symbols) 3 µM kirromycin. For experimental details see the text and (85).

does not occur either with a mixture of (EF-TuAr) · GDP and (EF-TuBo) · GDP. This failure of (EF-TuBo) · GDP to mediate the transfer of Phe-tRNA to the ribosomes, even in the presence of higher concentrations of the antibiotic (85), is not due to an inability to form the complex [(EF-TuBo) · GDP · (Phe-tRNA) · kirromycin]. This can be concluded from the experiments of Fig. 7B with the nitrocellulose filter technique. Mutant and wild-type species of (EF-Tu) · GDP were incubated with Phe-tRNA^{Phe} and kirromycin, the reaction mixtures were passed through the filters, and the filtrates were analyzed by isoelectric focusing. EF-TuBo appears in the filtrate only when kirromycin is included in the reaction mixture at a relatively high concentration (180 μM). (EF-TuAr) · GDP, which binds the antibiotic rather poorly (84), interacts very weakly with Phe-tRNA^{Phe} even at 180 μM kirromycin (lanes 3 and 4).

These data demonstrate that (EF-TuBo) · GDP can form a complex with aminoacyl-tRNA in the presence of kirromycin, but this complex then fails to bind to the ribosome. They also offer an explanation for the inhibition by kirromycin of the polypeptide synthesis mediated by EF-TuBo. Owing to the intrinsic GTPase of EF-TuBo, which can be induced by kirromycin (98), GTP hydrolysis may occur before complex formation with aminoacyl-tRNA or before association with the ribosome. In that case, formation of the complex [(EF-TuBo) · GDP · (aminoacyl-tRNA) · kirromycin] is possible, but this complex fails to associate with the ribosome, and polypeptide chain elongation does not occur. In case GTP hydrolysis occurs after accommodation of [(EF-TuBo) · GTP · (aminoacyl-tRNA)] on the ribosome, [(EF-TuBo) · GDP · kirromycin] will leave the ribosome, but the experimental data do not permit any conclusion as to whether or not this occurs concomitantly with aminoacyl-tRNA. More detailed studies, preferably with homogeneous EF-TuBo, are needed to determine to what extent aminoacyl-tRNA can "slip" into the aminoacyl site of the ribosome, permitting a limited polypeptide synthesis under these conditions.

Finally, notable in this context is that modification with labeled sulfhydryl agents failed to reveal an extra tRNA binding site on (EF-TuBo) · GDP (113). It means that [(EF-Tu) · GDP · kirromycin] cannot bind to peptidyl-tRNA on the ribosome, which may account for the fact that it is not retained by the ribosome like its wild-type counterpart. Recently, the mutant gene coding for EF-TuBo has been cloned. DNA sequencing revealed that Gly-222 at the end of β-strand 6 is replaced by Asp (113a).

III. Regulation of the Expression of *tufA* and *tufB*

It has been known for some time that the biosynthesis of ribosomes in *E. coli* and that of other components of the protein-synthesizing machinery, such as elongation factors and tRNA, display a high degree of coordination (*114–119*). Under steady-state growth conditions, all these components function at their maximal or near-maximal capacity, and the cell carefully adjusts the rate of synthesis of these components to changes in growth conditions. As a result the molar ratio of, for instance, ribosomes, EF-Ts and EF-G is maintained at about 1 : 1 : 1 (*120, 121*). The total amount of EF-Tu (EF-TuA plus EF-TuB) remains equimolar with that of tRNA (*115*). The ratio of EF-Tu per ribosome, however, varies somewhat under varying environmental conditions (between 7 and 14 according to refs. *12, 115*, between 10 and 20 according to ref. *15*).

The regulatory mechanisms that ensure that the amounts of these components are balanced and adjusted to the environment have remained obscure for a long time. Recently, our knowledge of the organization of the genes coding for ribosomal components and translational factors has expanded considerably (*116, 122, 123*), and a mechanism for the control of the synthesis of ribosomal proteins has been proposed (*124–127*). Here we restrict ourselves primarily to the regulation of expression of *tufA* and *tufB*.

A. Coordinate Regulation of the Expression of *tufA* and *tufB*

A fruitful experimental approach to study the expression of the two *tuf* genes has been the determination of intracellular levels of EF-TuA and EF-TuB in *E. coli* under varying conditions of steady-state growth (*15, 30, 38*). Such a determination obviously is hampered by the great structural similarity of the two proteins, but point mutations causing a shift in isoelectric point have enabled their separation. A prerequisite of this approach is that these mutations do not alter the regulation of the expression of *tufA* and *tufB*. The strains HAK88 (*66*) and LBE2020,AsBo (Table I) meet this requirement, and analyses of the intracellular *tuf* products revealed a constant ratio between the synthesis rates of EF-TuA and EF-TuB (*37*) and between the intracellular amounts of these proteins (*15, 38*) at all growth rates studied. Figure 9 illustrates the latter phenomenon for the strain LBE2020,AsBo. EF-TuAs and EF-TuBo were separated by submitting ribosome-free supernatants to isoelectric focusing, and their concentrations were de-

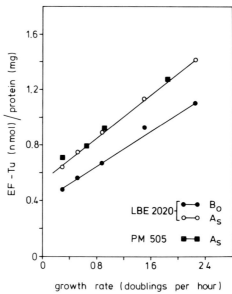

growth rate (doublings per hour)

FIG. 9. The cellular amounts of EF-TuAs and EF-TuBo in crude extracts of strain LBE2020,AsBo cultured at different growth rates. The total cellular amount of EF-Tu from strain PM505,As is also indicated. Isoelectric focusing and "rocket" immunoelectrophoresis were used for the quantitative determination of each protein (15, 38). Growth rates were varied by culturing the cells in media with different carbon sources. The EF-Tu symbols refer to the strains mentioned in Table I.

termined by "rocket" immunoelectrophoresis (15, 38). Figure 9 shows that the molar ratio between EF-TuAs and EF-TuBo in LBE2020,AsBo cells is maintained at a constant value of 1.4 at various growth rates. It may be concluded that the expression of *tufA* and *tufB* is regulated coordinately.

B. Intracellular EF-Tu Level and the Expression of *tufA*

Figure 9 also reveals that inactivation of *tufB* by insertion of bacteriophage Mu DNA does not affect the expression of *tufA*. The intracellular level of EF-TuAs in strain PM505,As is identical to that of cells from LBE2020,AsBo at comparable growth rates. It may be concluded, therefore, that cells from PM505,As do not compensate for the functional loss of the *tufB* gene and the lowering of the intracellular EF-Tu level by an enhanced expression of *tufA*. This conclusion can also be drawn from the data presented in Fig. 10. In this figure, the EF-TuAr level of cells from PM455,Ar is compared to that of LBE

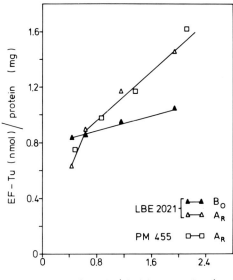

FIG. 10. The cellular amounts of EF-TuAr and EF-TuBo in crude extracts of strain LBE2021,ArBo cultured at different growth rates. The total cellular amount of EF-Tu from strain PM455,Ar is also presented. For further details, see legend to Fig. 9 and refs 15 and 38.

2021,ArBo cells. At comparable growth rates, both strains harbor identical amounts of EF-TuAr.

Interestingly, expression of *tufA* also is not affected by raising the intracellular EF-Tu level. This has been demonstrated by transforming cells of the strain LBE12020,AsBo with the plasmid pTuBo. Both the plasmid-borne *tufB* and the chromosomal *tufB* of the transformants code for EF-TuBo. This enabled the determination of EF-TuA concentrations in both the parental cells and the transformants. It is clear from Fig. 11 that they are the same under various growth conditions (15).

These data lead to the conclusion that neither reduction nor elevation of the intracellular level of EF-Tu influences the expression of *tufA*. A report that cells do compensate for the loss of a functional *tufB* by enhanced expression of *tufA* is unwarranted, since it was based on comparisons of nonisogenic strains (128).

C. Regulation of the Expression of *tufB*

In cells from the strain LBE2020,AsBo, EF-TuAs and EF-TuBo are present in a constant ratio of 1.4 at all growth rates studied. In contrast,

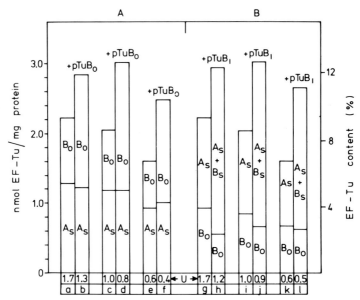

FIG. 11. Intracellular concentrations of chromosome and plasmid encoded EF-Tu species in strain LBE 12020,AsBo transformed with pTuBo (a–f) and pTuB1 (g–l). Cells were grown in rich (a, b, g, h), semi-rich (c, d, i, j), and minimal (e, f, k, l) medium under conditions described in (30). The growth rates are indicated under the bars.

this ratio varies with growth rate in cells from strain LBE2021,ArBo, as is illustrated in Fig. 10. Apparently, in the latter cells, the coordination in the expression of *tufA* and *tufB* is completely lost. This loss is due to the specific single-site mutation of *tufA*, rendering the EF-TuA product resistant to the antibiotic kirromycin. The mutant cells show an enhanced expression of *tufB* as compared to wild-type cells (Figs. 9 and 10), particularly at lower growth rates.

The effect of the mutation is specific in the sense that the expression of the *tsf* gene coding for EF-Ts and that of the ribosomal genes is not affected under all nutritional conditions studied. This strongly suggests a direct involvement of the EF-Tu protein itself in the expression of *tufB* (15, 38).

The findings described in this and the preceding section demonstrate that two distinct mechanisms control the expression of *tufA* and *tufB* during steady-state growth. Under non-steady-state growth conditions this is also the case. Starvation for charged valyl-tRNA in *rel*A[+] cells affects the synthesis of EF-TuA and EF-TuB in a different manner (*129*).

D. EF-Tu Itself Is Involved in the Regulation of tufB Expression

Both *in vitro* and *in vivo* experiments support the hypothesis that EF-Tu itself is involved in the regulation of *tufB* expression (*15, 30, 38*). Addition of EF-Tu to a cell-free coupled transcription–translation system, dependent on DNA from the plasmid pTuB1 (*28, 29*) as a template, suppresses the synthesis of EF-Tu considerably. This suppression is specific: synthesis of other proteins is not affected. It occurs already when EF-Tu is added in an amount that is only 2–5% of the EF-Tu protein endogenously present in the cell-free extract (*15*). Also *in vitro* EF-Tu synthesis directed by DNA, derived from the transducing phage λ*rif*d18, is suppressed by EF-Tu addition. Like the plasmid pTuB1, this phage harbors the entire tRNA-*tufB* transcription unit (*130*). Suppression is not observed with DNA from the plasmid pTuA1 (*15*) and with DNA from the transducing phage λ*fus*3. The latter phage carries the entire *str* transcription unit (*116*) (compare Fig. 1) in contrast to pTuA1, which carries part of the *fus* gene, the intercistronic region, and *tufA* (*27*).

Elevation of the intracellular EF-Tu level by transformation of cells with multicopy plasmids harboring either *tufA* or *tufB* also results in a lowered expression of *tufB* (*30*). This is illustrated in Table IV for cells transformed with plasmids carrying *tufA* and in Fig. 11B for cells transformed with pTuB1. In both cases, expression of the chromosomal *tufB* gene was monitored by assaying the cellular content of EF-TuBo, which is encoded by this gene and can be separated from the products of the chromosomal *tufA* and the plasmid-borne *tuf* gene owing to a difference in isoelectric point.

Three plasmids carrying *tufA* have been employed in the experiments of Table IV: pGp81, pGp82, and pTuA1. The latter was constructed (*27*) by cloning an *Eco*RI fragment derived from the transducing phage λ*fus*3 (*116*) harboring *tufA* into a *Col*EI derivative plasmid. Since *tufA* on the latter is only weakly expressed both *in vitro* (*27*) and *in vivo* (*29*) (Table IV) owing to a reported lack of the natural promoter (*23*), it has been put under the direction of the powerful major leftward promoter (pL) of λ (*131*). Two plasmids (derived from the vector pPLa2311) have thus been obtained: pGp81, carrying *tufA* in the sense orientation toward the pL promoter; and pGp82, with *tufA* in the opposite orientation. Transcription of *tufA* on pGp81 is controlled by a second plasmid pCI(857) compatible with pGp81 and bearing a CIts gene of phage λ coding for a temperature-sensitive repressor. When cultured at 37°C, transformants of the strain LBE12020,AsBo carrying

TABLE IV

Intracellular Amounts of EF-Tu and EF-Ts in Transformants of LBE12020, AsBo Carrying Different Multicopy Plasmids[a]

Strain	Medium	Growth rate	Total EF-Tu content (nmol/mg protein)	Total EF-Tu content (%)	EF-TuBo content (nmol/mg protein)	EF-TuBo content (%)	EF-Ts content (nmol/mg protein)
LBE12020, AsBo, pCI	LC[b]	1.1	2.34	10.1	0.96	4.1	0.35
LBE12020, AsBo, pCI, pGp81	LC	0.9	3.96	17.0	0.63	2.7	0.34
LBE12020, AsBo, pGp82	LC	1.0	4.10	17.6	0.65	2.8	0.34
LBE12020, AsBo, pTuA1	LC	1.2	2.21	9.5	ND[c]	ND	0.36

[a] For experimental details see (30) and the text (Section III,D).

[b] LC is a "rich" medium (defined in 15).

[c] ND, not done.

either pGp81 or pGp82 contain the same, almost twofold-elevated amount of EF-Tu (Table IV). Apparently at this temperature the two orientations of the plasmid-borne *tufA* have no differential effect on the total EF-Tu level. This indicates that under these conditions transcription is not initiated at the pL promoter but from an RNA polymerase binding site that, according to various authors (23, 32), is located in the C-terminal region of the *fus* gene and has been cloned together with *tufA*. Table IV shows that transformation with pTuA1, in contrast to that with pGp81 or pGp82, does not raise the EF-Tu level above that of the parental cells. It is not clear why expression of *tufA* on the former plasmid is so low while all three plasmids contain the same *Eco*RI fragment from λ*fus*3. Presumably it is the genetic environment of *tufA* on pTuA1 that reduces its expression in an unknown fashion.

The two plasmids harboring *tufB* employed in the experiments of Fig. 11 are identical except that pTuB1 codes for wild-type EF-Tu and pTuBo for EF-TuBo. Both carry the entire tRNA-*tufB* transcription unit (28).

Although suppression of the expression of chromosomal *tufB* occurs upon transformation with plasmids carrying either *tufA* or *tufB*, elevation of the EF-Tu level differs considerably. The growth behavior of the transformants is also differently affected. When transcription of *tufA* from the pL promoter on pGp81 is initiated by thermal inactivation of the temperature-sensitive λ repressor at 43°C, the EF-Tu content reaches values up to 30% of the total cellular protein and growth comes to a complete halt about three hours after the temperature shift up. Growth is already considerably affected when the λ repressor is not inactivated, and transcription from the pL promoter is blocked. Under these conditions, cells cultivated in rich medium show an extended lag phase in their growth. In semi-rich medium this lag is prolonged to such an extent that growth is virtually abolished. Transformants are able to overcome the initial block, however, in rich medium and reach thereafter a steady-state growth that does not differ from that of cells transformed with pCI only. Their EF-Tu content then amounts to about 17% of the cellular protein, which represents an increase of 75% over the wild-type content.

The consequences of transformation with pTuB1 or pTuBo are much less dramatic. Although the transformants grow somewhat slower than the parental cells, they do not have an extended lag phase. As illustrated in Fig. 11, their EF-Tu content is maximally 12.5% of the bacterial protein. It has been reported (29) that the rate of EF-Tu synthesis in cells transformed with pTuB1 is not appreciably increased although the copy number of pTuB1 is about 20. The presence of a regulatory mechanism that maintains the normal EF-Tu level in the cell has been suggested. The data of Fig. 11 reveal a limited increase in EF-Tu level of about 25% after transformation; this, however, is sufficient to suppress the expression of the chromosomal *tufB* gene (about 40% at the highest growth rate). For studies of the regulation of *tufB* expression, pTuB1 and pTuBo are therefore more suitable than pGp81 and pGp82. The latter raise the EF-Tu level too much, even when transcription is not initiated from the pL promoter. They also cause a complex cellular growth response.

It has been pointed out above that the intracellular amounts of ribosomes and elongation factors are positively correlated with the steady-state growth-rate of the cells. The question therefore may be raised whether the suppression of *tufB* expression possibly is the result of growth retardation rather than a specific effect of the rise in EF-Tu level. Determinations of the cellular contents of ribosomes and EF-Ts show, however, that the latter remains unaltered after transformation, strongly suggesting that we are dealing with a specific effect.

A failure to observe any effect of EF-Tu overproduction on the rate of synthesis of EF-TuA and EF-TuB has also been reported (33). However, the results, similarly obtained after transformation with plasmids carrying *tuf* genes, are not necessarily in contradiction with the data presented in Table IV and Fig. 11. Transformants were grown in a glycerol medium. Under comparable growth conditions, the expression of *tufB* in the transformants of Fig. 11 is only marginally affected.

E. EF-Tu as an Autogenous Repressor of *tufB*: A Hypothesis

The data discussed above indicate that EF-Tu specifically affects *tufB* expression. Although an indirect role cannot be ruled out entirely, a direct involvement seems more plausible. This particularly holds true for the results obtained *in vitro,* but the *in vivo* data are also in agreement with such an assumption. Neither the single-site mutation of *tufA* nor the modulations in *tuf* gene dosage affect the expression of *tsf* and that of the ribosomal genes.

The question then arises: At what level does EF-Tu exert such a regulatory function? It has been reported that the complex (EF-Tu) · (EF-Ts) stimulates transcription of rRNA genes (*132*), and a control function of EF-Tu in regulating *tufB* transcription may therefore be considered. Some investigators failed, however, to find any evidence for a specific effect of EF-Tu on rRNA synthesis or on RNA polymerase activity (*133, 134*), and it seems an attractive hypothesis to ascribe a posttranscriptional role to EF-Tu as an autogenous repressor of *tufB*. In this context it may be recalled that a number of ribosomal proteins appear to act as autogenous repressors of ribosomal protein genes (*123–127*). These proteins fulfill a key function in inhibiting the translation of mRNA, coding for themselves and for certain other ribosomal proteins (r-proteins) in the same transcription unit. Structural homologies have been found to exist between the binding sites on 16 S rRNA of some of these repressors, e.g., S4, S7 and S8, and the target sites on the mRNAs coding for the respective r-proteins (*123–127*). It may not be fortuitous that *tufB* is cotranscribed with four upstream tRNA genes. This could provide the primary transcript with one or more target sites for EF-Tu binding that are structurally homologous to aminoacyl-tRNA, the binding partner of (EF-Tu) · GTP during the elongation cycle.

A number of analogies may be noted between such a model and the models proposed for the regulation of r-protein genes. In the latter model, regulation can be regarded as competition between rRNA and r-protein mRNA for repressor r-proteins. The affinity of the repressor r-proteins for rRNA is supposed to be stronger than that for the target sites on their mRNA (*124*). Similarly, the affinity of (EF-Tu) · GTP for aminoacyl-tRNA presumably exceeds the affinity for the non-aminoacylated tRNA elements of the primary transcript of the tRNA-*tufB* transcription unit. Regulation of the latter unit may thus be due to competition between these tRNA elements and aminoacyl-tRNA for (EF-Tu) · GTP.

The finding that a specific point mutation of *tufA* enhances the expression of *tufB* is reminiscent of an analogous observation concerning the ribosomal protein S4 (*135*). A specific mutation of the S4-encoding gene *rps*D was shown to stimulate the *in vivo* expression of the r-protein genes of the so-called α-operon. Presumably this stimulation is the result of the lowered affinity of the mutant S4 repressor for its target on the mRNA. The finding mentioned in Section II,A, that EF-TuAr has a reduced affinity for aminoacyl-tRNA, lends suggestive support to the idea that the binding of EF-TuAr to the presumptive tRNA targets on the primary transcript is also impaired and causes the enhanced expression of *tufB*. This enhancement is more pronounced at low growth rates. Under the latter conditions, the degree of tRNA aminoacylation may be relatively low and the proportion of free EF-Tu molecules not taken up in ternary complexes, relatively high. Competition for aminoacyl-tRNA will then occur between (EF-TuAr) · GTP and (EF-TuBo) · GTP a competition that will be decided in favor of the latter. This means that the major part of free (EF-Tu) · GTP is (EF-

TuAr) · GTP, a poor repressor. The expression of tufB will then be enhanced, particularly under restrictive nutritional conditions, i.e., at lower growth rates.

A final analogy between the two models is that the repressor acts at a posttranscriptional level in both. In the case of the r-proteins, translation is inhibited. Binding of EF-Tu to the primary transcript of the tRNA-tufB transcription unit may influence the translation of the EF-TuB cistron in a similar fashion, but interference with the processing of the tRNA precursor with consequences for the maturation of the monocistronic EF-TuB mRNA and its translation may also be envisaged. The implication of the latter possibility is that autogenous repression of tufB would affect the intracellular concentration of certain specific tRNA species. In agreement with such a possibility are the pronounced effects of EF-Tu overproduction on bacterial growth, but not on the intracellular levels of EF-Ts and the ribosomes. Further analyses, particularly of the levels of specific tRNAs and of the primary transcripts of the tRNA-tufB transcription unit, are obviously needed to clarify the regulation of the expression of this interesting transcription unit.

In the light of the latter considerations it would not be surprising if this regulation appeared to be more complex than envisioned here. Preliminary indications that EF-Tu is not the only component involved in the control of tufB expression have been derived from experiments in which the expression of tufB on the plasmid pTuBo was studied (30). In contrast to expectation, this expression was lower in transformants that lacked a functional chromosomal tufB than in transformants haboring two active chromosomal tuf genes. Inactivation of the chromosomal tufB was achieved by insertion of Mu DNA. In the parental cells such an inactivation results in a 40% decrease of the EF-Tu content (see Fig. 9). Apparently a lowering of the intracellular EF-Tu level causes a suppression rather than an enhancement of the expression of the plasmid-borne tufB.

Insertion of Mu DNA occurred in the coding part of the chromosomal tufB. Since it may be assumed that this does not affect the expression of the tRNA genes cotranscribed with tufB, Mu insertion presumably has resulted in a decrease in the (EF-Tu)/tRNA ratio. Such a relative excess of tRNA clearly deviates from the 1 : 1 stoichiometry of EF-Tu and tRNA that apparently is maintained in wild-type cells under normal physiological conditions. Whether this excess is responsible for the lowered expression of the plasmid-borne tufB remains for further investigations. Possible physical differences in structure between the plasmid-borne and the chromosomal tufB gene should also be considered. Further studies of a possible regulatory role of tRNA in the expression of *tufB* and other genes involved in the translational machinery may, however, be promising.

ACKNOWLEDGMENT

The research of the authors is supported by the Netherlands Foundation for Chemical Research (S.O.N.), which is subsidized by the Netherlands Organization for the Advancement of Pure Research (Z.W.O.).

REFERENCES

1. D. L. Miller and H. Weissbach, *in* "Molecular Mechanisms of Protein Biosynthesis" (H. Weissbach and S. Pestka, eds.), p. 323. Academic Press, New York, 1977.
2. Y. Kaziro, *BBA* **505**, 95 (1978).
3. T. Blumenthal and G. G. Carmichael, *ARB* **48**, 525 (1979).
4. K. Arai, B. F. C. Clark, L. Duffy, M. D. Jones, Y. Kaziro, R. A. Laursen, J. L'Italien, D. L. Miller, S. Nagarkatti, S. Nakamura, K. M. Nielsen, T. E. Petersen, K. Takahashi, and M. Wade, *PNAS* **77**, 1326 (1980).
5. M. D. Jones, T. E. Petersen, K. M. Nielsen, S. Magnusson, L. Sottrup-Jensen, K. Gausing, and B. F. C. Clark, *EJB* **108**, 507 (1980).
6. W. Kalsch, W. H. Gast, G. E. Schulz, and R. Leberman, *JMB* **117**, 999 (1977).
7. F. Jurnak, A. Rich, and D. L. Miller, *JMB* **115**, 103 (1977).
8. J. R. Rubin, K. Morikawa, J. Nyborg, T. F. M. La Cour, B. F. C. Clark, and D. L. Miller, *FEBS Lett.* **129**, 177 (1981).
9. B. F. C. Clark, T. F. M. La Cour, J. Fontecilla-Camps, K. Morikawa, K. M. Nielsen, J. Nyborg, and J. R. Rubin, *FEBS Meeting on Cell Function and Differentiation*, Vol. 3, Symp. 12 (1982).
10. A. V. Furano, *PNAS* **72**, 4780 (1975).
11. G. R. Jacobson and J. P. Rosenbusch, *Nature* **261**, 23 (1976).
12. F. C. Neidhardt, P. L. Bloch, S. Pedersen, and S. Reeh, *J. Bact.* **129**, 378 (1977).
13. A. Miyajima and I. Kaziro, *J. Biochem.* **83**, 453 (1978).
14. S. Pedersen, P. L. Bloch, S. Reeh, and F. C. Neidhardt, *Cell* **14**, 179 (1978).
15. P. H. Van der Meide, E. Vijgenboom, A. Talens, and L. Bosch, *EJB* **130**, 397 (1983).
16. G. R. Jacobson, B. J. Tacks, and J. P. Rosenbusch, *Bchem* **15**, 2297 (1976).
17. M. Wurtz, G. R. Jacobson, A. C. Steven, and J. P. Rosenbusch, *EJB* **88**, 593 (1978).
18. B. D. Beck, P. G. Arscott, and A. Jacobson, *PNAS* **75**, 1250 (1978).
19. B. D. Beck, *EJB* **97**, 495 (1979).
20. A. F. M. Cremers, A. P. Sam, L. Bosch, and J. E. Mellema, *JMB* **153**, 477 (1981).
21. A. Travers, *Nature* **244**, 15 (1973).
22. S. R. Jaskunas, L. Lindhal, M. Nomura, and R. R. Burgess, *Nature* **257**, 458 (1975).
23. T. Yokota, H. Sugisaki, M. Takanami, and I. Kaziro, *Gene* **12**, 25 (1980).
24. G. An and J. D. Friesen, *Gene* **12**, 33 (1980).
25. P. G. Lemaux and D. L. Miller, *Mol. Gen. Genet.* **159**, 47 (1978).
26. D. L. Miller, S. Nagarkatti, R. A. Laursen, J. Parker, and J. D. Friesen, *Mol. Gen. Genet.* **159**, 57 (1978).
27. M. Shibuya, H. Nashimoto, and I. Kaziro, *Mol. Gen. Genet.* **170**, 231 (1979).
28. A. Miyajima, M. Shibuya, and I. Kaziro, *FEBS Lett.* **102**, 207 (1979).
29. A. Miyajima and I. Kaziro, *FEBS Lett.* **119**, 215 (1980).

124   L. BOSCH *et al.*

30. P. H. Van der Meide, R. A. Kastelein, E. Vijgenboom, and L. Bosch, *EJB* **130**, 409 (1983).
31. J. S. Lee, G. An, J. D. Friesen, and N. P. Fiil, *Cell* **25**, 251 (1981).
32. G. An, J. S. Lee, and J. D. Friesen, *J. Bact.* **149**, 548 (1982).
33. J. M. Zengel and L. Lindahl, *J. Bact.* **149**, 793 (1982).
34. J. A. M. Van de Klundert, E. Den Turk, A. H. Borman, P. H. Van der Meide, and L. Bosch, *FEBS Lett.* **81**, 303 (1977).
35. E. Fischer, H. Wolf, K. Hantke, and A. Parmeggiani, *PNAS* **74**, 4341 (1977).
36. J. A. M. Van de Klundert, P. H. Van der Meide, P. Van de Putte, and L. Bosch, *PNAS* **75**, 4470 (1978).
37. S. Reeh and S. Pedersen, in "Gene Expression" (B. F. C. Clark *et al.*, eds.), p. 89 (*FEBS Meet. 11th Copenhagen, 1977*).
38. P. H. Van der Meide, E. Vijgenboom, M. Dicke, and L. Bosch, *FEBS Lett.* **139**, 325 (1982).
39. A. Parmeggiani and G. Sander, in "Topics in Antibiotic Chemistry" (P. G. Sammes, ed.), Vol. 5, p. 159. Wiley, New York, 1980.
40. J. Lucas-Lenard and F. Lipmann, *ARB* **40**, 409 (1971).
41. B. J. Bachmann and K. B. Low, *Microbiol. Rev.* **44**, 1 (1980).
42. S. R. Jaskunas, A. M. Fallon, and M. Nomura, *JBC* **252**, 7323 (1977).
43. S. Pedersen, S. V. Reeh, J. Parker, R. J. Watson, J. D. Friesen, and N. P. Fiil, *Mol. Gen. Genet.* **144**, 339 (1976).
44. L. E. Post, A. E. Arfsten, M. Nomura, and S. R. Jaskunas, *Cell* **15**, 231 (1978).
45. K. Gausing, *Mol. Gen. Genet.* **184**, 272 (1981).
46. J. M. Zengel and L. Lindahl, *Mol. Gen. Genet.* **185**, 487 (1982).
47. M. Yamamoto and M. Nomura, *J. Bact.* **137**, 584 (1979).
48. J. J. Rossi and A. Landy, *Cell* **16**, 523 (1979).
49. L. Hudson, J. Rossi, and A. Landy, *Nature* **294**, 422 (1981).
50. M. Rosenberg and D. Court, *Annu. Rev. Genet.* **13**, 19 (1979).
51. W. E. Taylor and R. R. Burgess, *Gene* **6**, 331 (1979).
52. E. Calva and R. R. Burgess, *JBC* **255**, 11017 (1981).
53. J. Rossi, T. Egan, L. Hudson, and A. Landy, *Cell* **26**, 305 (1981).
54. T. Sekiva, R. Contreras, T. Takeya, and G. Khorana, *JBC* **254**, 5802 (1979).
55. A. V. Furano, *PNAS* **75**, 3104 (1978).
56. I. Smith and P. Paress, *J. Bact.* **135**, 1107 (1978).
57. D. Filer and A. V. Furano, *JBC* **255**, 728 (1980).
58. J. C. Watson and S. J. Surzycki, *PNAS* **79**, 2264 (1982).
59. O. Ciferri, personal communication.
60. J. Weiser, K. Mikulik, and L. Bosch, *BBRC* **99**, 16 (1981).
61. P. H. Van der Meide, Ph.D. Thesis, University of Leiden, The Netherlands, 1982.
62. T. Blumenthal, T. A. Landers, and K. Weber, *PNAS* **69**, 1313 (1972).
63. A. J. Wahba, M. J. Miller, A. Niveleau, T. A. Landers, G. G. Carmichael, K. Weber, D. A. Hawley, and L. I. Slobin, *JBC* **249**, 3314 (1974).
64. J. H. Lupker, G. J. Verschoor, F. W. M. De Rooij, and L. Bosch, *PNAS* **71**, 460 (1974).
65. F. S. Young and F. C. Neidhardt, *Annu. Meet. Am. Soc. Microbiol., 75th, Abstracts*, p. 161 (1975).
66. S. Pedersen, A. M. Blumenthal, S. Reeh, J. Parker, P. Lemaux, R. A. Laursen, S. Nagarkatti, and J. D. Friesen, *PNAS* **73**, 1698 (1976).
67. M. Kuwano, H. Endo, T. Kamiya, and K. Hori, *JMB* **86**, 689 (1974).
68. C. Vos, *Chem. Abstr.* **77**, 32742 (1972).

69. C. Vos and P. E. J. Verwiel, *Tetrahedron Lett.* **30**, 2823 (1973).
70. H. Wolf and H. Zahner, *Arch. Mikrobiol.* **83**, 147 (1972).
71. J. Berger, H. H. Lehr, S. Teitel, H. Maer, and E. Grunberg, *J. Antibiot.* **26**, 15 (1973).
72. H. Maer, M. Leach, L. Yarmchuk, and A. Stempel, *JACS* **95**, 8449 (1973).
73. H. Maer, M. Leach, T. H. Williams, W. Benz, J. F. Blount, and A. Stempel, *JACS* **95**, 8448 (1973).
74. H. Wolf, G. Chinali, and A. Parmeggiani, *PNAS* **71**, 4910 (1974).
75. G. Chinali, H. Wolf, and A. Parmeggiani, *EJB* **75**, 55 (1977).
76. H. Wolf, G. Chinali, and A. Parmeggiani, *EJB* **75**, 67 (1977).
77. A. Pingoud, C. Urbanke, H. Wolf, and G. Maass, *EJB* **86**, 153 (1978).
78. O. Fasano, W. Brums, J.-B. Crechet, G. Sander, and A. Parmeggiani, *EJB* **89**, 557 (1978).
79. G. Sander, R. Ivell, J-B. Crechet, and A. Parmeggiani, *Bchem* **19**, 865 (1980).
80. A. Parmeggiani and G. Sander, *Mol. Cell. Biochem.* **35**, 129 (1981).
81. V. Bocchini, G. Parlato, E. De Vendittis, G. Sander, and A. Parmeggiani, *EJB* **113**, 53 (1980).
82. R. Ivell, O. Fasano, J-.B. Crechet, and A. Parmeggiani, *Bchem* **20**, 1355 (1981).
83. P. H. Van der Meide, T. H. Borman, A. M. A. Van Kimmenade, P. Van de Putte, and L. Bosch, *PNAS* **77**, 3922 (1980).
84. P. H. Van der Meide, F. J. Duisterwinkel, J. M. De Graaf, B. Kraal, L. Bosch, J. Douglass, and T. Blumenthal, *EJB* **117**, 1 (1981).
85. F. J. Duisterwinkel, J. M. De Graaf, P. J. M. Schretlen, B. Krral, and L. Bosch, *EJB* **117**, 7 (1981).
86. K. Gausing, *Mol. Gen. Genet.* **184**, 265 (1981).
87. K. Gausing, *Mol. Gen. Genet.* **184**, 272 (1981).
88. E. Dubnau, S. Pifko, A. Sloma, K. Cabane, and I. Smith, *Mol. Gen. Genet.* **143**, 1 (1976).
89. W. Worner and H. Wolf, *FEBS Lett.* **146**, 322 (1982).
90. F. J. Duisterwinkel, J. M. De Graaf, B. Kraal, and L. Bosch, unpublished results.
91. O. Fasano and A. Parmeggiani, *Bchem* **20**, 1361 (1981).
92. A. P. Sam, A. Noort, C. W. A. Pleij, and L. Bosch, unpublished results.
93. G. W. M. Swart, B. Kraal, L. Bosch, and A. Parmeggiani, *FEBS Lett.* **142**, 101 (1982).
94. T. Blumenthal and T. A. Landers, *Bchem* **15**, 422 (1976).
95. T. Blumenthal, B. Saari, P. H. Van der Meide, and L. Bosch, *JBC* **255**, 5300 (1980).
96. A. P. Sam, A. Pingoud, and L. Bosch, unpublished results.
97. O. Fasano, E. De Vendittis, and A. Parmeggiani, *JBC* **257**, 3145 (1982).
98. F. J. Duisterwinkel, Ph.D. Thesis, University of Leiden, The Netherlands, 1981.
99. F. J. Duisterwinkel, J. M. De Graaf, B. Kraal, and L. Bosch, *FEBS Lett.* **131**, 89 (1981).
100. C. Branden, *Quant. Rev. Biophys.* **13**, 317 (1980).
101. J. F. Eccleston, M. R. Webb, D. E. Ash, and G. H. Reed, *JBC* **256**, 10774 (1981).
102. A. Wittinghofer, R. S. Goody, P. Roesch, and H. R. Kalbitzer, *EJB* **124**, 109 (1982).
103. J. F. Eccleston and M. R. Webb, *JBC* **257**, 5046 (1982).
104. J. Jonak, J. Smrt, A. Holy, and I. Rychlik, *EJB* **105**, 315 (1980).
105. G. Parlato, J. Guesnet, J. B. Crechet, and A. Parmeggiani, *FEBS Lett.* **125**, 257 (1981).
106. P. Bhuta, G. Kumar, and S. Chladek, *Bchem* **21**, 899 (1982).
107. J. Douglass and T. Blumenthal, *JBC* **254**, 5383 (1979).

108. G. Sander, M. Okonek, J. B. Crechet, R. Ivell, V. Bocchini, and A. Parmeggiani, *FEBS Lett.* **98**, 111 (1979).

109. J. M. Van Noort, F. J. Duisterwinkel, J. Jonak, J. Sedlacek, B. Kraal, and L. Bosch, *EMBO J.* **1**, 1199 (1982).

110. N. De Groot, A. Panet, and I. Lapidot, *EJB* **23**, 523 (1971).

111. L. Luhrmann, H. Eckhardt, and G. Stoffler, *Nature* **280**, 423 (1979).

112. S. Campuzano and J. Modolell, *EJB* **117**, 27 (1981).

113. J. M. Van Noort, B. Kraal, and L. Bosch, unpublished results.

113a. A. Talens and L. Bosch, unpublished results.

114. K. Gausing, in "Ribosomes: Structure, Function and Genetics" (G. Chambliss, G. R. Craven, J. Davies, K. Davis, L. Kahan, and M. Nomura, eds.), p. 693. Univ. Park Press, Baltimore, Maryland, 1979.

115. A. V. Furano, *PNAS* **72**, 4780 (1975).

116. M. Nomura, E. A. Morgan, and S. R. Jaskunas, *Annu. Rev. Genet.* **11**, 297 (1977).

117. A. Miyajima and Y. Kaziro, *J. Biochem.* **83**, 453 (1978).

118. O. Maaloe, in "Biological Regulation and Development" (R. F. Goldberger, ed.), p. 487. Plenum, New York, 1979.

119. A. Skjold, H. Juarez, and C. Hedgcoth, *J. Bact.* **115**, 117 (1973).

120. J. Gordon, *Bchem* **9**, 912 (1970).

121. J. Gordon and H. Weissbach, *Bchem* **9**, 4233 (1970).

122. M. Nomura and L. E. Post, in "Ribosomes: Structure, Function and Genetics" (G. Chambliss, G. R. Craven, J. Davies, K. Davis, L. Kahan, and M. Nomura, eds.), p. 671. Univ. Park Press, Baltimore, Maryland 1979.

123. L. Lindahl and J. M. Zengel, *Adv. Genet.* **21**, 53 (1982).

124. M. Nomura, J. L. Yates, D. Dean, and L. E. Post, *PNAS* **77**, 7084 (1980).

125. P. O. Olins and M. Nomura, *NARes* **9**, 1757 (1981).

126. P. O. Olins and M. Nomura, *Cell* **26**, 205 (1981).

127. J. L. Yates and M. Nomura, *Cell* **24**, 243 (1981).

128. F. S. Young and A. V. Furano, *Cell* **24**, 695 (1981).

129. S. Reeh, S. Pedersen, and J. D. Friesen, *Mol. Gen. Genet.* **149**, 279 (1976).

130. J. B. Kirschbaum and E. B. Konrad, *J. Bact.* **116**, 517 (1973).

131. E. Remaut, P. Stanssens, and W. Fiers, *Gene* **15**, 81 (1981).

132. A. Travers, *Nature* **263**, 641 (1976).

133. A. J. J. Van Ooijen, Ph.D. Thesis, University of Groningen, The Netherlands (1976).

134. C. K. Biedricher and M. Druminsky, *PNAS* **77**, 866 (1980).

135. M. O. Olsson and L. A. Isaksson, *Mol. Gen. Genet.* **169**, 271 (1979).

Small Nuclear RNAs and RNA Processing[1]

RAM REDDY AND
HARRIS BUSCH

*Department of Pharmacology,
Baylor College of Medicine,
Houston, Texas*

I. Summary[2]

Ribosomal RNA, transfer RNA, and messenger RNAs, which comprise about 99% of the cellular RNA, are part of the protein-synthesizing machinery. Many studies in the last 15 years have established the presence of another class of RNA, "small nuclear RNAs" (snRNAs) that account for 0.1–1% of the total cellular RNA. There is evidence for at least 15 distinct small RNAs in rat and human cells. Of these, six (designated U1- to U6-RNAs) are capped, metabolically stable, synthesized by polymerase II, present as ribonucleoprotein particles, and present in concentrations comparable to that of ribosomes. U3-RNA, found only in the nucleolus, is associated with preribosomal RNA and is involved in maturation of ribosomal RNAs, although the precise mechanism is not known. U1-, U2-, U4-, U5-, and U6-RNPs,

[1] Work in our laboratory has been supported by grants from Cancer Center Program, Grant 10893, awarded by DHEW; the Bristol-Myers Fund; the Michael E. DeBakey Medical Foundation; the Pauline Sterne Wolff Memorial Foundation; the Taub Foundation; and the William S. Farish Fund.

[2] *Abbreviations:* snRNA(s), small nuclear ribonucleic acid(s); snRNP(s), small nuclear ribonucleoprotein(s); U-RNA(s), RNA(s) rich in uridylic acid; IVS, intervening sequence; anti-Sm (-Ro, etc.), antibodies produced by patient Sm (Ro, etc.) with autoimmune disease(s); Alu-family DNA, highly repeated, interspersed DNA containing an "alu" restriction enzyme site (EC 3.1.23.1).

Progress in Nucleic Acid Research
and Molecular Biology, Vol. 30

found in nucleoplasm, are in part associated with hnRNP particles and are implicated in messenger RNA transport and processing; the detailed mechanism(s) are under study.

The discovery that patients with autoimmune diseases produce antibodies against RNP particles containing small nuclear RNAs made improved methods for studies on small RNPs available to researchers in many disciplines. The availability of these immunological reagents for selective immunoprecipitation of specific U-snRNPs and other snRNPs offers a powerful approach to study their structures, intracellular localization, and function. In addition, the attractive hypothesis that snRNAs, like U1-RNA, may be involved in properly aligning splice junctions, of pre-mRNA, brought snRNAs to the attention of many researchers.

Unlike the capped U-snRNAs, which are transcribed by RNA polymerase II, the noncapped RNAs are transcribed by RNA polymerase III; they have diverse functions. Cytoplasmic 7 S RNA is an integral part of the "signal recognition particle" involved in synthesis and transport of secretory proteins (181a). RNase-P (EC 3.1.26.5) RNA has been reported (200, 201) to be part of an RNP particle involved in processing precursor tRNAs. P-snRNA is implicated in making chromatin accessible for crossing-over during meiosis (34), and CEH-RNA is thought to induce embryonic heart-cell differentiation (198). In addition, several RNAs, including 4.5 and 4.5 SI, 6 S, 7 S RNAs, exhibit homologies to reiterated DNA sequences, whose significance is not understood. Although the structures of the small RNAs are now well defined, much remains to be learned about their relationship to proteins in snRNP particles and the functions of the snRNP particles.

II. Small Nuclear RNAs: Characteristics, Nomenclature, Occurrence

Approximately 15 small nuclear RNAs (snRNAs) from rat and human tissues have been well characterized; these RNAs are broadly divided into two groups, the capped U-snRNAs and the noncapped snRNAs. There have been several recent reviews on these RNAs (1–4). The general properties of these two groups of snRNAs are summarized in Table I. Some snRNAs are virtually found only in nuclei (e.g., the U-snRNAs and the 4.5 S and 4.5 SI snRNAs). Others that are also found in the cytoplasm include the 4, 5, 5.8, 7, and 8 S and the Y-RNAs. (Figure 9 shows the cellular distribution of these species.) In this essay, "snRNAs" includes only the U-snRNAs and the 4.5 S RNAs. Other RNAs are referred to as "small RNAs."

TABLE I
CHARACTERISTICS OF SMALL RNAs OF NOVIKOFF HEPATOMA

Property	U-snRNAs	Other snRNAs
RNAs	U1, U2, U3, U4, U5, and U6	4.5, 4.5 SI, 6 S, Y1, Y2, 7 S, 7-3, 7-2, 8-2 RNAs
5′ ends	All RNAs capped, U1- to U5-RNAs with trimethyl-guanosine, and U6-RNA with an unidentified nonnucleotide	pppG; in some instances, pG
Size	100–250 nucleotides	90–400 nucleotides
Posttranscriptional modifications	Yes	None
Copies per cell	0.2 to 1×10^6	Less than 1×10^3 to 0.5×10^6
Present in ribonucleo-protein particles	Yes	Yes
Subcellular localization	U3-RNA in nucleolus; others in nucleoplasm	7 S, 8-2, Y1, and Y2 RNAs in cytoplasm; 4.5, 4.5 SI in nucleoplasm; others not clearly established
Metabolic stability	Stable; half-lives of up to one cell cycle	Stable; half-lives of up to one cell cycle where studied
Synthesized by:	Polymerase II	Polymerase III

The uridylic-acid-rich and capped small nuclear RNAs are termed U1- to U6-snRNAs (5). [Several investigators have suggested that the U in U-snRNAs was intended to mean Ubiquitous, nUclear, Unusual, or Unique, but the terminology was actually devised by Hodnett and Busch in 1968 (5) to indicate Uridylic-acid-rich and is so used here.] The noncapped RNAs are numbered by their apparent sedimentation values, although these estimates were based upon their electrophoretic mobilities on polyacrylamide gels. The 4.5 S RNA migrates between 4 S and 5 S RNA. Several RNAs of the size of 7 S RNA are numbered 7-1, 7-2, 7-3, etc.; these are all unique small RNAs. The suffixes A, B, C, etc., indicate minor structural variants in primary sequence, or the absence of some nucleotides near the 3′ end, or conformational isomers, but all these variants presumably carry out the same function; examples of these are U1A and U1B; U3A, U3B, and U3C. For alternative nomenclatures, see reviews (1, 2, 4).

After small RNAs were found in human, rat, and mouse cells, systematic studies led to the conclusion that snRNAs are present in all vertebrates (6) and invertebrates (7, 8). snRNAs are present in all cell types and in malignant cells (9–11). Table II shows the cell types, tissues, and species from which small RNAs have been isolated and characterized (7–47).

The occurrence of each of the 18 small RNAs is indicated in Table III only where definite evidence appears in the literature. Each of these RNAs is presumably present in other species. The capped RNAs U1 to U6 have been found in vertebrates, invertebrates, and plants. Dinoflagellates, which are considered to link prokaryotes and eukaryotes, contain each of the six U-snRNAs, indicating that these RNAs arose very early in evolution. There are less exhaustive studies on the occurrence of noncapped RNAs in many species. Also, many other noncapped RNAs may be identified in the future.

III. Uridylate-Rich Small Nuclear RNAs

A. Cap Structure

One unique feature of the U-RNAs is the "cap" structure at their 5′ ends. The trimethylguanosine in snRNAs (48) was first found only in U1-, U2-, and U3-RNAs (49). It is on the 5′ end of U1-RNA (50, 51) and U2-RNA (51, 52) in an unusual 5′-5′ triphosphoric linkage. This struc-

TABLE II
SPECIES FOR WHICH STUDIES ON SMALL RNAS HAVE BEEN REPORTED

Human	HeLa cells (9, 11, 12), lymphocytes (13), fibroblasts (14), intestine cells. Chang liver cells (8), KB cells (15)
Monkey	Vero cells (8)
Rat	Novikoff hepatoma cells (5, 16), liver, kidney, Yoshida cells (8), brain (8, 17)
Rabbit	Heart, kidney, liver, leg muscle, blood cells, lung (8)
Mouse	Ehrlich ascites cells (18), myeloma (19, 20), erythroleukemia (21), lung, liver, L cells (8)
Hamster	Baby hamster kidney cells (22), Chinese hamster ovary (23)
Chicken	Brain (24), heart, kidney, liver, leg muscle, blood cells (8)
Lizard	Heart, lung, liver, tail (8)
Frog	Erythrocytes, brain, heart, liver, muscle (8)
Insects	Drosophila (25, 26, 26a), fall army worm (27)
Protozoans	Amoeba (7); Dictyostelium (28, 29); Tetrahymena (30); sea urchins (31); sea urchin embryos (32); yeast, Physarum, Psammechinus, Paracentrotus (8); Calliphora, Tenebrio, Hylotrupes (8, 33)
Plants	Wheat (J. Skuzeski, personal communication), lilies (34), dinoflagellates (35)
Fungi	Neurospora (36), Mycoplasma (8)
Bacteria	Escherichia coli (37–40)
Viruses	Adenovirus (41), SV40 (42, 43), vesicular stomatitus virus (VSV) (44, 45), Epstein–Barr virus (EBER) (46, 47)

TABLE III
Species from Which Small RNAs Have Been Isolated and Characterized[a]

RNA	Human	Rat, mouse, hamster	Chicken	Drosophila	Xenopus	Amoeba	Dinoflagellates	Wheat	Tomato	Lilies	E. coli
U1	X	X	X	X	X	X	X	—	X	—	—
U2	X	X	X	X	X	X	X	X	—	—	—
U3	X	X	X	X	X	X	X	—	—	—	—
U4	X	X	X	X	—	—	X	—	—	—	—
U5	X	X	X	X	—	—	X	—	—	—	—
U6	X	X	X	X	—	—	X	—	—	—	—
4.5	—	X	—	—	—	—	—	—	—	—	—
4.5 I	—	X	—	—	—	—	—	—	—	—	—
Y1	X	X	—	—	—	—	—	—	—	—	—
Y2	X	X	—	—	—	—	—	—	—	—	—
5 S	—	X	—	—	—	—	—	—	—	—	—
7-2	X	X	—	—	—	—	—	—	—	—	—
8-2	X	X	X	—	—	—	—	—	—	—	—
7 S	X	X	X	—	X	—	—	—	—	—	—
7-3	X	X	—	—	—	—	—	—	—	—	—
CEH-RNA	—	—	X	—	—	—	—	—	X	—	—
P-snRNA	—	—	—	—	—	—	—	—	—	X	—
RNase P	—	—	—	—	—	—	—	—	—	—	X

[a] X indicates the presence of RNA; P, pachytene; CEH, chicken embryonic heart.

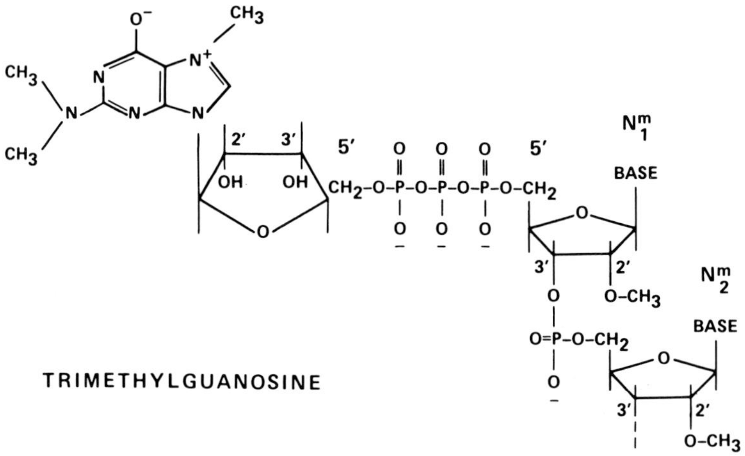

TRIMETHYLGUANOSINE

FIG. 1. The 5'-terminal cap structure on eukaryotic U1- to U5-RNAs (2). The 2'-O-methylations occur only in higher eukaryotes, such as rat and HeLa cells, but not in amoebae or dinoflagellates.

ture (Fig. 1) was first found in these small RNAs; subsequently, a similar cap containing 7-methylguanosine was found in eukaryotic messenger RNAs and in viral mRNAs (53, 54). Our studies showing the trimethylguanosine-containing cap structure in very early eukaryotes, like dinoflagellate snRNAs, indicate that it arose very early in eukaryotic evolution.

B. U1-RNA

U1-RNA is the most abundant of the small RNAs (9); the amount of it in the nuclei of rat or human cells (1×10^6 copies per cell) is comparable to that of ribosomal RNA (28). The localization of U1-RNA to nucleoplasm, shown initially by cell fractionation procedures (5, 9), was confirmed by the use of U1-RNP-specific antibodies (55). In most species, including human, rat, chicken, *Drosophila*, and dinoflagellates, the U1-RNA is a single homogeneous species with no detectable heterogeneity. Mouse contains two U1-RNA species, designated U1A and U1B, that differ in the nucleotide sequence in the center of the molecule (18). The two forms of U1-RNA found (56) in Novikoff hepatoma appear to be isomers. The complete nucleotide sequences of the U1-RNAs of human, rat, chicken, and fruit fly have been defined (27, 57, 58). Those of the human and fruit fly are 72% homologous (Fig. 2).

In addition to establishing its unique structure, U1-RNA sequence analysis led to a concept of hydrogen bonding to specific pre-mRNA

Human $m_3^{2,2,7}$GpppAUACψψACC   UGGCAGGGGA   GAUA.CCAUGA   UCACGAAGGU   40
$\phantom{m_3^{2,2,7}GpppAUAC}$mm
Insect   '   '''''''''   '''GUA'AG   'U''A''G'''   ''''''''''C

GGUUUUCCCA   GGGCGAGGCU   UAUCCAUUGC   ACUCCGGAUG   UGCUGACCCC   90
                                              m
''''CCU''G   'A'U'''''''   'GG'''''''   A'CU'''C''   A'U'''''U'

UGCGAUUUCC   CCAAAUGUGG   GAAACUCGAC   UGCAUAAUUU   GUGGUAGUGG   140
'''''''AUU   ''U'''''''A   AU''''''UG   C'UG''''''   U''''''CC'

GGGACUGCGU   UCGCGCUUUC   CCCUG$_\text{OH}$ 165
''A'UG''''   ''''''CG''   ''CA$_\text{OH}$

FIG. 2. Comparison of primary sequences of U1-RNA from HeLa cells (57) and from *Drosophila* (26, 26a). The nucleotides identical in both are shown by ditto marks. Rat (57, 58) and chicken (57) U1-RNA sequences are also defined. An "m" beneath a symbol indicates a 2'-O-methyl group.

"consensus" IVS sequences[2] and to analysis of the secondary structures of U1-RNA, and later to analysis of homologies with other U-snRNAs. Diener (59) has suggested that base-pairing of U1-RNA to intron "ancestors" may be part of a mechanism for viroid formation. Multiple secondary structures are possible with similar stability numbers (60). With the techniques developed for specific immunoprecipitation of the U1-snRNP particles, it is possible to conduct direct studies on the conformational state of the U1-RNA in U-snRNP particles (61) (Fig. 3). When RNase-T1 digestion is followed by immunoprecipitation of the U1-snRNP particles, only one major site-specific cleavage is found, at position 107 (61). The additional fragments produced by RNase-A cleavage permit a more detailed analysis of the RNA structure within the particles. This secondary structure is in good agreement with the U1-RNA secondary structure determined for human (60), chicken (60), and fruit fly (26) U1-RNAs.

C. U2-RNA

U2-RNA is the second most abundant snRNA in eukaryotes. Its most remarkable feature is the large number of modifications in its 5' end (62). The presence of 2'-O-methylated nucleotides and the remarkable number of pseudouridine residues on the 5' end of U2-RNA distinguish it clearly from U1-RNA. Like U1-RNA, U2-RNA is found in the nucleoplasm. The complete sequence of rat U2-RNA is known (62, 63), and partial nucleotide sequences of human (64, 64a), bird

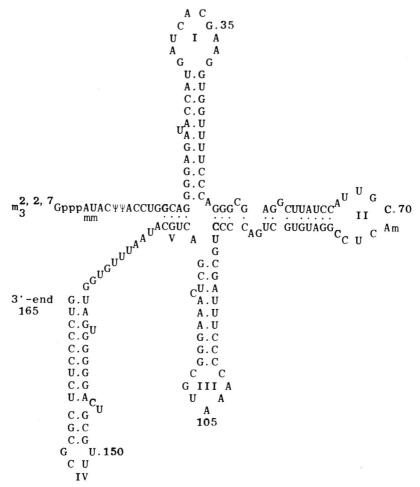

FIG. 3. One possible secondary structure of rat U1-RNA (60). The RNA appears to contain five hydrogen-bonded stems (indicated I to V). U1-RNAs of other species fit well into this model (26, 60).

(64a), and wheat U2-RNAs have been established (J. Skuzeski, personal communication). Figure 4 shows the homology between rat and wheat U2-snRNAs.

D. U3-RNA

U3-RNA (1, 65) is of interest because of its specific localization in the nucleolus and its hydrogen bonding to nucleolar 35 S and 28 S RNA (66). This RNA was first purified by molecular sieve chromatography (67). It is associated with protein and is present in nucleoli as an

```
                                                             6m
Rat      m2,2,7Gppp AUCGCψ. ψCU  CGGCCψUUUG  GCUAAGAUCA  AGUGψAGψAψ   40
          3          mm              mm     m         m       m
Wheat              '  ''AC''U'''   '.''''''''.   ''.''.''.'   .''''''.'


         CψGψψCUUAU  CAGUψUAAψA  UCUGAUACGU  CCUCUAUCCG  AGGACAAUAU   90
          m        m                m
         .''''''''''  ''''''''''''  XX''''''U'X  GGGXC'(---  ?-----)G''


         A UAAAUGGA  UUUUUGGAAC  UAGGAGUUGG  AAUAGGAGCU  UGCUCCGUCC  140
         '''''''UU'  '''''U'UGG  GG'AG'GA(-  ---?------  -) AUG'GGX


         ACUCCACGCA  UCGACCUGGU  AUUGCAGUAC  CUCCAGGAAC  GGUGCACC(A)OH  189
         XX'UGGGUGU  'GUC'AGU''  G''''XX''U  G'''U''GUA  ''C'''''CCAAOH
```

FIG. 4. Comparison of sequences of U2-RNA from rat (63) and wheat (J. Skuzeski personal communication). Identical nucleotides are indicated by ditto marks. Modified nucleotides in wheat U2-RNA are not yet localized. HeLa cell U2-RNA (3' end) is defined (64, 64a). X = unknown nucleotide.

RNP (68). No significant amount of U1- and U2-RNA are present in nucleoli. Rat U3-RNA is heterogeneous (66). The hydrogen bonding of U3-RNA to the 28 S and 325 S RNA is not stoichiometric; accordingly, one suggestion is that U3-RNA is involved in the processing of 32 S RNA (66).

Two of the three U3-RNA species found in Novikoff hepatoma cells have been sequenced (69, 70), and minor differences were found in their sequences (70). The U3-RNA sequence of *Dictyostelium* (71) is homologous (40%) to rat U3-RNA (Fig. 5). Secondary structures common to rat and *Dictyostelium* U3-RNAs have been constructed, and some evidence for these models has been presented (71a).

E. U4-RNA

U4-RNA is another nucleoplasmic RNA; its concentration is 200,000 copies per cell. Its sequence, determined for human (72), rat (72, 73), mouse (74), and chicken (72) tissues, contains the same trimethylguanosine cap as U1-, U2-, and U3-RNAs. Comparison of the primary structures of human and chicken tissues (Fig. 6) shows that this RNA structure is highly conserved. It has extensive homologies to U1-RNA (72, 73).

F. U5-RNA

When U5-RNA was first purified, it was referred to as 5 S-III RNA (75). It has at least two or more subspecies (2). Like U1- to U4-RNAs,

Rat $m_3^{2,2,7}$GpppAAGACUAΨA CUΨUCAGGGA UCAUUUCUAU AGU.UCGUUAC   40
                               mm
Dictyostelium   '   AU'''C'A' ''C'U'''.A ''''''''''G '''A''''··'

           UAGAGAAGUU UCUCUGACUG UGUAGAGCCC ACGAAACCAC GAGGACGA.GA   90
           ''UUA''A'' AU''AUCAAU AA'UUUU''U CUUUC'UAG' U''''U''U''

           ..CAUAGCGUCC CCUCCUGAGC GUGAAGCCGG CUCUAGGUGC UGCUUCUGUG 140
           UA''''CUCA'U AUA'GAA''' '''''A'''U UAU''UCGAA ''A'''AU'U

           CAGCUGCCUC UUGCCAUUGA UGAUCGUUCU UCUCUCCUUC GGGGG.GGUAA   190
           AUUUGUUA'U AA..''''''' '''C'' ''' AA'UCAGGGA U'AAUU'''UG

           GAGGGAGGGA ACGCAGUCUG AGUGGA$_{OH}$ 216
           UGU''U''''' UUCGUA.''' .'CU$_{OH}$

FIG. 5. Comparison of sequences of U3-RNA from rat (modified from 69) and *Dictyostelium* (71). Identical nucleotides are marked by ditto marks.

U5-RNA contains a trimethylguanosine-containing cap structure, and the complete nucleotide sequence is known for it from human (76), rat (2, 76, 77), mouse (78), and chicken (76) sources. Of the U-snRNAs, U5-RNA is the most enriched in uridine (35%) and, like other U-snRNAs, has been highly conserved through evolution (Fig. 7).

G. U6-RNA

U6-RNA is associated with purified perichromatin granules (79, 80). These dense granules are specifically juxtaposed to chromatin (80, 81) and appear in electron micrographs as dense cores surrounded by white halos. Because of their association with newly synthesized mRNA (80, 81), they could be "carriers" or processing elements in or near the functional chromatin. Accordingly, U6-RNA and U6-RNP

Human $m_3^{2,2,7}$GpppAGCΨUUGCG CAGUGGCAGU AUCGUAGCCA AUGAGGUUUA   40
                      mm   m
Chicken   '   ''''''''' '''''''''' '''''''''' ''''''''A'

UCCGAGGCGC GAUUAUUGCU AAUUGAAAAC UUΨUCCCAAΨ ACCCCGCCAU GACG   94
                                m
'''''''''' '''''''''' '''''''''' '''''''''' '''''''G' ''''

ACUUGA AAUAUAGUCG GCAUUGGCAA UUUUUGACAG UCUCUACGGA GACUG(G)$_{OH}$146
'''''C '''''''''' '''''''''' '''''''''' '''''''''' '''''''

FIG. 6. Comparison of sequences of U4-RNA from human (72) and chicken (72). The nucleotides identical in tLe two RNAs are shown by ditto marks.

Human $m_3^{2,2,7}$GpppAUACUCUGG   UUUCUCUUCA   GAUCGCAUAA   AUCUUUCGCC   40
              mm
Chicken   '   ' ' ' ' ' ' ' ' '   ' ' ' ' ' ' ' ' ' '   ' ' ' ' ' U ' ' ' '   ' ' ' ' ' ' ' ' ' '

UUUψACψAAA   GAUψUCCGUG   GAGAGGAAUA   ACUCUGAGUC   UUAACCCAAU   90
 m   m
' ' ' ' ' ' ' ' ' '   ' ' ' ' ' ' ' ' ' '   ' ' ' ' ' ' ' C '   ' ' ' ' ' ' ' ' ' '   ' ' ' ' A ' ' ' ' '

UUUUUGAGCC   UUGCUCCGAC   AAGGCUA$_{OH}$ 117
' ' ' ' ' ' ' ' ' '   ' ' ' U ' ' ' G '   ' ' ' ' ' ' '

FIG. 7. Comparison of sequencs of U5-RNA from human (76) and chicken (76). The nucleotides identical between the two RNAs are indicated by ditto marks.

may be the first U-snRNPs to combine with newly synthesized heterogeneous nuclear RNP (hnRNP).

The structure of U6-RNA (82, 83; Fig. 8) differs from that of the other U-snRNAs in two major respects. First, the cap does not contain trimethylguanosine. It is not known what structure is linked to the nucleotide chain, but it is not a normal nucleotide (82). Second, U6-RNA has several clusters of modified nucleotides in the center of the molecule (Fig. 8); in other U-snRNAs, most modifications are in the 5′ third of the structure. The U6-RNA contains several 2′-O-methylated nucleotides in addition to m^6A and m^2G. This molecule appears to be highly hydrogen-bonded (82, 83). Interestingly, the U1- to U5-RNAs have 2′-O-methyladenosine (Am) as their first nucleotide in the RNA sequence, but U6-RNA has an unmodified terminal G.

H. Homologies in U-snRNAs

The nucleotide sequences of the U-snRNAs show significant homologies (2, 84), the most striking of which are those between U1- and U4-RNAs (72, 73). Since all nucleoplasmic U-snRNPs contain one or more common proteins, these homologous regions may serve as binding sites for the protein(s). U1-, U4-, and U5-RNAs contain some

                                                     6
      10   20   30   40   m   50
XpppGUGCUCGCU   UCGGCAGCAC   AUAUACUAAA   AψUGGAACGA   ψACAGAG$\underset{m}{A}$AG

           60   70   2   90   100
                                 m
AUUAGCAUGG   CCCCUGCGCA   AGGAUGACAC   GCAAAUψCGU   GAAGCGUUCC
  mm   m mm   m   m

      108
AUAUUUU(U)$_{OH}$

FIG. 8. Nucleotide sequences of U6-RNA of Novikoff hepatoma (82) and mouse (83). For HeLa cell U-6 RNA sequences, see (64).

138 RAM REDDY AND HARRIS BUSCH

common secondary structure features (72). These results suggest that some U-snRNAs contain homologies in both their primary and their secondary structures. Nucleotide sequences of U-snRNAs from different species fit into a common secondary structure model with high stability numbers. For example, the U1-RNA of HeLa cells, rat, chicken and fruit fly fit well into one secondary structure (26, 57) (Fig. 3).

Enzymatic digestions and precipitation of the U1-RNP particles by antibodies (61) indicate that there are two regions of U1-RNA that are very susceptible to enzymatic digestion: the first seven nucleotides at the 5' end; and near nucleotide 107. Since the association of snRNP and hnRNP appears possibly to be in part caused by RNA · RNA hydrogen bonding, these two regions are the most likely ones to be involved in such association(s). Of the two proteins characterized and shown to be associated with U1-RNP, the 28 kDa protein (Sm-antigen)[2] binds nucleotides 120–145 of U1-RNA (84a). A 69-kDa protein (RNP-antigen) appears to bind (85) near the 5' end (20–60 nucleotides).

IV. Small Nuclear RNA in Ribonucleoproteins

A. Isolation of U-snRNP Particles

In recognition that snRNAs are functional as RNP particles, efforts have been made to isolate U-snRNPs (68, 86–88). Raj et al. (89) purified U1- and U2-RNPs and showed that they contain approximately 10 proteins. The first attempts to isolate U-snRNPs made use of Sepharose–gel filtration and sucrose-gradient centrifugation, starting from nuclear extracts (89). Several methods [including ammonium sulfate fractionation, isoelectric focusing, DEAE-Sepharose chromatography, PEI-cellulose chromatography, Cibacron blue columns, DEAE-cellulose chromatography, hydrophobic chromatography on ω-aminobutyl agarose columns (89a, 89b), and CsCl centrifugation (64)] have been utilized by various workers in various combinations. At present, these methods yield several fractions containing one or more U-snRNPs. The proteins associated with these RNP particles appear to be the same, based on migration of proteins on dodecyl sulfate/acrylamide gels, that are immunoprecipitated with U-RNP specific antibodies (17). The data at present indicate that U1-RNP separates well from U2-, U4-, U5-, and U6-RNPs on DEAE-Sepharose or PEI-cellulose chromatography, but U2-, U4-, U5-, and U6-RNPs do not separate from one another. There appears to be at least one protein on U2-RNP not found in U1-RNP, suggesting that U-snRNPs have both common and different proteins bound to them (S. Berget, personal communication).

B. Antibodies against snRNPs

RNP antibodies and Sm-antibodies[2] were found to be directed against U-snRNPs (17), and antibodies designated La[2] and Ro[2] were also found to be directed against small RNPs. The antibodies presently characterized and found to be directed against small RNPs are shown in Table IV. These antibodies, which in many instances cross-react against evolutionarily distant species, are useful in isolating and identifying new RNA species and proteins associated with RNAs. However, the RNPs isolated using antibodies may not be useful to test biological activity, since partially denaturing conditions have to be employed to dissociate the RNP · antibody complex.

C. Proteins Associated with U-snRNPs

In the first studies on the snRNP proteins, 11 were identified on two-dimensional gels (89). These had molecular weights of 50,000 to 70,000 in the fractions that contained the U1- and U2-snRNP particles. However, it is not certain that all these proteins are associated with the particles. Several subsequent studies (17, 85, 90–101), utilizing antibodies against U-snRNPs, discovered 2–11 proteins ranging in molecular weight from 10,000 to 70,000 (Table V). At present, definitive data are lacking on the number and types of proteins associated with

TABLE IV
ANTIBODIES AGAINST RNP PARTICLES CONTAINING SMALL RNA FROM
PATIENTS WITH AUTOIMMUNE DISEASES[a]

Antibody	RNAs present in immunoprecipitates	Species showing reactivity
Anti-RNP	U1	Rat, chicken, *Drosophila*
Anti-Sm	U1, U2, U4, U5, U6	Rat, chicken, frog, *Drosophila,* dinoflagellates
Anti-Ro/SS-A	Y1 to Y5	Rat, chicken
Anti-La/SS-B/Ha	Many cellular RNAs including 4.5, 4.5 I 5 S*, 7-2*, rRNAs, VA-RNAs, EBER RNAs, precursor tRNAs	Rat, chicken
Anti-To	7-2, 8-2	Rat, mouse

[a] VA, virus-associated; EBER, Epstein–Barr virus; for Sm, Ro, La, Ha, To, see footnote 2.

TABLE V
PROTEINS ASSOCIATED WITH U1- TO U6-RNPs

Specificity of antibodies	Source of antigen	Method employed[a]	Number	Proteins ($M_r \times 10^{-3}$)	References
Sm	Ehrlich ascites	Im.P.	7	11 to 33	17
	Friend cells	Im.P.	4	<10 to 30	95
	HeLa cells	Im.P.	8	10 to 32	94
		Im.P.	6	<10 to 31	90
		Im.P.	10	<10 to 67	96
	Calf thymus	I.A.C.	8	12 to 65	85
	Rabbit thymus	I.A.C.	7	11 to 70	99
		I.A.C.	11	10 to 42	100
	Pig thymus	Im.P.	5	10 to 12	101
	Drosophila	Im.P.	6	10 to 26	94
	HeLa cells	Im.P.	7	40 to 60	97, 98
		Im.P.	8	10 to 70	94
		Im.P.	6	<10 to 31	90
		Im.P.	10	<10 to 67	96
RNP	Rat liver	I.A.C.	2	13, 30	91–93
	Drosophila	Im.P.	2	14, 26	94
	Ehrlich ascites	Im.P.	7	11 to 33	17
	Friend cells	Im.P.	4	<10 to 30	95
	Calf thymus	I.A.C.	6	13 to 65	91
		I.A.C.	8	12 to 65	85
	Rabbit thymus	I.A.C.	7	11 to 70	99
		I.A.C.	5	10 to 15	100
	Pig thymus	Im.P.	5	10 to 30	101
Sm + RNP	Rabbit thymus	I.A.C.	9	9 to 44	91

[a] Im.P. = immunoprecipitation; I.A.C. = immunoaffinity chromatography. For Sm, see footnote 2.

each of the U-snRNPs. However, several studies conclude that (1) U1-RNP contains a 68–70-kDa protein not found on other U-snRNPs that may be part of the RNP antigen, and (2) U1-, U2-, U4-, U5-, and U6-RNPs contain a common antigen (Sm-antigen), which may be the 26–28-kDa protein available for antibody binding and enzymatic digestions.

D. Synthesis of Small Nuclear RNAs

Transfer RNA (tRNA) and 5 S RNA are synthesized by RNA polymerase III (102–104); 5.8 S RNA is synthesized as part of 45 S ribosomal RNA precursor by RNA polymerase I (105–107). RNA polymerase II, which synthesizes hnRNA (108), also synthesizes U2 snRNA (109–115). The sensitivity of U1- and U2-RNA biosynthesis to α-amanitin in whole-cell systems (109–112) and in cell-free systems

(*113, 114*), and to 5,6-dichloro-1-β-D-ribofuranosylbenzimidazole (*111, 115*) indicate that RNA polymerase II is responsible for U1- and U2-RNA biosynthesis.

The U1-RNA genes were transcribed in *in vitro* systems using HeLa cell extracts, and RNA transcripts longer than U1-RNA were observed (*114*). Analysis of the transcribed RNAs suggested that U1-RNA might be transcribed from nucleotide 183 (considering the cap site of U1-RNA to be nucleotide 1). Attempts to isolate this precursor from RNAs labeled *in vivo* have not been successful, suggesting that this precursor may be rapidly processed *in vivo* (*114*). U2-RNA genes were transcribed in frog oocytes to yield mature U2-RNA, but pseudogenes were not (H. Nojima and R. Kornberg, personal communication).

The noncapped RNAs are the products of RNA polymerase III. This was demonstrated for 7 S RNA (*116, 117*), 7-3 RNA (*116, 117*), 7-2 and 8-2 RNAs (*117a*), Y-RNAs (*118*), P-snRNA (*34*), adenovirus RNAs (*119*), Epstein–Barr virus RNAs (*47*), 4.5 S RNA (*120*) and 4.5 SI RNA (*118*). An intragenic promoter was found for all these RNAs. A table of intragenic promoters in small RNAs was compiled (*47, 121*). The results obtained thus far indicate that capped small U1- to U6-RNAs are synthesized by polymerase II, and other small RNAs are synthesized by polymerase III.

E. Precursors of Small Nuclear RNAs

Some precursors of U1- and U2-RNA slightly larger than the mature U-snRNAs have been detected in the cytoplasmic fraction within 10 minutes of [^{3}H]uridine labeling (*12, 122, 123*). Precursors of U1- and U2-RNAs have been analyzed by chromatography (*124*). Since these RNAs are capped, the larger size of the precursors was presumed to reflect elongation at the 3' ends. Salditt-Georgieff *et al.* (*125*) found $m_3^{2,2,7}G$ in the cap I structures isolated from the <750-base nuclear RNA fraction of Chinese hamster ovary cells labeled briefly with [*methyl*-^{3}H]methionine. These observations suggest that longer precursor molecules for snRNAs than previously reported might exist. Tamm *et al.* (*115*) also found evidence for long precursors for snRNAs, but did not find trimethylguanosine in hnRNAs longer than 1000 nucleotides. From the sensitivity of snRNA synthesis to UV irradiation, it appears that U1- and U2-RNAs may be derived from transcription units as long as 5000 bases (*126*). Precursors to U1-RNA were observed when human U1-RNA genes were transcribed *in vitro* (*114*). However, there is controversy regarding the existence of these precursors (*113*), and unequivocal structural proof of their identity is required.

F. Subcellular Localization

Several attempts have been made (5, 9, 12, 16, 112, 122, 127–130) to show the subcellular localization of different snRNAs (Fig. 9). The methods used to fractionate the nuclei from cytoplasm include both aqueous and nonaqueous methods and also the citric acid method. The results obtained by different investigators for the location of small RNAs vary slightly; however, the data point to the localization of small RNAs, as shown in Fig. 9. The U-RNPs (U1, U2, U4, U5, and U6) are nucleoplasmic, as shown by indirect immunofluorescence using specific antibodies directed against these RNPs (55). Similar studies show La[2] 4.5 and 4.5-I RNPs to be located in the nucleus and Y-RNPs to be located in the cytoplasm (118). U-snRNAs injected into the cytoplasm are stable and are transported into the nucleus; these RNAs associate readily with snRNP proteins to form immunoprecipitable RNP particles (131). Experiments with labeled nuclei of amoebae transplanted into unlabeled amoebae indicate that U-snRNAs shuttle between cytoplasm and nucleus during the cell cycle (132).

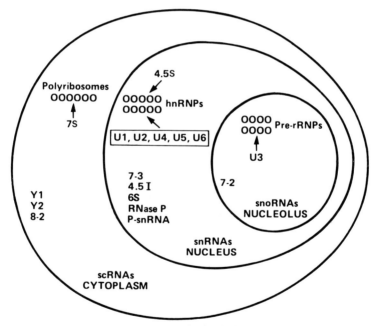

FIG. 9. Diagrammatic representation of subcellular localization of small RNAs of rat. The three categories of small RNAs, based on subcellular localization, are small cytoplasmic RNAs (scRNAs), small nuclear RNAs (snRNAs), and small nucleolar RNAs (snoRNAs).

G. Small Nuclear RNAs and Precursor RNAs

All capped snRNAs are associated with precursor RNAs. U3-RNA is hydrogen-bonded to nucleolar 28 S and 32 S RNAs, and this bonding is stable to treatment with phenol and dodecyl sulfate at 25° (66). U3-RNA was the first snRNA to be shown associated with precursor RNAs. The nucleoplasmic U1- and U2-RNAs are found in hnRNP particles (133) as are other snRNAs (64, 134–144). U4-, U5-, and U6-RNAs are also bound to hnRNP particles (145). Other studies show that U6-RNA is in perichromatin granules (79), 7 S RNA is bound to mRNA in polysomes (146), 7 S and 7-3 RNA are in polysomes (147), 4.5 S RNA is hydrogen-bonded to hnRNA (23), and 7-1 and 8 S RNA are hydrogen-bonded to nucleolar 28 S RNA (16). Small RNAs appear in nuclear matrix preparations from the rat (148) and from lower eukaryotes, such as *Tetrahymena* (149). The extent of association of U-snRNPs with nuclear matrix was quantitated using anti-Sm^2 antibodies, and it appears that about 70% of the total U-snRNPs are associated with nuclear matrix (150).

H. Genes Coding for Small Nuclear RNAs

Several groups have isolated cloned DNA fragments containing genes for snRNAs; a summary of the snRNA clones presently available is shown in Table VI. Very interesting results have emerged from these studies. (1) No intervening sequences have been found in any of the snRNA genes. (2) The genes for U-snRNAs are not clustered in the genome, but rather are dispersed throughout the genome (113, 151, 152); genes for several human Y-RNAs appear to be clustered (152a). (3) Seven U1-RNA genes characterized were found to be surrounded by a very similar genomic environment (153); the nucleotide sequences 100 nucleotides upstream from the U1-RNA sequences were identical, and restriction enzyme mapping showed similarities as far as 2,700 bases upstream from the U1-RNA genes (153). (4) There appear to be more pseudogenes dispersed throughout the genome in an approximate ratio of 10 : 1 compared to the true genes (151). (5) There is uncertainty about the presence of a Hogness, or TATAAA, box in snRNA genes. If there is one, it is further upstream from the cap site than the 25 base-pairs of most mRNA genes.

Other features of sequenced eukaryotic genes, such as the putative adenylylation signal (AATAAA, 25 base-pairs prior to the 3′ end of the RNA) and the termination signal (TTT, at the 3′ end of the RNA) are not found for the U1-RNA gene (113, 153). As expected, the adenylylation signal is missing, since U1-RNA is not polyadenylylated. It is

TABLE VI
CLONED GENES FOR SMALL NUCLEAR RNAs

RNA	Source	References for		
		Sequence identical to RNA	Pseudogenes	cDNA clones
U1-RNA	Human	114, 152, 153	151, 152, 154, 155	—
	Mouse	—	156	—
	Rat	156a	—	—
	Chicken	113	—	113
	Drosophila	26	—	—
U2-RNA	Human	—	151, 154, 157	—
	Mouse	A, B[a]	—	—
U3-RNA	Human	—	151, 154	—
	Dictyostelium	71	—	—
U4-RNA	Human	—	158	—
U6-RNA	Mouse	159	159, 160	—
7 S RNA	Human	—	—	161–163
7-3 RNA	Human	—	—	162
Y-RNAs	Human	152a	—	—

[a] (A) H. Nojima and R. Kornberg, personal communication; (B) R. Huang, personal communication.

interesting that the termination signal is missing, since the presence of this signal seems to be a general feature of genes transcribed by RNA polymerases II and III (113). The lack of a Hogness box and of the putative termination signal (113) is consistent with the possibility that U1-RNA and other snRNAs are transcribed in larger primary transcripts.

Are the genes for the isolated and sequenced snRNAs the same as those transcribed *in vivo*? The genes for U1- and U2-RNAs are transcribed in frog oocytes and U1-RNA genes in *in vitro* systems with apparent fidelity (114). The pseudogenes are not transcribed in these systems (H. Nojima and R. Kornberg, personal communication).

Early studies estimated the number of genes coding for U1-, U2-, and U3-RNAs by DNA · RNA hybridization (20, 164). It has been suggested that 2000 genes code for each snRNA in baby hamster cells (163a). Analyses of mouse genome sequences for snRNAs led to the suggestion (20) that there are 100–2000 copies per genome. However, these values are much higher than the approximately 10 determined by cloning studies; they probably include many pseudogenes and reflect the problems of the hybridization systems employed.

I. Functions of U-snRNPs

Over the years, several suggestions have been made as to the possible functions of U-snRNAs. It is clear that U-snRNPs exist in (U-snRNP) · (hnRNP) complexes as well as in a free RNP state. The suggestion that received most attention is that U1-RNA may properly align splice junctions of pre-mRNAs (27, 164–166). Although this hypothesis has not been proved, some observations are consistent with the idea that U1-RNA is involved in splicing mRNAs; however, other observations are not.

In favor of this hypothesis are the following findings. (a) U-snRNPs are associated with hnRNPs, where splicing is supposed to be occurring (133). (b) U-snRNAs are hydrogen-bonded to hnRNAs (134, 135). (c) U1-RNA (143) and U2-RNA (144) have been identified after crosslinking snRNAs and hnRNAs *in vivo*. (d) The sequence of the 5' end of U1-RNA (50), implicated in binding to splice junctions, (27, 165) is conserved in all known U1-RNA sequences. (e) U1-RNPs lacking the 5'-terminus are not associated with hnRNPs (27). (f) Splicing of adenovirus hnRNA is inhibited in nuclei incubated with anti-RNP antibodies (167). When nuclei are incubated with anti-Ro² or anti-La antibodies, splicing is not inhibited. Since other cellular functions, e.g., polyadenylylation, are not inhibited, and since anti-Ro or anti-Sm antibodies react with and presumably inactivate the U-snRNPs, it seems possible that U1-snRNPs are required for splicing. The differing structures in the other U-snRNPs suggest they are less likely to play such a splicing role. It is also known that the 5'-end cap-containing regions of U1- to U5-snRNAs are accessible to antibody binding, indicating that the 5'-end portion of U-snRNAs are available for binding to splice junctions (167a). U1-snRNP binds selectively a 5' splice site *in vitro*; the U1-snRNA-associated proteins appear to be necessary for specific binding to the splice site (167b). (g) In the processing of collagen hnRNA (168), several splicing steps are required for the removal of one IVS, and the polarity is 3' → 5'. This multistep removal of the IVS has been shown to be correlated to complementarity between U1-RNA and sites within the IVS.

In addition to these lines of evidence, the data on the abundance of U1-RNP, which correlates positively with the prevalence of splicing, the presence of U1-RNP in hnRNP where splicing takes place, and the higher amounts of U1-RNP in rapidly dividing cells, are all consistent with a role for U1-RNP in splicing hnRNA.

However, there are results that are not consistent with the above hypothesis. (a) Weissman et al. (169) quantitated the efficiency of splic-

ing of globin pre-mRNAs in which nucleotides in the consensus sequence near the splice junctions have been substituted. The results
obtained indicate no correlation between the efficiency of splicing and
complementarity between U1-RNA and altered splice junctions.
Splice junctions with poor complementarity to U1-RNA were spliced
with relatively high efficiency. These results indicate that complementarity to U1-RNA is not a requirement for splicing of pre-mRNAs (169).
(b) Analyses of globin genes coding for defective mRNAs in thalas-
semia (170) show that single-base alterations in regions of IVS away
from the splice junctions and sometimes in the exon sequences have
profound effects on splicing, indicating that complementarity of consensus sequences near splice junctions to U1-RNA is not sufficient for
accurate splicing. (c) In addition, a careful examination of the small
RNAs of yeast did not indicate the presence of an RNA structurally
homologous to U1-RNA (D. Tollerway and C. Guthrie, personal communication). Since yeast mRNAs contain intervening sequences and
are spliced as in higher eukaryotes, U1-RNP may not be necessary for
mRNA splicing. (d) In addition, tRNAs and mitochondrial mRNAs and
rRNAs are derived in some instances from precursors containing IVS
and require splicing (171, 172). In all the above instances, enzymes
with no RNA requirement carry out splicing. In the case of rRNA
precursors, the splicing appears to require GTP with no enzymatic
requirement (172a), indicating that IVS sequences can acquire conformations that are unstable and cleave without the aid of enzymes.

In view of the accumulating evidence that does not support the
involvement of U-RNAs in splicing, alternative possible functions require consideration.

Various other functions have been suggested for U-snRNPs, among
them, transport. It is hypothesized that the trimethylguanosine-
containing cap or other regions recognize and bind a protein or RNA
sequence on hnRNP particles and transport the pre-mRNA- and
mRNA-containing particles from the site of synthesis to the nuclear
membrane (173). Figure 10 presents a scheme of assembly and transport of hnRNP · snRNP complexes. A likely site of the assembly of
such complexes and their entry into the nuclear RNP network matrix is
the perinucleolar chromatin, a structure described in early studies on
the nucleolus; the perinucleolar chromatin is known to be composed
of highly repetitive DNA. At this site, the snRNPs that are either float-
ing free in the nucleoplasm or being transported to the nucleolus (by
as yet undefined nuclear elements) are linked to the hnRNP; the 5' cap
of snRNP could be the binding site for hnRNP proteins. Either
through binding of the snRNP or hnRNP or the snRNP · hnRNP com-

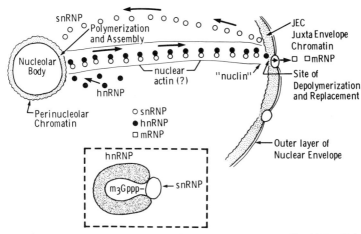

FIG. 10. "Ski-lift" model of the role of snRNPs in transport of hnRNPs. Polymerization of matrix elements and entry of snRNPs into the matrix are considered to occur
either in or adjacent to the repetitive DNA of the perinucleolar chromatin. There is
unidirectional movement of matrix elements from the perinucleolar chromatin to the
juxta-envelope chromatin. Entry of hnRNPs into this moving stream may occur as
polymerization and assembly occurs, or along the moving stream toward the nuclear
envelope. Depolymerization, replacement, and maturation of the hnRNP to mRNP are
considered to occur either in the juxta-envelope chromatin or in or around the nuclear
pore. It is also considered possible that the linkage between the snRNP (inset) occurs
through the 5' cap and adjacent nucleotides of snRNPs and one or more protein or RNA
regions of the hnRNPs.

plex, this complex is linked to a "conveyer belt" or "moving stream" of
nuclear contractile elements such as nuclear actin, which is
polymerized in or adjacent to the perinucleolar chromatin. Further
transport occurs by unidirectional flow or "pulsatile" effects exerted
by these contractile elements.

Several events are postulated to occur at the inner layer of the
nuclear envelope in the juxta-envelope chromatin (JEC). One is depolymerization of the moving or "conveyor belt" system. The second
is separation of the hnRNP and U-snRNP; the U-snRNP is returned to
the nucleoplasm. The third is further processing of the hnRNP to
mRNP by displacement of the "information" proteins and addition of
the specific mRNP proteins. The mRNP then moves through the nuclear pore complex or the nuclear envelope either alone or in complexes with ribosomes.

This concept provides a basis for new experiments on the
polymerization and assembly reactions in the perinucleolar chromatin,
the mechanisms of transport of the hnRNP · snRNP complexes, and

the reactions involved in dissociation and maturation of the mRNP particles. A related hypothesis was proposed by Sekeris (174). Other cellular functions in which U-snRNAs are implicated include nucleocytoplasmic transport (33), DNA replication (175), modulation of transcription (33, 66, 176, 176a), structural role in hnRNP particles (136), and as part of chromatin structure (177).

V. Noncapped Small RNAs

A. 7 S RNA

The 7 S RNA first found in RNA viruses (178) is a host-coded, conserved RNA species (179, 179a). It is the most abundant of the noncapped small RNAs (500,000 copies per cell) in rat liver or human cells. The complete nucleotide sequence of 7 S RNA in rat (180) and human cells (161) has been determined (Fig. 11). The 7 S RNA is the only small RNA present in HeLa cells that hybridizes to Alu-family DNA sequences (181). The regions of 7 S RNA homologous to Alu-family[2] DNA sequences, indicated in Fig. 11, are near the 5' end and 3' end, and near the boundaries of these homologous sequences is a hexanucleotide direct repeat, GUAGUG. Accordingly, the suggestion has been made that 7 S RNA may have arisen by insertion of a 150-nucleotide sequence into an Alu-family sequence to generate 7 S RNA genes (161).

The first indication of the possible function of 7 S RNA was that it is found in cytoplasm in association with polysomes (146). More recently, it was shown that 7 S RNA is an integral component of "signal recognition particle." This particle is an essential component for protein translocation across the lipid bilayer of the endoplasmic re-

```
                          AC
pppGCCGGGCGCG  GUGGCGCGUG  CCUGUAGUCC  CAGCUACUCG  GGAGGCUGAG    50
   A A
   GCUGGAGGAU  CGCUUGAGUC  CAGGAGUUCU  GGGCUGUAGU  GCGCUAUGCC   100

   GAUCGGGUGU  CCGCACUAAG  UUCGGCAUCA  AUAUGGUGAC  CUCCCGGGAG   150

   CGGGGGACCA  CCAGGUUGCC  UAAGGAGGGG  UGAACCGGCC  CAGGUCGGAA   200

   ACGGAGCAGG  UCAAAACUCC  CGUGCUGAUC  AGUAGUGGGA  UCGCGCCUGU   250

   AAUAGCCACUGCA  CUCCAGCCUG  GGCAACAUAG  CGAGACCCCG  UCUCU(A)_{OH}   300
```

FIG. 11. Nucleotide sequence of 7 S RNA of HeLa cells (161). The nucleotide substitutions found in rat 7 S RNA (180) are shown above the sequence. The portions of 7 S RNA homologous to Alu-family DNA sequences and the hexanucleotide direct repeat flanking these sequences are underlined.

ticulum (181a). It functions in "decoding" the information contained in the signal peptide of nascent secretory, lysosomal, and certain membrane proteins, and it mediates the attachment of this class of polysomes to the microsomal membrane (182–184). The 7 S RNP particle was purified and shown to contain six polypeptides ranging from 6.5 to 94 kDa (185). The 7 S RNA is one of the small RNAs for which a transport function is supported by other observations.

B. 7-3 RNA

The 7-3 RNA (K-RNA) is structurally distinct from 7 S RNA (16). The subcellular localization of this RNA is not clearly established. Two reports (16, 112) show most of the 7-3 RNA in the nucleus, but others indicate a cytoplasmic location (12). One study found 7-3 RNA in association with polysomes (147). The total sequence of 7-3 RNA is shown in Fig. 12; this sequence is structurally distinct from other small RNAs (our unpublished results). Chromatography of 7-3 RNAs of rat and human cells shows that this RNA is well conserved (16).

C. 4.5 S RNA

4.5 S RNA migrates on gels between 4 S and 5 S RNA and hence was named 4.5 S RNA. This RNA was first shown (23) to be a group of RNAs 90–100 nucleotides long, hydrogen-bonded to poly(A)-containing nuclear or cytoplasmic RNA from cultured Chinese hamster ovary cells. This RNA is found in rat and mouse cells, but not in human cells; it is found in some RNA viruses (120) and is heterogeneous at the 3' end in having up to 30 uridylic acid residues (120). The sequences of the 4.5 S RNAs of mouse (186) and of hamster (187) have been determined. This species of RNA has extensive homology to Alu-family sequences (Fig. 13), and its binding to mRNAs is presumed

```
pGGAUGUGAGG CGAUCUGGCU GCGACAUCUG UCACCCUAUU GAUCGCCAGG    50

 GUUGAUUCGG CUGAUCUGGC UGGCUAGGCG GGUGUCCCCU UCCUCCCUCA   100

 CCGCUCCAUG UGCGUCCCUC CCGAAGCUGC GCGCUCGGUC GAAGAGGACG   150

 ACCUUCCCCG AAUAGAGGAG GACCGGUCUU CGGCUAAGGG UAUACGAGUA   200

 GCUGCGCUCC CCUGCUAGAA CCUCCAAACA AGCUCUCAAG GUCCAUUGUA   250

 GGAGAACGUA GGGUAGUCAA GCUUCCAAGA CUCCAGACAC AUCCAAAUGA   300

 GGCGCUGCAG GGGCAGUCUG CCUUUCUUU(A)$_{OH}$    330
```

FIG. 12. Total nucleotide sequence of 7-3 RNA of rat (our unpublished results). X = unidentified nucleotide.

```
Mouse 4.5S RNA  pppGCCGGUAGUG  GUGGCGCACG  CCGGUAG GAU  UUGCUGAAGG  AGGCA  55
Type I Alu DNA      ''''GCA''   ''''''''''A  ''UU'''UCCC  CA''ACUC''   '''''

GAGGC  AGAGGGAU  CA  CGAGUUCGAG  GCCAGCCUGG  GCUACACAUU  UUUU_OH  94
'''''   ''GC''''UU'U  ''''''''''  ''''''''''   U''U''G'G'  'CC'
```
FIG. 13. Comparison of nucleotide sequences of rat (189) and modi-hamster (187) with mouse B1 DNA sequences (187a). Identical nucleotides are indicated by ditto marks.

to be by this type of hydrogen-bonding (23, 188). Its functions are not known. This RNA is developmentally regulated and short-lived in the cytoplasm; a role in transporting mRNA has been suggested for it (188a).

D. 4.5 SI RNA

The 4.5 SI RNA was the first small RNA to be sequenced (189) (Fig. 14). This RNA, like 4.5 S RNA, appears in rodent tissues (rat, mouse) but not in human tissues. It also has sequence homologies to repeated DNA sequences different from Alu-family-type DNA (190, 191) (Fig. 11).

E. 6 S snRNA

The 6 S snRNA was first found and characterized in Chinese hamster ovary cells (191). The sequence of this 184-nucleotide RNA was deduced from the DNA sequence; it is homologous to the type-2 Alu-family DNA sequences. This is a minor RNA in terms of its abundance; an RNA with similar properties is found in Novikoff hepatoma cells (unpublished results). It is a polymerase III product and has pppG at the 5' terminus and UUUUU (OH) at the 3' terminus (191). Cloned DNA fragments are good templates for RNA polymerase III transcription (192, 193). Whether any of these repeated sequences are actually transcribed in vivo is not certain at this time.

An RNA of about 160 nucleotides found in rat brain is absent from liver and kidney (191a). It hybridizes to several randomly selected cDNA clones made from rat brain poly(A)-containing RNA. This indicates that some small RNAs may be tissue-specific.

F. 7-2 snRNA

The 7-2 snRNA is present in about 50,000 copies per cell in human, rat, and mouse cells (193a). This RNA may correspond to RNA-M (12). Chromatographic analysis of 7-2 snRNA of human and rat cells indicates that it is partially conserved in structure. It can be precipitated from rat, human, or mouse cells as an RNP particle by antibodies from patients with scleroderma (193a). The subcellular localization of this

```
                                                                              U
Rat 4.5I RNA    pppGGCUGGAGAG  AUGGCUCAGC  CGUUAAAG GC  UAGGCUCACA  ACCAAAAAUA 50
Type 2 Alu DNA  ··········     ··········   G······A··    GCCCGACUGC  UCUUCCAAAG

    UAA  GAGUUCG  GUUCCCAGCA  CCCACGGCUG  UCUCUCCAGC  CACCUUUUU_OH  99
    GUCCU·····A  A·········   A····AUGGU  GGCUCACAAC   CAUCUGUAAAGAG
```

FIG. 14. Comparison of nucleotide sequence of rat 4.5 SI RNA (189, modified) with type-2 Alu-family DNA sequences (190, 191). Identical nucleotides are shown by ditto marks. The continuous underline indicates a sequence present in the type-2 Alu-equivalent sequence that is also present in the rat 4.5 SI RNA sequence, but different in position from one another.

RNA is not well established. Initial studies showed it to be nucleolar, since it was enriched in isolated nucleoli (16). A small proportion of 7-2 RNA, presumed to be longer on its 3′ end and newly synthesized, is found in the cytoplasmic fraction; however, most of the 7-2 RNA is found associated with larger cellular components (117a, 193a). The function of this RNA is not known.

G. 8-2 snRNA

This RNA was identified by means of antibodies from patients with autoimmune diseases. It is present in human, rat, and mouse tissues and does not appear, from chromatography, to be conserved between rat and human tissues. The RNA is a primary transcription product, since the 5′ end of RNA is pppG and is present in the cytoplasm as an RNP particle with a sedimentation value of around 10 S (193a). The function of this RNP particle is not known.

H. Y-RNAs

These RNAs were designated Y-RNAs because of their localization in the cYtoplasm (3). They were detected in mouse (118), rat (unpublished), and human (118) cells using anti-Ro[2] (SS-A) antibodies. They are metabolically stable, are synthesized by polymerase III, and are primary transcription products as they contain pppG or pppA at their 5′ ends (118). Mouse cells contain two distinct RNAs designated Y1 and Y2; rat cells contain the same Y1- and Y2-RNAs, since the chromatograms of rat and mouse Y1- and Y2-RNAs are identical (our unpublished results, and J. Steitz, personal communication). Rat Y1-RNA has two bands designated Y1A and Y1B that differ in only a few nucleotides. The human cells contain four structurally distinct Y-RNAs, designated Y1 to Y5; these RNAs are only partially conserved between rodent and human tissues (118). The human Y1, Y2, Y3 (152a) and Y5 (193b) sequences are known.

I. Nucleolar 8 S and 7-1 RNAs

These two RNAs are enriched in nucleoli of rat cells and are hydrogen-bonded to preribosomal RNA (16). The 8 S RNA was sequenced and found to be a precursor of ribosomal 5.8 S RNA (194). This 274-nucleotide-long RNA contains the 156-nucleotide 5.8 S RNA on its 5' end. All the extra nucleotides are on its 3' end. An RNA with similar characteristics, designated 7 S RNA, was found in yeast cells. The 7-1 RNA has not yet been fully characterized. There are other reports on RNAs 8 S to 18 S in size (195–197); in some instances, these have been identified as polymerase I products (196, 197). One study ascribed small RNAs with sequence homologies to nontranscribed spacer regions of rDNA (197). However, it is still not certain that any of these RNAs are distinct snRNAs. It is possible that many are intermediates in pre-rRNA processing.

J. P-snRNA

This abbreviation for "pachytene small nuclear RNA" refers to a group of snRNA molecules 125 nucleotides long and transcribed by RNA polymerase III (34). These RNA molecules were found in *Lilium,* and a corresponding RNA appears to be present in mouse cells (34). P-snRNA is synthesized during meiotic prophase, when chromosomes are undergoing homologous pairing or are already paired. Accessibility to the meiotically active DNA sequences depends on an as-yet-undefined alteration in chromatin structure. P-snRNA is a critical factor in this alteration, which makes specific DNA sequences accessible to endonuclease cleavage (34). The mechanism by which P-snRNA achieves its site-specific effect is suggested to be by DNA · RNA complementarity. Its sequence is not known.

K. CEH-RNA

This RNA was isolated from chicken embryonic heart (CEH); it is about the size of 7 S RNA and is capable of inducing specific changes in the early embryonic cells of stage-4 chick blastoderm cultivated *in vitro* (198). These changes are similar to those of embryonic heart differentiation. It has been suggested (198) that CEH-RNA has a gene-regulating role, since heartlike differentiation appears to be dependent on this RNA species. This RNA has been characterized; the nucleotide sequence of the 45 nucleotides at the 5' end is established, and the 3' end is polyadenylylated (~50 residues) (199). It is not capped, and it contains no modified nucleotides. CEH-RNA is not present in adult heart tissues, but can be found in the hearts of mice treated with drugs that produce embryonic heart differentiation (R. Manikyam, personal communication). These results suggest that the synthesis of CEH-RNA is linked to embryonic heart development.

L. RNase-P-RNA (M2-RNA)

RNase P (EC 3.1.26.5) consists of a 375-nucleotide RNA and a 20-kDa basic protein. This complex was detected and purified as an endoribonuclease that specifically removes a 41-base fragment from the 5′ portion of a precursor tRNA (200, 201). RNase-P cleavage is required for 5′ maturation of most, perhaps all, tRNA species of *Escherichia coli* and its bacteriophages (202). RNase-P activity was found in higher eukaryotes, including human cells (203); in eukaryotes, it also appears to be an RNA-containing particle (203).

Comparison of all the RNase-P substrates indicates that since no primary sequence similarities exist, secondary and tertiary conformations play a major role in determining its substrate specificity. The complete nucleotide sequence of *E. coli* RNase-P-RNA (M2-RNA) was deduced from the DNA sequence (203a). It has a tight secondary structure. It is proposed that M2-RNA recognizes invariant nucleotides in tRNAs and binds to the tRNA structures. Although this enzyme is specific for precursor tRNAs, it also can process *E. coli* 4.5 S RNA, but much less efficiently (202). The site of *in vitro* endonuclease (RNase P) cleavage is shown in Fig. 15.

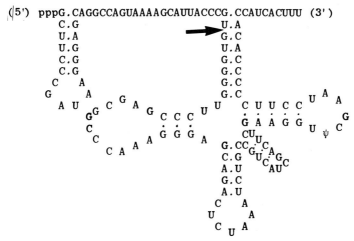

FIG. 15. Nucleotide sequence of a precursor to *Escherichia coli* tyrosine-tRNA (200, 201). The arrow indicates the site of RNase P cleavage.

VI. Other Small RNAs

There are several other small RNAs in *E. coli* (37–40). Some of these, such as 4.5 S RNA (40) and 6 S RNA (39), have been sequenced. However, their functions are not known.

VII. Small RNAs of Yeast

Initial studies on small RNAs of yeast (33) did not detect small RNAs other than 5 S RNA and 5.8 S RNAs. However, recent studies indicate that yeast contains nine "capped" small RNAs (D. Tollerway and C. Guthrie, personal communication). Interestingly, these RNAs appear to be capped with 2,7-dimethylguanosine, not with 2,2,7-trimethylguanosine. One of the RNA sequences was deduced from the DNA sequence; it had no apparent homology to any known eukaryotic capped small RNA. Surprisingly, mutants of yeast lacking this RNA grew normally, suggesting that it is not required for cell growth, or that another RNA can substitute for it (D. Tollerway and C. Guthrie, personal communication). There is at least one noncapped RNA in yeast cells about 250 nucleotides in length (our unpublished results).

VIII. Small RNAs of Viruses

Several viruses code for small RNAs, and these viral RNAs are required for virus production. An snRNA encoded by adenovirus that infects human cells, identified in 1966 (41), was one of the first small RNA species to be identified and characterized.

The adenovirus genome codes for two species of small RNAs, designated VA-I and VA-II because they are Virus-Associated. The VA-RNAs are synthesized by polymerase III, and their complete nucleotide sequences are known (204, 205). The VA-RNAs were thought to be involved in splicing pre-mRNAs (164). However, studies (205a) indicate a role for VA-RNAs as inhibitors of host mRNA translation.

Small viral RNAs have been characterized as products of the Epstein–Barr virus (46, 47). These RNAs appear to be analogous to VA-RNAs in structure (47) and possibly in function. Other viruses whose small RNAs have been characterized include vesicular stomatitis (44, 45) and SV40 (42, 43). Many viruses, like retroviruses (206–208), incorporate host-coded RNAs including tRNAs, 4.5 S RNA, 7 S RNA, etc. In some instances, as with tRNAs, these RNAs act as primers for reverse transcription of the RNA genome (209).

IX. Conclusions and Future Studies

Small nuclear RNAs, discovered over 15 years ago, are metabolically stable, conserved through evolution, and located in specific subcellular compartments. The sequencing of small RNAs resulted in the discovery of "cap" structures, and the nucleotide sequences of all six capped U-snRNAs have been determined, in some instances for several species. All the capped snRNAs appear to be synthesized by polymerase II. The other small RNAs are synthesized by polymerase III. Genes having sequences identical to U1-, U2-, U3-, and U6-RNAs have been isolated, and, interestingly, the human genome appears to contain up to 10 times more pseudogenes for small RNAs than real genes.

Table VII lists functions suggested for small RNAs. Different small RNAs appear to have different functions that may be varied and diverse. There is conclusive evidence for the involvement of an RNA component as part of RNase-P in processing tRNA precursors. It is also established that 7 S RNA is an integral part of a signal recognition particle involved in the translocation of secretory proteins. In the case of other snRNAs, the functions are largely unknown and the suggested functions are not supported by experimental data.

TABLE VII
FUNCTIONS SUGGESTED FOR SMALL RNAs

Function	References
Splicing of hnRNA	18, 27, 164–166
Processing tRNA precursors	200–203a
Processing ribosomal precursors	66, 217
Intranuclear or nucleocytoplasmic transport	33, 173, 174
DNA replication	175, 188
Modulators of transcription	33, 66, 176, 176a
Stimulator of transcription	210–212
Genetic reprogramming	132
Gene regulation and differentiation	176
Chromosome organization	132
Part of nuclear or chromatin structure	12, 177
Structural role in hnRNP particle	136
Induces embryonic heart differentiation	198
Control of translation	213, 213a, 214
Acts as incompatibility factor	216
Control of cell division	215
Involved in crossing-over during meiosis	34

156 RAM REDDY AND HARRIS BUSCH

Future studies of importance include (a) identification of new small RNAs, (b) identification of corresponding snRNAs in other species, (c) identification of protein(s) associated with each snRNA, (d) identification of the nature of interaction(s) between snRNPs and other cellular components, (e) isolation of purified snRNP particles, and (f) identification of the function(s) of each snRNP particle. Although much has been learned about snRNAs and snRNPs, clearly the studies on function are of much consequence for the future.

REFERENCES

1. H. Busch, R. Reddy, L. Rothblum, and Y. C. Choi, *ARB* **51**, 617 (1982).
2. R. Reddy and H. Busch, in "The Cell Nucleus" (H. Busch, ed.), Vol. 8, p. 261. Academic Press, New York, 1981.
3. M. Lerner and J. A. Steitz, *Cell* **25**, 298 (1981).
4. G. Zieve, *Cell* **25**, 296 (1981).
5. L. Hodnett and H. Busch, *JBC* **243**, 6334 (1968).
6. A. Rein and S. Penman, *BBA* **190**, 1 (1969).
7. L. Goldstein and C. Ko, *Cell* **2**, 259 (1974).
8. P. Hellung-Larsen and S. Frederiksen, *Comp. Biochem. Physiol. B* **58B**, 273 (1977).
9. R. A. Weinberg and S. Penman, *JMB* **38**, 289 (1968).
10. E. Yazdi and F. Gyorkey, *J. Natl. Cancer Inst.* **47**, 765 (1971).
11. K. Nohga, R. Reddy, and H. Busch, *Cancer Res.* **41**, 2215 (1981).
12. G. Zieve and S. Penman, *Cell* **8**, 19 (1976).
13. P. H. Larsen, G. Tyrsted, J. Engberg, and S. Frederiksen, *Exp. Cell Res.* **85**, (1974).
14. M. Ringuette, W. C. Liu, E. Jay, K. K. Y. Yu, and M. O. Krause, *Gene* **8**, 211 (1980).
15. C. J. Larsen, F. Galibert, A. Hampe, and M. Boiron, *Bull. Soc. Chim. Biol.* **51**, 649 (1969).
16. R. Reddy, W. Li, D. Henning, Y.-C. Choi, K. Nohga, and H. Busch, *JBC* **256**, 8452 (1981).
17. H. Gallinaro-Matringe, J. Stevenin, and M. Jacob, *Differentiation* **9**, 147 (1977).
18. M. Lerner and J. A. Steitz, *PNAS* **78**, 2737 (1979).
19. A. Brown and W. Marzluff, *BBA* **521**, 662 (1978).
20. W. F. Marzluff, E. L. White, R. Benjamin, and R. C. C. Huang, *Bchem* **14**, 3715 (1975).
21. E. F. Howard, *Bchem* **17**, 3228 (1978).
22. S. Frederiksen, T. R. Pederson, P. H. Larsen, and J. Engberg, *BBA* **340**, 64 (1974).
23. W. Jelinek and L. Leinwand, *Cell* **15**, 205 (1978).
24. P. L. Jeffrey, L. Austin, and P. W. Gunning, *Neurosci. Lett.* **2**, 153 (1976).
25. L. Ireland, J. Szyszko, and M. Krause, *JMB* **8**, 97 (1982).
26. S. Mount and J. A. Steitz, *NARes* **8**, 4143 (1982).
26a. J. C. Wooley, R. D. Cone, D. Tartof, and S. Chung, *PNAS* **79**, 6762 (1982).
27. M. R. Lerner, J. A. Boyle, S. M. Mount, S. L. Wolin, and J. A. Steitz, *Nature* **283**, 220 (1980).
28. J. A. Wise and A. M. Weiner, *JBC* **256**, 956 (1981).
29. K. Takeishi and S. Kaneda, *J. Biochem. (Tokyo)* **90**, 299 (1981).
30. P. H. Larsen, S. Frederiksen, and P. Plesner, *BBA* **254**, 78 (1971).
31. S. Frederiksen, P. Hellung-Larsen, and J. Engberg, *Exp. Cell Res.* **78**, 287 (1973).
32. P. Nijhawan and W. F. Marzluff, *Bchem* **18**, 1353 (1979).

33. P. Hellung-Larsen and S. Frederiksen, *Comp. Biochem. Physiol. B* **58**, 273 (1977).
34. Y. Hotta and H. Stern, *Cell* **27**, 309 (1981).
35. R. Reddy, D. Spector, D. Henning, and H. Busch, *FP* **42**, 1883 (1983).
36. K. T. Kim, D. Apirion, and B. K. Ghora, *Mol. Gen Genet.* **160**, 25 (1978).
37. J. Hindley, *JMB* **30**, 125 (1967).
38. S. Y. Lee, S. C. Bailey, and D. Apirion, *J. Bact.* **133**, 1015 (1978).
39. G. G. Brownlee, *Nature NB* **229**, 147 (1971).
40. B. E. Griffin, *JBC* **250**, 5426 (1975).
41. P. R. Reich, B. G. Forget, S. M. Weissman, and J. A. Rose, *JMB* **17**, 428 (1966).
42. J. C. Alwine, R. Dhar, and G. Khoury, *PNAS* **77**, 1379 (1980).
43. M. A. Hutchinson, T. Hunter, and W. Eckhart, *Cell* **15**, 65 (1979).
44. R. J. Colonno and A. K. Banerjee, *Cell* **8**, 197 (1976).
45. D. Testa, P. K. Chands, and A. K. Banerjee, *Cell* **21**, 267 (1980).
46. M. R. Lerner, N. C. Andrews, G. Miller, and J. A. Steitz, *PNAS* **78**, 805 (1981).
47. M. D. Rosa, E. Gottleib, M. R. Lerner, and J. A. Steitz, *Mol. Cell. Biol.* **1**, 785 (1981).
48. A. G. Saponara and M. D. Enger, *Nature* **223**, 1365 (1969).
49. R. Reddy, T. S. Ro-Choi, D. Henning, H. Shibata, Y. C. Choi, and H. Busch, *JBC* **247**, 7245 (1972).
50. R. Reddy, T. S. Ro-Choi, D. Henning, and H. Busch, *JBC* **249**, 6486 (1974).
51. T. S. Ro-Choi, R. Reddy, Y. C. Choi, N. B. Raj, and D. Henning, *FP* **33**, 1548 (1974).
52. T. S. Ro-Choi, Y. C. Choi, D. Henning, J. McCloskey, and H. Busch, *JBC* **250**, 3921 (1975).
53. F. Rottman, A. Shatkin, and R. Perry, *Cell* **3**, 1977 (1974).
54. A. J. Shatkin, *Cell* **9**, 645 (1976).
55. E. A. Lerner, M. R. Lerner, C. A. Janeway, and J. A. Steitz, *PNAS* **78**, 2737 (1981).
56. H. Shibata, R. Reddy, D. Henning, T. S. Ro-Choi, and H. Busch, *Mol. Cell. Biochem.* **4**, 3 (1974).
57. C. Branlant, A. Krol, J.-P. Ebel, E. Lazar, H. Gallinaro, M. Jacob, J. Sri-Widada, and P. Jeanteur, *NARes* **8**, 4143 (1980).
58. R. Reddy, D. Henning, and H. Busch, *BBRC* **98**, 1076 (1981).
59. T. O. Diener, *PNAS* **78**, 5014 (1981).
60. A. Krol, C. Branlant, E. Lazar, H. Gallinaro, and M. Jacob, *NARes* **9**, 841 (1981).
61. P. Epstein, R. Reddy, and H. Busch, *PNAS* **78**, 1562 (1981).
62. H. Shibata, T. S. Ro-Choi, R. Reddy, Y. C. Choi, D. Henning, and H. Busch, *JBC* **250**, 3909 (1975).
63. R. Reddy, D. Henning, P. Epstein, and H. Busch, *NARes* **9**, 5645, (1981).
64. J. Sri-Widada, J. P. Liautard, C. Assens, and C. Brunel, *Mol. Biol. Rep.* **8**, 29 (1981).
64a. C. Branlant, A. Krol, J. Ebel, E. Lazar, B. Haendler, and M. Jacob, *EMBO J.* **1**, 1259 (1982).
65. H. Busch and K. Smetana, "The Nucleolus," p. 285. Academic Press, New York, 1970.
66. A. W. Prestayko, M. Tonato, and H. Busch, *JMB* **47**, 505 (1971).
67. T. Nakamura, A. W. Prestayko, and H. Busch, *JBC* **243**, 1368 (1968).
68. A. W. Prestayko, M. Tonato, C. Lewis, and H. Busch, *JBC* **246**, 182 (1971).
69. R. Reddy, D. Henning, and H. Busch, *JBC* **254**, 11097 (1979).
70. R. Reddy, D. Henning, and H. Busch, *JBC* **255**, 7029 (1980).
71. J. A. Wise and A. M. Weiner, *Cell* **22**, 109 (1980).
71a. L. B. Bernstein, S. M. Mount, and A. M. Weiner, *Cell* **32**, 461 (1983).
72. A. Krol, C. Branlant, E. Lazar, H. Gallinaro, and M. Jacob, *NARes* **9**, 2699 (1981).

73. R. Reddy, D. Henning, and H. Busch, *JBC* **256**, 3532 (1981).
74. N. Kato and F. Harada, *BBRC* **99**, 1477 (1981).
75. T. S. Ro-Choi, R. Reddy, D. Henning, and H. Busch, *BBRC* **44**, 963 (1971).
76. A. Krol, H. Gallinaro, E. Lazar, M. Jacob, and C. Branlant, *NARes* **9**, 769 (1981).
77. N. Okada, K. Sakamoto, Y. Itoh, and Y. Ohshima, *Bchem* **91**, 1281, 1982.
78. N. Kato and F. Harada, *BBRC* **99**, 1468 (1981).
79. Y. Daskal, L. Komaromy, and H. Busch, *Exp. Cell Res.* **126**, 39 (1980).
80. Y. Daskal, in "The Cell Nucleus" (H. Busch, ed.), Vol. 8, p. 117. Academic Press, New York, 1981.
81. E. Puvion and G. Moyne, in "The Cell Nucleus" (H. Busch, ed.), Vol. 8, p. 59. Academic Press, New York, 1981.
82. P. Epstein, R. Reddy, and H. Busch, *JBC* **255**, 8901 (1980).
83. F. Harada, N. Kato, and S. Nishimura, *BBRC* **95**, 1332 (1980).
84. H. Busch, R. Reddy, D. Henning, and P. Epstein, in "International Cell Biology" (H. Schweiger, ed.), p. 47. Springer Verlag, Berlin and New York, 1981.
84a. J. Liautard, J. Sri-Widada, C. Brunel, and P. Jeanteur, *JMB* **162**, 623 (1982).
85. M. Takano, S. S. Golden, G. C. Sharp, and P. F. Agris, *Bchem* **20**, 5929 (1981).
86. M. D. Enger and R. A. Walters, *Bchem* **9**, 3551 (1970).
87. A. Rein, *BBA* **232**, 306 (1971).
88. E. F. Howard, *Bchem* **17**, 3228 (1978).
89. N. B. Raj, T. S. Ro-Choi, and H. Busch, *Bchem* **14**, 80 (1975).
89a. M. Hinterberger, I. Petterson, and J. A. Steitz, *JBC* **258**, 2604 (1983).
89b. C. Kinlaw, S. Schwartz, and S. Berget, *JBC* **258**, 7181 (1983).
90. L. Matter, K. Schopfer, J. A. Wilhelm, T. Nyffenegger, R. F. Parisot, and E. M. DeRobertis, *Arthritis Rheum* **25**, 1278 (1982).
91. P. J. White, W. D. Gardner, and S. O. Hoch, *PNAS* **78**, 626 (1981).
92. A. S. Douvas, W. E. Stumph, P. Reyes, and E. M. Tan, *JBC* **254**, 3608 (1979).
92a. A. Douvas, *PNAS* **79**, 5401 (1982).
93. P. J. White and S. O. Hoch, *BBRC* **102**, 365 (1981).
94. E. D. Wieben and T. Pederson, *Mol. Cell. Biol.* **2**, 914 (1982).
95. J. P. Barque, P. Yeni, L. Peraudeau, F. Danon, and C. J. Larsen, *BBRC* **99**, 284 (1981).
96. C. Kinlaw, S. Schwartz, and S. Berget, *Mol. Cell. Biol.* **2**, 1159 (1982).
97. R. Lenk, J. V. Maizel, and R. Crouch, *EJB* **121**, 475 (1982).
98. P. B. Billings, R. W. Allen, F. C. Jensen, and S. O. Hoch, *J. Immunol.* **128**, 1176 (1982).
99. J. J. Gibbons, C. C. Tsai, and S. T. Roodman, *FP* **39**, 1023 (1980).
100. D. A. Augustynek, J. J. Gibbons, C. C. Tsai, and S. T. Roodman, *Arthritis Rheum.* (in press).
101. A. J. MacGillivray and A. R. Carroll, in "Biochemistry and Biology of the Cell Nucleus: Non-histone Proteins" (L. S. Hnilica, ed.), Vol. 2, p. 123. CRC Press, Boca-Raton, Florida, 1982.
102. W. F. Marzluff, E. C. Murphy, and R. C. Huang, *Bchem* **13**, 3689 (1974).
103. L. McReynolds and S. Penman, *Cell* **1**, 139 (1974).
104. R. Weinmann and R. G. Roeder, *PNAS* **71**, 1790 (1974).
105. R. G. Roeder and W. J. Rutter, *PNAS* **65**, 675 (1970).
106. C. J. Chesterton and P. H. Butterworth, *FEBS Lett.* **12**, 301 (1971).
107. R. H. Reeder and R. G. Roeder, *JMB* **70**, 433 (1972).
108. E. A. Zybler and S. Penman, *PNAS* **68**, 2861 (1971).
109. T. S. Ro-Choi, N. B. Raj, L. M. Pike, and H. Busch, *Bchem* **15**, 3823 (1976).

110. S. Frederiksen, P. Hellung-Larsen, and E. Gram-Jensen, *FEBS Lett.* **87**, 227 (1978).
111. E. Gram-Jensen, P. Hellung, and S. Frederiksen, *NARes* **6**, 321 (1979).
112. G. L. Eliceiri, *J. Cell. Physiol.* **102**, 199 (1980).
113. D. R. Roop, P. Kristo, W. E. Stumph, M. J. Tsai, and B. W. O'Malley, *Cell* **23**, 671 (1981).
114. J. T. Murphy, R. R. Burges, J. E. Dahlberg, and E. Lund, *Cell* **29**, 265 (1982).
115. I. Tamm, T. Kikuchi, J. E. Darnell, and M. Salditt-Georgieff, *Bchem* **19**, 2743 (1980).
116. G. Zieve, B. J. Benecke, and S. Penman, *Bchem* **16**, 4520 (1977).
117. R. Reichel, and B. Benecke, *NARes* **8**, 225 (1980).
117a. C. Hashimoto, and J. A. Steitz, *JBC* **258**, 1379 (1983).
118. J. P. Hendrick, S. L. Wolin, J. Rinke, M. R. Lerner, and J. A. Steitz, *Mol. Cell. Biol.* **1**, 1138 (1981).
119. H. Soderland, U. Pettersson, B. Vennstrom, L. Philipson, and M. B. Mathews, *Cell* **7**, 585 (1976).
120. F. Harada, N. Kato, and H. O. Hoshino, *NARes* **7**, 95 (1979).
121. C. J. Shen and T. Maniatis, *J. Mol. Appl. Genet.* **1**, 343 (1982).
122. G. L. Eliceiri, *Cell* **3**, 11 (1974).
123. S. Frederiksen and P. Hellung-Larsen, *FEBS Lett.* **58**, 374 (1975).
124. G. L. Eliceiri and M. S. Sayavedra, *BBRC* **72**, 507 (1976).
125. M. Salditt-Georgieff, M. Harpold, S. Chen-Kiang, and J. E. Darnell, *Cell* **19**, 69 (1980).
126. G. L. Eliceiri, *Nature* **279**, 80 (1979).
127. M. Muramatsu, J. L. Hodnett, and H. Busch, *JBC* **241**, 1544 (1966).
128. S. Frederiksen, H. Flodgard, and P. Hellung-Larsen, *JBC* **193**, 743 (1981).
129. P. W. Gunning, L. Austin, and P. L. Jeffrey, *Neurochemistry* **32**, 1725 (1979).
130. T. Gurney and G. Eliceiri, *J. Cell Biol.* **87**, 398 (1980).
131. E. M. DeRobertis, S. Lienhard, and R. F. Parisot, *Nature* **295**, 572 (1982).
132. L. Goldstein, G. E. Wise, and C. Ko, *J. Cell Biol.* **73**, 322 (1977).
133. C. E. Sekeris and J. Niessing, *BBRC* **62**, 642 (1975).
134. W. Northemann, M. Scheurlen, V. Gross, and P. C. Heinrich, *BBRC* **76**, 1130 (1977).
135. W. Northemann, H. Klump, and P. C. Heinrich, *EJB* **99**, 447 (1979).
136. G. Zieve and S. Penman, *JMB* **145**, 501 (1981).
137. E. S. Maxwell, K. Maundrell, and K. Scherrer, *BBRC* **97**, 875 (1980).
138. E. S. Maxwell, K. Maundrell, F. Puvion-Dutilleul, and K. Scherrer, *EJB* **113**, 233 (1981).
139. C. Flytzanis, A. Alonso, C. Louis, L. Krieg, and C. E. Sekeris, *FEBS Lett.* **96**, 201 (1978).
140. B. Deimel, C. Louis, and C. E. Sekeris, *FEBS Lett.* **73**, 80 (1977).
141. C. Guimont-Ducamp, J. Sri-Widada, and P. Jenateur, *Bchem* **59**, 755 (1977).
142. H. Gallinaro and M. Jacob, *BBA* **228**, 585 (1981).
143. J. P. Calvet and T. Pederson, *Cell* **26**, 363 (1981).
144. J. P. Calvet, L. M. Meyer, and T. Pederson, *Science* **217**, 456 (1982).
145. C. Brunel, J. Sri-Widada, M. N. Lelay, P. Jeanteur, and J. P. Liautard, *NARes* **9**, 815 (1981).
146. T. A. Walker, N. R. Pace, R. L. Erikson, E. Erikson, and F. Behr, *PNAS* **71**, 3390 (1974).
147. P. W. Gunning, P. Beguin, E. M. Shooter, L. Austin, and P. L. Jeffrey, *JBC* **256**, 6670 (1981).

148. T. E. Miller, C. Y. Huang, and A. O. Pogo, *J. Cell Biol.* **76**, 692 (1978).
149. G. Herlan, W. A. Eckert, W. Kaffenberger, and F. Wunderlich, *Bchem* **18**, 1782 (1979).
150. B. Vogelstein and B. F. Hunt, *BBRC* **105**, 1224.
151. R. A. Denison, S. W. VanArsdell, L. B. Bernstein, and A. M. Weiner *PNAS* **78**, 810 (1981).
152. T. Manser and R. F. Gesteland, *J. Mol. Appl. Genet.* **1**, 117 (1981).
152a. S. Wolin and J. A. Steitz, *Cell* **32**, 735 (1983).
153. T. Manser and T. Gesteland, *Cell* **29**, 257 (1982).
154. S. W. VanArsdell, R. A. Denison, L. B. Bernstein, A. M. Weiner, T. Manser, and B. F. Gesteland, *Cell* **26**, 11 (1981).
155. R. Denison and A. M. Weiner, *Mol. Cell. Biol.* **2**, 815 (1982).
156. M. Piechaczyk, M. N. Lelay-Taha, J. Sri-Widada, C. Brunel, J. Liautard, and P. Jeanteur, *NARes* **10**, 4627 (1982).
156a. N. Watanabe-Nagasu, Y. Itoh, T. Tarri, K. Okano, N. Koga, N. Okada, and Y. Ohshima, *NARes* **11**, 1791 (1983).
157. G. Westin, H. Monstein, J. Zabielski, L. Philipson, and V. Petterson, *NARes* **9**, 6323 (1981).
158. K. Hammarstrom, G. Westin, and V. Petterson, *EMBO J.* **1**, 737 (1982).
159. Y. Ohshima, N. Okada, T. Tani, Y. Itoh, and M. Itoh, *NARes* **9**, 5145 (1981).
160. K. Hayashi, *NARes* **9**, 3379 (1981).
161. E. Ullu, S. Murphy, and M. Melli, *Cell* **29**, 195 (1982).
162. E. Ullu and M. Melli, *NARes* **10**, 2209 (1982).
163. A. Balmain, R. Krumlauf, J. K. Vass, and G. D. Birnie, *NARes* **10**, 4259 (1982).
163a. J. Engberg, P. Hellung-Larsen, and S. Frederiksen, *EJB* **41**, 321 (1974).
164. V. Murray and R. Holliday, *FEBS Lett.* **106**, 6 (1979).
165. J. Rogers and R. Wall, *PNAS* **77**, 1877 (1980).
166. Y. Ohshima, M. Itoh, N. Okada, and T. Miyata, *PNAS* **78**, 4471 (1981).
167. V. W. Yang, M. Lerner, J. A. Steitz, and S. J. Flint, *PNAS* **78**, 1371 (1981).
167a. P. Bringmann, R. Reuter, J. Rinke, B. Appel, R. Bald, and R. Luhrmann, *JBC* **258**, 2475 (1983).
167b. S. M. Mount, I. Pettersson, M. Hinterberger, A. Karmas, and J. A. Steitz, *Cell* **33**, 509 (1983).
168. V. E. Avvedimento, G. Vogeli, Y. Yamada, J. E. Maizel, I. Pastan, and B. Crombrugghe, *Cell* **21**, 689 (1980).
169. C. Weissman, *in* "Gene Regulation" (B. W. O'Malley and C. F. Fox, eds.), Vol. 26, p. 65. Academic Press, New York, 1982.
170. R. A. Spritz, P. Jagadeeswaran, P. V. Chowdary, P. A. Biro, J. T. Elder, J. K. Deriel, J. L. Manley, M. L. Gefter, B. G. Forget, and S. M. Wiessman, *PNAS* **78**, 2455 (1981).
171. J. Abelson, *ARB* **48**, 1035 (1979).
172. R. Breathnach and P. Chambon, *ARB* **50**, 349 (1981).
172a. K. Kruger, P. Grabowski, A. Zang, J. Sands, D. Gottschling, and T. R. Cech, *Cell* **31**, 147 (1982).
173. H. Busch, R. Reddy, D. Henning, D. Spector, P. Epstein, M. Liu, S. Chirala, W. Schrier, and L. Rothblum *in* "Gene Regulation" (B. W. O'Malley and C. F. Fox, eds.), Vol. 26, p. 167. Academic Press, New York, 1982.
174. C. E. Sekeris and A. Guialis, *in* "The Cell Nucleus" (H. Busch, ed.), Vol. 8, p. 247. Academic Press, New York, 1981.
175. A. O. Pogo, *in* "The Cell Nucleus" (H. Bush, ed.), Vol. 8, p. 337. Academic Press, New York, 1981.

176. R. J. Britten and E. H. Davidson, *Science* **165**, 349 (1969).
176a. J. Light and S. Molin, *EMBO J.* **2**, 93 (1983).
177. T. Pederson and J. S. Bhorjee, *JMB* **128**, 451 (1979).
178. J. M. Bishop, W. Levinson, D. Sullivan, L. Farrshier, N. Quintrell, and J. Jackson, *Virology* **42**, 927 (1970).
179. E. Erikson, R. L. Erikson, B. Henry, and N. R. Pace, *Virology* **53**, 40 (1973).
179a. E. Ullu, V. Esposito, and M. Melli, *JMB* **161**, 195 (1982).
180. W. Y. Li, R. Reddy, D. Henning, P. Epstein, and H. Busch, *JBC* **257**, 5136 (1982).
181. A. M. Weiner, *Cell* **22**, 209 (1980).
181a. P. Walter and G. Blobel, *Nature* **299**, 691 (1982).
182. P. Walter and G. Blobel, *J. Cell Biol.* **91**, 557 (1981).
183. P. Walter and G. Blobel, *J. Cell Biol.* **91**, 551 (1981).
184. P. Walter, I. Ibrahimi, and G. Blobel, *J. Cell Biol.* **91**, 545 (1981).
185. P. Walter and G. Blobel, *PNAS* **77**, 7112 (1980).
186. F. Harada and N. Kato, *NARes* **8**, 1273 (1980).
187. S. R. Haynes, T. P. Toomey, L. Leinwand, and W. R. Jelinek, *Mol. Cell. Biol.* **1**, 573 (1981).
187a. A. S. Krayev, D. A. Kramerov, K. G. Skryabin, A. P. Kyskov, A. A. Bayev, and G. P. Georgiev, *NARes* **8**, 1201 (1980).
188. W. R. Jelinek, T. P. Toomey, L. Leinwand, C. H. Duncan, P. A. Biro, P. V. Choudary, S. M. Weissman, C. M. Rubin, C. M. Houck, P. L. Deininger, and C. W. Schmid, *PNAS* **77**, 1398 (1980).
188a. L. Leinwand, R. Wydro, and B. Nadal-Ginard, *Mol. Cell. Biol.* **2**, 1320 (1982).
189. T. S. Ro-Choi, R. Reddy, D. Henning, T. Takano, C. Taylor, and H. Busch, *JBC* **247**, 3205 (1972).
190. W. R. Jelinek and C. W. Schmid, *ARB* **51**, 813 (1982).
191. S. Haynes and W. Jelinek, *PNAS* **78**, 6310 (1981).
191a. J. G. Sutcliffe, R. J. Milner, F. E. Bloom, and R. A. Lerner, *PNAS* **79**, 4942 (1982).
192. C. H. Duncan, P. Jagadeeswaran, R. Wang, and S. M. Weissman, *NARes* **9**, 1161 (1981).
193. P. Jagadeeswaran and S. Weissman, *Cell* **26**, 141 (1981).
193a. R. Reddy, E. Tan, D. Henning, K. Nohga, and H. Busch, *JBC* **258**, 1383 (1983).
193b. N. Kato, H. Hoshino, and F. Harada, *BBRC* **108**, 363 (1982).
194. R. Reddy, L. I. Rothblum, C. Subrahmanyam, M. Liu, D. Henning, and H. Busch, *JBC* **258**, 584 (1983).
195. H. Savage, V. Grinchishin, W. Fang, and H. Busch, *Physiol. Chem. Phys.* **6**, 113 (1974).
196. B. Benecke and S. Penman, *Cell* **12**, 939 (1977).
197. R. Reichel, H. Monstein, H. Jansen, L. Philipson, and B. Benecke *PNAS* **79**, 3106 (1982).
198. A. K. Deshpande, S. B. Jakowlew, H. Arnold, P. A. Crawford, and M. A. Q. Siddiqui, *JBC* **252**, 6521 (1977).
199. H. J. Drabkin and M. A. Q. Siddiqui, *Biochem. Int.* **3**, 533 (1981).
200. S. Altman, E. Bowman, R. Garber, R. Kole, and B. C. Stark *in* "Transfer RNA: Biological Aspects" (D. Söll, J. N. Abelson, and P. R. Schimmel, eds.), p. 71. Cold Spring Harbor Laboratory, 1980.
201. R. Kole and S. Altman, *PNAS* **76**, 3795 (1979).
202. P. Gegenheimer and D. Apirion, *Microbiol. Rev.* **45**, 502 (1981).
203. R. Kole, M. F. Baer, B. C. Stark, and S. Altman, *Cell* **9**, 881 (1980).
203a. R. E. Reed, M. F. Baer, C. Guerrier-Takada, H. Donis-Keller, and S. Altman, *Cell* **30**, 627 (1982).

204. M. L. Celma, J. Pan, and S. M. Weissman, *JBC* **252**, 9032 (1977).
205. G. Akusjarvi, M. B. Mathews, P. Andersson, B. Vennstrom, and U. Petterson, *PNAS* **77**, 2424 (1980).
205a. B. Thimmappaya, C. Weinberger, R. J. Schneider, and T. Shenk, *Cell* **31**, 543 (1982).
206. R. A. Bonar, L. Sverak, D. Bolognesi, A. J. Langlors, D. Beard, and J. W. Beard, *Cancer Res.* **27**, 1138 (1967).
207. P. H. Duesberg, *PNAS* **60**, 1511 (1968).
208. M. M. Bishop, W. E. Levinson, N. Quintrell, D. Sullivan, L. Fanshier, and J. Jackson, *Virology* **42**, 182 (1970).
209. J. E. Dahlberg, R. C. Sawyer, J. M. Taylor, A. J. Faras, W. E. Levinson, H. M. Goodman, and J. Bishop, *J. Virol.* **13**, 1134 (1974).
210. M. O. Krause and M. J. Ringuette, *BBRC* **76**, 796 (1977).
211. M. Ringuette, W. C. Liu, E. Jay, K. K. Yu, and M. O. Krause, *Gene* **8**, 211 (1980).
212. T. Kanehisa, Y. Oki, and K. Ikuta, *BBA* **277**, 584 (1974).
213. A. J. Bester, D. S. Kennedy, and S. M. Heywood, *PNAS* **72**, 1523 (1975).
213a. T. L. McCarthy, E. Siegel, B. Mroczkowski, and S. M. Heywood, *Bchem* **22**, 935 (1983).
214. M. S. Rao, M. Blackstone, and H. Busch, *Bchem* **16**, 2756 (1977).
215. E. Howard and E. Stubblefield, *Exp. Cell Res.* **70**, 460 (1971).
216. J. Tomizawa, T. Itoh, G. Selzer, and T. Som, *PNAS* **78**, 1421 (1981).
217. C. Denoya, P. C. Costa-Giomi, E. A. Scodeller, C. Vasquez, and J. L. Latorre, *EJB* **115**, 375 (1981).

Ribosome Evolution: The Structural Bases of Protein Synthesis in Archaebacteria, Eubacteria, and Eukaryotes

JAMES A. LAKE

The Molecular Biology Institute
and Department of Biology,
University of California, Los Angeles,
Los Angeles, California

Considerable progress has been made during the last decade to understand the structure and the function of the ribosome. In general, current knowledge of the *Escherichia coli* ribosome is more detailed than that of other ribosomes since *E. coli* is the organism of choice for studying protein synthesis. Almost all known techniques in the fields of immunology, genetics, and biochemistry have been employed in conjunction with structural studies to probe this particular ribosome.

In this chapter, I review the detailed structural and biochemical information available for the *E. coli* ribosome, and use it as a basis for interpreting the less specific structural and biochemical information available for archaebacterial and eukaryotic ribosomes. In this way, I hope to present a unified view of the structural bases of protein synthesis and of the evolution of the ribosome.

I. Functional Sites

A. Structure of the *Escherichia coli* Ribosome

Electron microscopy has been used to study the gross structure of ribosomes for more than 20 years (reviewed in *1*, see also *2*). Although

Progress in Nucleic Acid Research
and Molecular Biology, Vol. 30

three-dimensional reconstruction has advanced our understanding of ribosome structure (3, 4), perhaps the largest advances have come through immunoelectron microscopy (5–7). This technique, by combining immunology and electron microscopy, allows one to map specific ribosomal components and to determine their locations in three dimensions. Before these mapping studies can be reviewed, however, one needs to describe the structure of the ribosome and provide a few details concerning the interpretation of electron micrographs.

An electron micrograph (like a medical X-ray) is a transmission image. It is the two-dimensional projection of a three-dimensional structure that results from directing a beam of electrons through the structure. When one is looking at images of three-dimensional ribosomes one sees different images depending upon the particular orientation of the ribosome that is making the image. The structures of the small and large subunits of the *E. coli* ribosome and some of the characteristic images they produce are illustrated in Fig. 1.

The 30 S subunit (Fig. 1A, B) is divided into two unequal parts by an indentation and a region of accumulated negative stain (1, 8). The parts are referred to as the "upper one-third," or "head," and the "lower two-thirds," or "base." A region of the subunit, called "the platform," extends from the base of the small subunit and forms a cleft between it and the upper one-third (9). Nearly all models used for mapping studies are asymmetric and can be related to the model shown in Fig. 1. The asymmetric 30 S model derived from images of heavy-metal-shadowed subunits (10) is similar to that shown in Fig. 1, although it lacks a cleft. The platform and cleft have been confirmed in *E. coli* ribosomes (11) and in eukaryotic ribosomes (12). In addition, neutron diffraction studies on the locations of ribosomal small subunit proteins (13) have fully confirmed the asymmetric model of the small subunit.

The large subunit, like the small subunit, is asymmetric (Fig. 1C, D) (1, 8, 14). It consists of a central protuberance (Fig. 1C, first frame), the site of 5 S rRNA, and protrusions inclined approximately 50° to either side of the central protuberance. One of these projections, the "L7/L12 stalk," is at the right and contains the only multiple-copy proteins present in the *E. coli* ribosome. In a projection approximately orthogonal to this (shown in the right frames of Fig. 1C, D), the large subunit is characterized by a notch on the upper surface. The model of Boublik *et al.* (15) is also an asymmetric structure in general agreement with our results, as are the models of Vasiliev *et al.* (16) and Stöffler *et al.* (17).

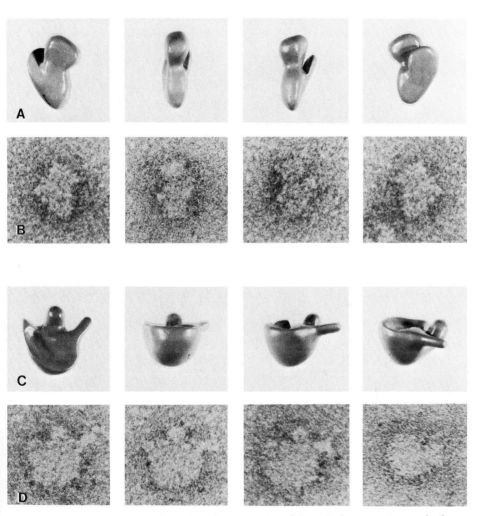

FIG. 1. A comparison of the three-dimensional models with electron micrographs for small subunits (A, B) and for large subunits (C, D). Adapted from Lake (14).

In the monomeric ribosome, the small subunit is positioned asymmetrically on the large subunit (1) as shown in Fig. 2. The platform of the small subunit is in contact with the large subunit, so that the one-third–two-thirds partition of the small subunit is approximately aligned with the notch of the large subunit (14). Two alternative orientations, in which the long axis of the small subunit is rotated ±90 degrees with respect to that shown in Fig. 2, have been proposed (18, 19). These conclusions were based on the interpretation of micro-

166

JAMES A. LAKE

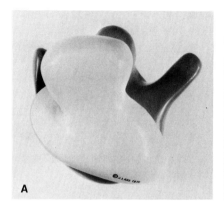
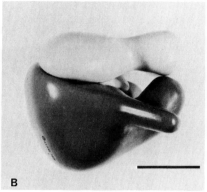

A   B

FIG. 2. Model of the 70 S *Escherichia coli* ribosome showing the relative orientations of the subunits (the 30 S subunit is light, the 50 S subunit is dark). Adapted from Lake (*14*).

graphs of a single view of the subunit (the one shown in Fig. 2B), and 70 S antibody-labeling studies were not performed. While the possibility of an alternative 70 S model should be kept in mind, I much prefer the alternative in Fig. 2 since it is derived from two different, mutually perpendicular views of the ribosome, and the detailed orientation of the 30 S subunit has been deduced by antibody-labeling studies of 70 S ribosomes using anti-S13 IgGs (*14*) and, since it is strongly supported by double-labeling immunoelectron microscopy (*20*; see also *21*). The model is also consistent with data of Stöffler and co-workers (*22*).

Using these three-dimensional structures, preliminary locations of a majority of the ribosomal proteins have been mapped (*6, 9, 23–26*). Their locations provide insights into the functioning of the ribosome that are described in the following sections. Ribosomal proteins have also been extensively mapped by Stöffler and co-workers (*27*). While their experimental results are quite similar to ours, their three-dimensional locations were initially interpreted using their symmetric model. In those cases where they have reinterpreted their 50 S protein locations using the asymmetric model (L1 and L7/L12), their 50 S mappings match ours and are included. Small subunit proteins mapped by neutron diffraction (*28–30*) are also included.

B. The Translational and Exit Domains

The ribosome is divided into two general functional regions, the translational domain and the exit, or secretory, domain (*31*). These two domains are at opposite ends of the ribosome, as illustrated in Fig. 3,

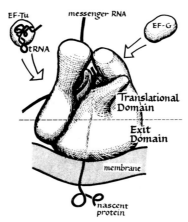

FIG. 3. Diagrammatic representation of the exit and translational domains of the ribosome and their orientations with respect to the membrane binding site. The binding sites of mRNA and elongation factors EF-Tu and EF-G are those inferred from the locations of ribosomal proteins. Adapted from Bernabeu and Lake (31).

with the exit domain in contact with the membrane of the rough endoplasmic reticulum (RER). The translational domain includes the head and platform of the small subunit and the L7/L12 stalk, the central protuberance, and the L1 ridge of the large subunit.

   In general, all the proteins of the E. coli small ribosomal subunit that have been mapped are located in the translational domain (see Figs. 4 and 5) (for a review of these locations see 1). In the large subunit, many ribosomal proteins are found in the translational domain, although at least one (L17) is located in the exit domain (see Fig. 9).

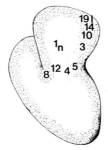

FIG. 4. Locations of some exterior proteins discussed in this chapter This view corresponds to the surface of the subunit exposed to the cytoplasm, i.e., the exterior surface.

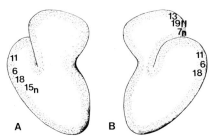

FIG. 5. Locations of proteins S6, S11, S13, S18, and S19 are shown on the exterior (A) and interface (B) surfaces of the small subunit.

C. Functions of the Translational Domain

Within the translational domain itself, several functional regions are found; these regions are discussed in the following sections.

1. tRNA Binding and Recognition Proteins Map on the External Surface of the Small Subunit

The orientation of the small subunit on the large subunit makes possible an operational distinction between 30 S proteins located on the "exterior" of the subunit (i.e., the side away from the 50 S subunit) and those at the interface between subunits. In the view of the 30 S subunit characterized by a platform and a cleft shown in Fig. 1A (third frame), exterior proteins map on the side of the subunit opposite the platform. Ultimately, the spatial features that distinguish exterior proteins from interior ones reflect functional differences. Several different types of experiments suggest that the cluster of proteins located at the concave edge of the upper one-third of the subunit containing S3, S10, S14, and S19 may be involved in tRNA binding (see Fig. 4). Single-component-omission experiments (32), for example, suggested an important role for proteins S3, S10, S14, and S19 in poly(U)-dependent Phe-tRNA binding. When these proteins were omitted, poly(U)-dependent Phe-tRNA binding was reduced to less than one-third of that obtained with subunits reconstituted with all 30 S proteins present. Other experiments have also suggested an involvement of these proteins in tRNA binding (see, for example, 33, 34).

Adjacent to this group is a second region of small subunit proteins mapping on the external surface. It includes the proteins located at the constriction between the base and the head, i.e., S4, S5, and S12. These proteins have all been implicated in tRNA recognition by drug-induced "misreading" studies. S4, for example, is the *ram*-A gene-product (35), and modifications in both S12 and S5 alter (i.e., restrict and restore, respectively) the suppressor activity of mutant strains resistant to streptomycin (36–38). Furthermore, a mapping of the EF-Tu binding site (J. A. Langer and J. A. Lake, unpublished) indicates that this general region functions in binding the EF-Tu ternary complex.

2. THE CODON–ANTICODON INTERACTION PROBABLY OCCURS ON THE PLATFORM OF THE SMALL SUBUNIT

Another group of small subunit proteins maps on the platform. Proteins S6, S11, and S18 are in this group (see Fig. 5B). Because of the thinness (approximately 30 Å) of the platform, it is possible for a protein to be exposed on both the exterior and the interface surfaces of the platform.

Several lines of experimentation have linked these proteins to mRNA binding. Single-component-omission experiments (32; discussed in 39) suggest that S11 may be participating directly in the selection of the correct tRNA, i.e., in the codon–anticodon interaction. Protein S18 has been cross-linked to mRNA using a variety of affinity-labeling analogs (these are comprehensively reviewed in 40).

Additional evidence placing the codon–anticodon interaction site near the platform comes from the interaction (41) of the 3' end of the 16 S RNA with between four and seven base-pairs of a "leader" sequence located about ten nucleotides before (i.e., on the 5' side of) the initiation codon. Consistent with this sequence being located on the platform, dimethyladenines located on the 16 S RNA near the leader sequence pairing region have been mapped (42) there by immunoelectron microscopy. Also, the platform has been implicated as the decoding site by affinity immunoelectron microscopy (43). Thus, a considerable body of evidence suggests that the platform proteins S6, S11, and S18 are close to the site of codon–anticodon interaction.

3. INITIATION FACTORS MAY BIND AT THE INTERFACE BETWEEN SUBUNITS

The locations of proteins S13 and S19, the locations of the platform proteins (shown in Fig. 6), and the location of S12, taken together, suggest a binding site for initiation factors IF-1, IF-2, and IF-3 (9). Consideration of the results of both cross-linking (44–48) and protein localization by immunoelectron microscopy suggests that IF-3, IF-2, and IF-1 are positioned across the cleft between S13, S19-II, and S12 on the head of the small subunit and S11 on the platform in the general region indicated in Fig. 6 (see also 39). In eukaryotic small subunits, eIF-3 binds in a similar region on the platform (12).

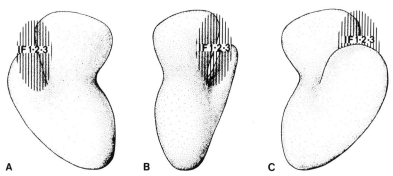

FIG. 6. Locations suggested for IF-1, IF-2, and IF-3: (A) on the exterior; (B) in the clef; (C) on the interface surface of the 30 S subunit.

4. PROTEINS L7 AND L12, BOTH IMPLICATED IN THE HYDROLYSIS OF GTP, FORM THE STALK OF THE LARGE SUBUNIT

Ribosomal proteins L7 and L12 have several unique properties (for reviews, see 49, 50). Proteins L7 and L12 have identical amino-acid sequences except that the amino terminus of L7 is acetylated, whereas that of L12 is not. L7 and L12 are the only ribosomal proteins present in multiple copies, and the total number of L7 and L12 copies per ribosome is most likely four. Both proteins are intimately involved in elongation factor Tu (EF-Tu), in elongation factor G (EF-G), and in IF-2-dependent GTP hydrolysis. The location of L7/L12 and the L7/L12 stalk (25) is illustrated in Fig. 7. Also indicated are the binding sites mapped for EF-G (51) and for EF-Tu (J. A. Langer and J. A. Lake, unpublished). Crosslinks have been observed between L7/L12 and the elongation factors EF-G (52) and EF-Tu (53), suggesting that the stalk itself may have some flexibility during protein synthesis.

The stalk appears to be a constant feature of the eubacterial ribosome. Indeed, large subunits from gram-negative bacteria, gram-positive bacteria, cyanobacteria, and chloroplasts are nearly indistinguishable (54; see Fig. 8). More recent studies show the stalk to be a relatively constant structural feature, even across the archaebacterial, eubacterial, and eukaryotic lineages (J. A. Lake, E. Henderson, M. Clark, and A. T. Matheson, unpublished; see also Section II below). The L7/L12 proteins for several diverse organisms have been sequenced and characterized. Rather unexpectedly, in archaebacteria and eukaryotes the L7/L12 sequences are more closely related than they are in eubacteria (55). This important landmark appears to be a universal ribosomal structure.

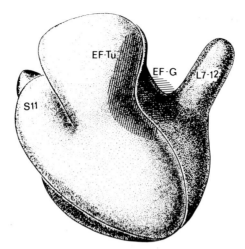

FIG. 7. The location of the L7/L12 stalk relative to the small subunit. The morphology of the stalk is shown as it is normally observed in fields of subunits. The locations of some proteins are included for reference.

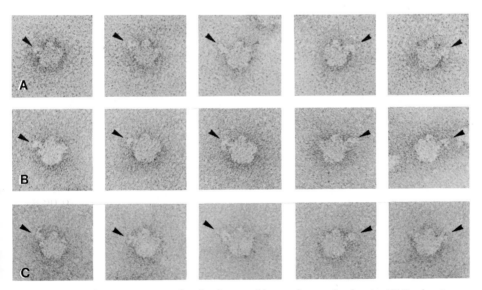

FIG. 8. Electron micrographs of eubacterial large ribosomal subunits. 50 S subunits from *B. stearothermophilus, Thermus aquaticus, and Synechocystis 6701* are shown in (A), (B), and (C), respectively. Adapted from Fahnestock *et al.* (*54*).

5. THE PEPTIDYLTRANSFERASE AND 5 S rRNA ARE ON THE CENTRAL PROTUBERANCE OF THE LARGE SUBUNIT

The first evidence suggesting that the central protuberance is the site of the peptidyltransferase center was provided by immunoelectron microscopy. In particular, this was suggested by the location of the codon–anticodon site on the platform of the small subunit (14). This location for the peptidyltransferase is shown in Fig. 9. More direct evidence was provided by a direct mapping of protein L27 on the side of the central protuberance opposite the L7/L12 stalk (26, 56). This protein is consistently found among the proteins labeled by modified aminoacyl-tRNAs when they are bound to either the peptidyl site or the aminoacyl site (for reviews and discussions, see 57, 58). The most common affinity labels for peptidyl-site studies have been electrophilic derivatives of N-acylphenylalanyl-tRNA^{Phe}. Using these affinity labels, the principal labeled proteins are L2, L11, L18, and L27. Cooperman (58) has emphasized that the electrophilic nature of the labels should be kept in mind. More recently, the binding site of an analog of puromycin has been mapped on the central protuberance in the vicinity of L27 (59). Thus the case for the transferase being contained on the central protuberance is quite strong.

This same region is also the location of the 3' end of 5 S rRNA (16,

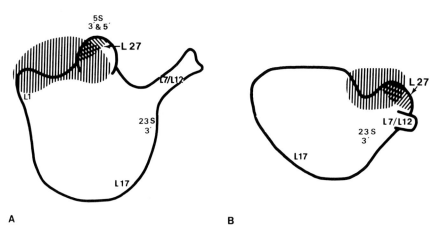

FIG. 9. Location of the peptidyltransferase in the quasi-symmetric (A) and the asymmetric (B) projections of the subunit. The vertical stripes correspond to a possible region of contact of the acceptor end of the tRNA, assuming that the codon–anticodon interaction occurs on the platform. The diagonal stripes correspond to the localization of protein L27. Adapted from Lake and Strycharz (26). Also shown are the locations of the 5' and 3' ends of 5 S rRNA and the 3' end of 23 S rRNA.

60) and the 5' end of the same molecule (61). This latter mapping is illustrated using covalently linked 23 S and 5 S rRNAs from *E. coli* mutant AB301-105 (Fig. 10). Also shown in Fig. 9 is the location of the 3' end of the 23 S rRNA (62).

6. SUMMARY OF THE TRANSLATIONAL DOMAIN

The broad outlines of the energetics of the chain-elongation cycle of protein synthesis are quite well understood (for reviews, see 63, 64). Typically, the major events that occur are summarized as (a) codon recognition, (b) peptide-bond formation, and (c) translocation. The process of tRNA binding progresses through three stages (in Fig. 11B, C, and D). These correspond to binding at three sites that are distinguished structurally according to their reactivity with puromycin. These are the R, the A, and the P tRNA binding sites, respectively (65).

These steps are illustrated in Fig. 11. In the first frame, a peptidyl-tRNA occupies the P site and the next codon is available to be read by the correct tRNA. The first step of elongation, indicated by three lines on the mRNA, is codon recognition (Fig. 11B). During this step, the codon is initially recognized and bound to the ribosome as an (aminoacyl-tRNA) · (EF-Tu) · GTP complex at the R site. If the initial reading indicates that the correct tRNA is present, the GTP is cleaved, the (EF-Tu) · GDP complex and P_i are released from the ribosome,

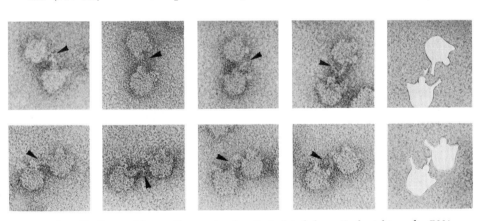

FIG. 10. Pairs of large ribosomal subunits isolated from *Escherichia coli* rRNA processing mutant AB301-105. This strain is deficient in RNase III processing activity. In the top row, the RNA strand leaves the lower subunit of the pair from the central protuberance (the 5' end of the 5 S rRNA) and enters the other subunit just below the base of the L7/L12 stalk (the 3' end of the 23 S rRNA). In the bottom row, the RNA strand leaves the right-most subunit just below the base of the L7/L12 stalk and enters the left-most subunit at its central protuberance.

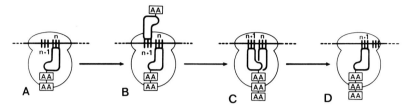

FIG. 11. The elongation cycle of protein synthesis. (A) Peptidyl-tRNA in the P site; (B) aminoacyl-tRNA in the R site; (C) peptidyl-tRNA in the A site; (D) peptidyl-tRNA in the P site. Adapted from Lake (65).

and the aminoacyl tRNA is (very likely) read a second time. After this, the peptide bond is made (Fig. 11C) and the new tRNA occupies the aminoacyl site (A site). The third event, translocation, is accompanied by the hydrolysis of a second GTP, in the presence of EF-G, and represents a switching of the peptidyl-tRNA from the aminoacyl site (Fig. 11C) to the peptidyl site (Fig. 11D). During this step EF-G, GDP, P_i, and the deacylated tRNA are released. At the completion of this step, a single tRNA occupies the peptidyl (P) site and the cycle is ready to be repeated.

Given the locations of the functional regions discussed in this essay, one can begin to ask where these tRNA-binding regions of the ribosome are. Obviously the process of combining data on the functional roles of ribosomal proteins is subject to interpretation regarding which experiments are significant and to what extent structural inferences can be obtained from them. Nevertheless, the locations of the proteins suggest functionally consistent domains. In the following paragraph, I put forth what I regard as the current "best guess."

First, a likely site for the A and P tRNA binding sites is that shown in Fig. 12B. This fits the previously discussed observations on (a) the location of the codon–anticodon site on the platform, (b) the binding site for IF-1, IF-2, and IF-3 in the cleft, (c) the localization of eIF-3 in native eukaryotic small subunits (discussed in the next section), (d) the location of the peptidyltransferase on the central protuberance of the large subunit, and (e) the location of the EF-G binding site at the interface between subunits.

Second, a possible location of the recognition site is shown in Fig. 12A. This site is consistent with (a) a direct role for external proteins S3, S5, S8, S10, S12, S14, and S19-I in aminoacyl-tRNA binding to the recognition site, (b) location of the codon decoding site, (c) the location mapped for EF-Tu on the exterior of the small subunit, and (d) the proximity of L7/L12 to the EF-Tu binding site. In addition, the D stem of a tRNA in the recognition site would be near proteins S4, S5, and

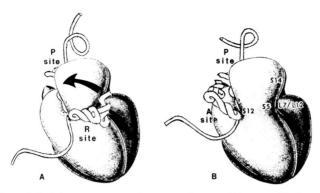

FIG. 12. Model of the monomeric ribosomes showing (A) a possible location for the recognition site and (B) suggested aminoacyl and peptidyl-tRNA binding sites. Adapted from Lake (45).

S12, consistent with the roles of those proteins in altering of nonsense mutations.

Thus our detailed knowledge of the translational domain is gradually being synthesized into a mechanistic structural–functional understanding of translation.

D. Functions of the Exit Domain

In contrast with the detailed knowledge of the translational domain, relatively little was known until recently about the ribosomal exit domain. In particular, all translational functions of the ribosome are found in the upper half of the small subunit and in the adjacent region of the large subunit. Information on the role of the other half of the ribosomal surface is, by comparison, meager. Yet by focusing on the role of the ribosome in accommodating the nascent protein chain, and on its role in binding to the membranes of the rough endoplasmic reticulum, we are obtaining some information about the functioning of the ribosomal exit domain.

1. THE EUBACTERIAL EXIT DOMAIN

Our information on the exit domain in *E. coli* comes from immune mapping of the nascent chain as it emerges from the ribosome, a function associated with protein secretion rather than with the translation steps just described. Using antibodies directed against the enzyme β-galactosidase to map the exit site of the nascent protein chain, it was found that the nascent chain exits from the ribosome at a single region, located on the large subunit (31). Electron micrographs of 70 S ribo-

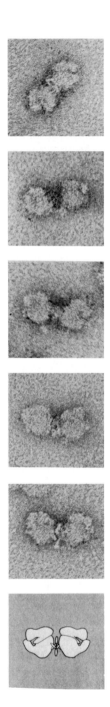

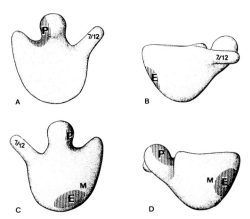

FIG. 14. Diagrammatic representation of the exit site on the surface of the large ribosomal subunit. The subunit surface contacting the small subunit is visible in (A) is at the top of the model in (B) and (D), and faces away from the viewer in (C). Regions indicated are the exit site (E) the peptidyltransferase (P), the membrane binding site (M), and the stalk proteins (L7/L12).

somes labeled with IgGs are shown in Fig. 13. In these micrographs, the IgGs are bound at the end of the ribosome *opposite* the head of the small subunit. Hence the nascent chain emerges from the large subunit nearly 150 Å from the central protuberance of the large subunit, the location of the peptidyltransferase.

For reference, both the peptidyltransferase (shown by the letter P) and the exit site (shown by the letter E) are labeled in Fig. 14. In our measurements of the distances obtained from electron micrographs and from the three-dimensional model of the 50 S subunit (assuming ±20% uncertainty in ribosome dimensions), the transferase and the exit site are separated by 150 (±30) Å.

2. THE EXIT DOMAIN IS IN THE SAME RELATIVE REGION IN BOTH EUKARYOTIC AND EUBACTERIAL RIBOSOMES

Our understanding of the structure and function of the eukaryotic ribosome has lagged behind that of the *E. coli* ribosome (for reviews, see 66, 67). This is primarily because relatively less biochemical and

FIG. 13. Electron micrographs of ribosomes linked by antibodies against nascent chains of β-galactosidase. Pairs of ribosomes in the nonoverlap projection connected by IgGs. The orientation of the ribosomes is shown diagrammatically in the sixth frame. No significant IgG reaction occurred with puromycin-treated ribosomes. Adapted from Bernabeu and Lake (31).

genetic information is available for eukaryotic ribosomes. Scientists studying protein synthesis in eukaryotes—unlike those studying prokaryotes, who have selected *E. coli*—have not focused on a single organism. Thus, cell biologists interested in the field of secretion may use mammalian pancreas or liver whereas others may study protein secretion in protists. Elongation and initiation studies have used a range of organisms and organs from the brine shrimp to the reticulocytes of various vertebrates.

Structural studies on eukaryotic ribosomes have not always lagged behind the prokaryotic ones. Some of the earliest structural studies used eukaryotic ribosomes. Of these, two in particular showed features that can be recognized today. These were electron microscopic studies of monomeric ribosomes and of isolated subunits (68) and a three-dimensional reconstruction of the *Entamoeba invadens* ribosome (3, 69). Nonomura *et al.* in their analysis of rat liver ribosomes observed a subdivision of the small subunit into unequal parts, observed an approximately circular profile of the large subunit, and also noted the asymmetric placement of the small subunit on the large subunit. Their structural interpretations are shown in Figs. 15 and 16. The three-dimensional reconstruction of the amoeba ribosome revealed similar features, such as the circular profile of the large subunit and the asymmetrically positioned small subunit on the large subunit. Because the same profiles could be recognized in images of both eukaryotic and prokaryotic subunits and ribosomes (Fig. 16), it was anticipated that a similar structure applied to both prokaryotic and eukaryotic ribosomes.

As the structure of the *E. coli* ribosome was studied more intensively, structural features were observed that had not previously been noted in the eukaryotic ribosome. These included principally the platform and the cleft of the small subunit (6, 9) together with the central protuberance of the large subunit (5, 8, 70) and quasi-symmetrically related projections on either side (5, 7, 8) of the central protuberance. These last two included the L7/L12 stalk (*14, 25*) and the L1 ridge (*17, 26*). Many of the newly discovered morphological features of the prokaryotic small subunit were related to the eukaryotic small subunit when the location of the eukaryotic initiation factor eIF-3 was mapped (*12*) on the platform of native small subunits from rabbit reticulocytes. Their model of the small subunit, together with the correspondingly scaled model for the *E. coli* ribosome, is shown in Fig. 17. Most of the additional mass in the larger eukaryotic subunit is concentrated in the lower two-thirds, or base, of the subunit. Shortly after, similar models were derived for the eukaryotic small subunits of rat liver and the

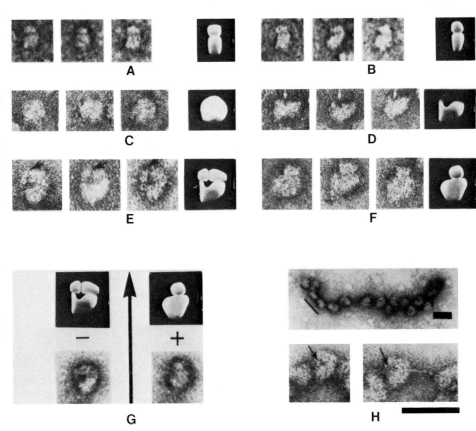

FIG. 15. A gallery of rat liver ribosome monomers and subunits and corresponding
views of the model shown in Fig. 1. (A,B). Two approximately orthogonal views of the
small subunit; (C,D) two approximately orthogonal views of the large subunit; (E,F)
two views of the monomer; (G) views of a monomer taken at two different tilt angles
showing the conversion of one type of monomer image into another; (H) polysomes
showing the path of the strand of mRNA. Scale bars = 50 nm. Adapted from Lake *et al.*
(8).

brine shrimp, and a eukaryotic feature resembling the prokaryotic
L7/L12 stalk was noted (71, 72).

Many of the structural features present in the translational domain
in prokaryotes are also present in eukaryotes, suggesting that the translation mechanisms function similarly in both. Even those translational
functions that are quite different, such as initiation, seem to occur on
comparable surfaces in ribosomes of both types (e.g., eIF-3, ref. 12).
For other aspects of ribosomal organization, particularly those in-

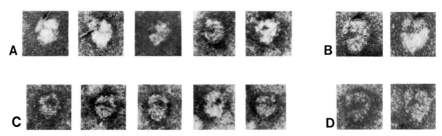

FIG. 16. A gallery of *Escherichia coli* and rat liver ribosome monomers. (A) An overlap view of *E. coli* monomers; (C) view of *E. coli* monomers enantiomorphic to that shown in (A). (B and D) views of rat liver monomers in orientations comparable to those shown for *E. coli* in (A) and (C), respectively. Adapted from Lake *et al.* (8).

volved with protein secretion and processing, it was thought that perhaps they could differ extensively in eukaryotic and prokaryotic ribosomes, since the rough endoplasmic reticulum has no obvious counterpart in the prokaryotic cell. Thus we were interested in determining whether the exit domain had a similar arrangement in both prokaryotes and eukaryotes.

Only a general knowledge is available, but it now appears that the exit domain in both types of organisms has a similar organization. In particular, the exit site of the nascent protein chain in eukaryotic ribosomes has been mapped (73) using antibodies directed against the enzyme ribulose-1,5-biphosphate carboxylase ("rubisco"). In the duckweed *Lemna gibba* the polypeptide nascent chain emerges from the large subunit at a region on the opposite side of the ribosome from the translational domain and in the same relative position as found in the *E. coli* ribosome. The results of both the eubacterial (prokaryotic) and eukaryotic mapping are compared in Fig. 18 (73).

The exit sites are at a single region located at comparable positions

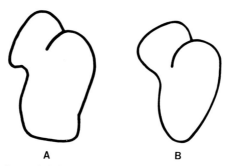

FIG. 17. An early model for the asymmetric projection of small subunits from eukaryotic and prokaryotic ribosomes are shown in (A) and (B), respectively.

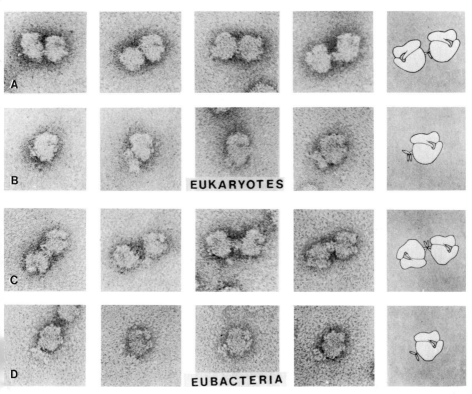

FIG. 18. Electron micrographs of ribosomes allowed to react with IgGs against their nascent protein chains. In (A) and (B) eukaryotic ribosomes are allowed to react with IgGs directed against rubisco, and in (C) and (D) prokaryotic ribosomes are allowed to react with IgGs directed against β-galactosidase. Pairs of ribosomes (the nonoverlap projection) linked by an IgG are shown in (A) and (C), and single ribosomes with an attached IgG are shown in (B) and (D). Adapted from Bernabeu *et al.* (*73*).

on the large subunits of both ribosomal types. In eukaryotes, this site is approximately 160 Å from the site of the peptidyltransferase. Hence, in spite of the greater complexity of eukaryotic as compared with prokaryotic ribosomes, the overall organization of the exit domain on ribosomes, as reflected by the location mapped for the exit site, seems to be similar in both.

3. Structural Features of Ribosomes Bound to Rough Endoplasmic Reticulum Are Similar to Eubacterial Ones

Eukaryotic cells contain two populations of actively synthesizing ribosomes, which are distinguished according to whether they are free in the cytoplasm or are bound to membranes. In general, the two populations synthesize different sets of proteins. Membrane-bound ribosomes of the rough endoplasmic reticulum (RER) function to synthesize proteins for export from the cell (74). During synthesis these proteins are vectorially discharged through the membrane (75). It is this set of membrane-bound ribosomes that has been used to study the site of membrane attachment.

These ribosomes of the RER are attached by two types of interaction (76). One attachment can be released by treatment with the antibiotic puromycin, indicating that it occurs through an anchoring effect of the nascent chain. The other interaction is sensitive to high concentrations of monovalent salts and possibly involves integral membrane proteins (76–78) and a "signal recognition" particle (79).

Ordered arrays of membrane-bound ribosomes are found in the ovarian follicles of a lizard (*Lacerta sicula*) during its winter hibernation period (80), and their structures have been studied at low (approximately 1/90 Å) resolution using three-dimensional reconstruction (4, 81, 82). These crystals appear to be representative of a general class of ribosome attachment to the RER. Although the ribosomes are crystallized, Unwin has argued that structural details of their attachment to

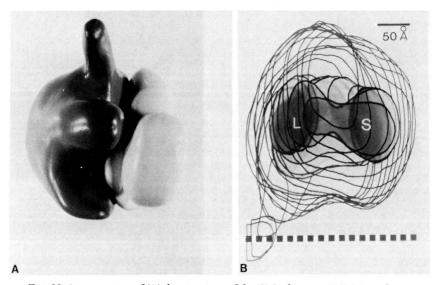

A   B

FIG. 19. A comparison of (A) the structure of the 70 S ribosome (14) (viewed approximately down the division between large and small subunits) with a corresponding view (B) of the eukaryotic ribosome (82). The arrow indicates the membrane attachment particle. Adapted from Lake (83).

the RER are probably the same, in general, as the true ribosome–membrane interaction. The structure of this ribosome–membrane complex is shown in Fig. 19B, and adjacent to it is our model of the *E. coli* ribosome in the corresponding orientation (82; discussed in 83).

This comparison, based on using the structure of the *E. coli* ribosome as a guide, indicates that the attachment site of membrane-bound ribosomes is near the exit site found in both eubacteria and eukaryotes.

This membrane site is indicated in Fig. 14, by the letter M. By this criterion, both the membrane-binding site and the nascent-chain-exit site are adjacent (within 60 Å of each other). Hence, in a general sense, protein synthesis appears to be organized into translational domains and exit domains in both prokaryotes and eukaryotes. Within each of these two major structural domains, the model illustrated in Fig. 3 appears to be applicable to both prokaryotes and eukaryotes.

II. Evolution of Ribosome Structure

A. Archaebacteria, Eubacteria, and Eukaryotes

In using ribosome structure to study the evolutionary relationships between eukaryotic and prokaryotic ribosomes, one is faced with an apparent gulf between the very different prokaryotic and eukaryotic ribosome structures. Clearly, it would be helpful if a third form of ribosome existed that could provide a baseline for judging which ribosome properties are ancestral and which are derived. In 1977, Woese and Fox (84), from their analysis of 16 S rRNA primary sequences, proposed that archaebacteria, eubacteria, and eukaryotes represented three aboriginal lines of cellular descent. Hence archaebacteria could, for our purposes, represent just such a third class of organism. The phylogenetic relationships of these lines were unclear, however. In certain aspects, archaebacteria resemble eukaryotes, whereas in others they resemble the eubacteria (55–57, 85–87). Phylogenetic trees based on accumulated nucleotide differences in rRNA sequences suggest that all three lines diverged at approximately the same time (84), but owing to extensive divergence of the sequences, the technique cannot determine their phylogenetic relationships. These unusual bacteria provide a unique opportunity for studying the evolution of ribosome structure. Just as three dimensional molecular structure has been successfully used to measure bacterial evolution within lineages

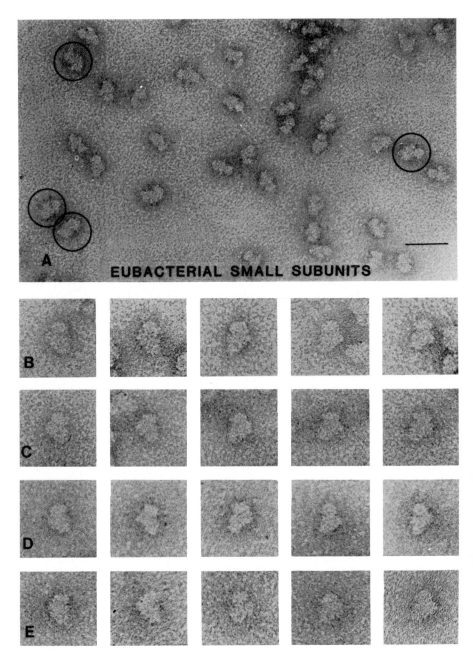

EUBACTERIAL SMALL SUBUNITS

(88), the divergences among these three types of ribosomes can be used to measure the evolution of the three lineages (89).

Electron micrographs of small ribosomal subunits from eubacteria (89), from archaebacteria (89), and from eukaryotes (cytoplasmic ribosomes) (89) are shown in the electron micrographs in Figs. 20–22, respectively. Because the ribosomal subunits are randomly oriented on the carbon support film, the images vary accordingly, and we have displayed images corresponding to the asymmetric projections of the *E. coli* small subunit. The eukaryotic structure and images corresponding to its characteristic projections were identified by analogy with the asymmetric projection of the eubacterial structure (12, 71, 72, 83, 89, 90), and the projections of the archaebacterial subunits were similarly identified (89). Differences between the eukaryotic, archaebacterial, and eubacterial structures are most apparent in the asymmetric (90°) projection of the eubacterial subunit (14). That projection, or its enantiomorph, is illustrated in the micrographs that follow.

A field of eubacterial (*E. coli*) small subunits is shown in Fig. 20. Also present are several eukaryotic small subunits that have been included as size markers. They are quite apparent because of their larger size and different shape (four of them have been circled and a fifth is left unmarked). A striking feature of small subunits from eubacteria is the extreme constancy of the characteristic projections. These profiles, representing the three major divisions of the eubacteria (84), are nearly indistinguishable. A generalized eubacterial profile is shown schematically in Fig. 23.

A field of archaebacterial small ribosomal subunits is shown in Fig. 21. These subunits contain a structure that resembles a duck bill—the archaebacterial bill. The "bill" is not present in eubacterial ribosomes. It extends from the head of the subunit and is estimated, from a comparison of its size with that of the L7/L12 stalk, to have a molecular weight (±SEM) of 44,000 ± 7000. The maximum dimensions of archaebacterial and eubacterial subunits are, within measurement, the same. The structure of the archaebacterial small subunit (shown

---

FIG. 20. Electron micrographs of small ribosomal subunits from the three principal lineages of eubacteria. (A) A field of *Escherichia coli* subunits, which also contains four circled (and one not circled) eukaryotic subunits for use as a control. The scale bar represents 500 Å. Rows B–E contain ribosomal small subunits in the asymmetric projection from the following sources: (B) *Thermus aquaticus*, a gram-negative thermophilic bacterium; (C) *Bacillus stearothermophilus*, a gram-positive thermophilic bacterium; (D) *Synechocystis* 6701, a cyanobacterium; and (E) *Spinacia oleracea* chloroplast, a spinach. Adapted from Lake *et al.* (89).

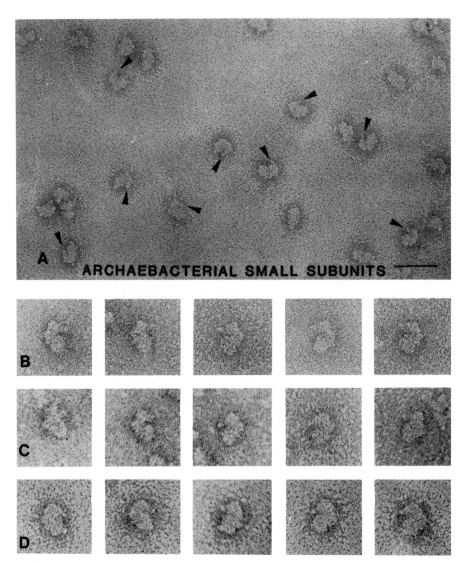

FIG. 21. Electron micrographs of small ribosomal subunits from the three lineages of archaebacteria. In the field in (A), small subunits from *Sulfolobus* are marked with arrowheads to indicate the archaebacterial bill. The scale bar is 500 Å. Rows B–D illustrate the asymmetric projection of small subunits from the following sources: (B) *Methanobacterium thermoautothrophicum*, a methanogenic bacterium; (C) *H. cutirubrum*, an extreme halophile; and (D) *Sulfolobus acidocaldarius*, a thermoacidophile. Adapted from Lake *et al.* (89).

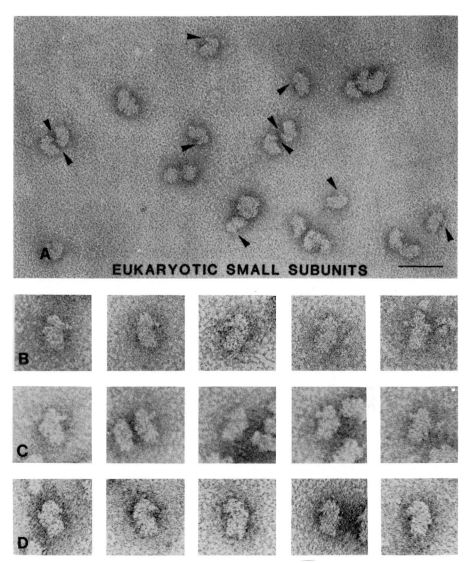

FIG. 22. Electron micrographs of small subunits of cytoplasmic ribosomes from three main divisions of eukaryotes. In the field in (A), small subunits from *Triticum aestivum* (wheat germ) are marked with arrows to indicate the archaebacterial bill. The scale bar is 500 Å. Rows B–D illustrate the asymmetric projection of the small subunits from the following sources: (B) *Saccharomyces cerevisiae*, a yeast; (C) *Triticum aestivum*, a wheat; and (D) *Rattus rattus*, a rat. Adapted from Lake *et al.* (89).

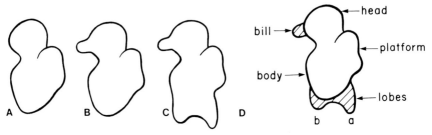

FIG. 23. Generalized profiles of small ribosomal subunits, in the asymmetric profile. The eubacterial, archaebacterial, and eukaryotic profiles are shown in (A), (B), and (C), respectively. The common ribosomal regions are named in (D), and the archaebacterial bill and eukaryotic lobes (a and b) are shown in diagonal stripes. Adapted from Lake *et al.* (*89*).

schematically in Fig. 23) is that of the eubacteria with the addition of the bill.

A field of eukaryotic small subunits, from the cytoplasmic ribosomes of a plant, is shown in Fig. 22A. In the Figs. 22B–D, subunits from three branches of the eukaryotic lineage are shown. These subunits are highly similar in organization. In addition to containing all the features of the eubacterial subunits, they also contain the archaebacterial bill and possess additional structures at the bottom of the subunit called the eukaryotic lobes (see Fig. 23D). These lobes are absent in both eubacteria and archaebacteria.

Biochemical and structural evidence, although indirect, suggests that the bill may function in the factor-related steps of protein synthesis, since the bill is located near the factor binding sites (*89*). Similarly, the eukaryotic lobes are thought to be composed primarily of RNA (*89, 91*). Measurements of the lobes from several projections suggest that they are large enough to contain ($\pm$SEM) 305 $\pm$ 20 nucleotides of RNA.

The stability of small subunit morphology within each of the three lineages is remarkable, when one considers that major subgroupings of each lineage have been surveyed. The observed intralineage ribosomal stability is taken to imply that each line descended from its own common ancestor, and that this ancestor had ribosomes representative of the lineage. This is not the only possible interpretation, but it is the simplest. Hence the three-dimensional structures of ribosome, although separate and independent observations, fully support the proposal of Woese and Fox (*84*) that archaebacteria, eubacteria, and eukaryotes are separate and primitive lineages.

Ribosome structure, conserved as it is within lineages, provides a

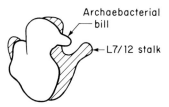

FIG. 24. Diagrammatic representation of the 70 S archaebacterial ribosome showing the location of the archaebacterial bill, as inferred from the eubacterial 70 S model and from preliminary results on *H. cutirubrum* 50 S subunits and 70 S ribosomes (89). The physical proximity of the bill and of the L7/L12 stalk is indicated.

simple, rapid, and accurate method for classifying new organisms. In addition, new lineages, if they exist, can be detected by identifying ribosomes that do not fit the three currently recognized groups.

B. Comparison of Eukaryotic and Prokaryotic Ancestors

Before one can relate the ribosomes of these three lineages to the evolution of cells, both cell structures need to be related to a common structural form. Hence it is usually assumed that the ancestor of the eukaryotic cell had prokaryotic organization (84). Certainly this assumption is strongly supported by the fossil record (92). (Fossil evidence, however, probably cannot exclude completely the alternative assumption, that the eukaryotic cell arrangement could be primitive.) In order to compare the evolution of both cell types, Woese and Fox (84) proposed that the evolution of the eukaryotic cell could be compared with that of the two prokaryotic lineages by devising a hypothetical ancestor of the eukaryotic cell. This cell, the "urkaryote," has a prokaryotic organization and represents the species that contributed its ribosomes to the eukaryotic cell. They assumed that the urkaryote evolved nuclear membranes during its transformation into the primitive eukaryote (for a discussion, see 93). We refer to this hypothesis as the "Karyogenic Hypothesis" and have illustrated it in Fig. 25A. An alternative hypothesis, the "Endokaryotic Hypothesis" (89), shown in Fig. 25B, postulates that the nucleus of the eukaryotic cell was formed when the urkaryote was engulfed by another cell. This proposal posits that the double membranes of the nucleus, like those of the other eukaryotic organelles, also enclosed in double membranes (chloroplast and mitochondrion), were derived as a result of capture by an engulfing species. In this second hypothesis the ribosomes found in the cytoplasm of the eukaryotic cell are derived from the nucleus.

The "Endokaryotic Hypothesis" has the virtue that it is simple. It

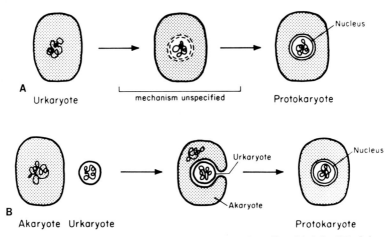

FIG. 25. A comparison of (A) the "Karogenic Hypothesis" and (B) the "Endokaryotic Hypothesis" for the evolution of the nucleus of the eukaryotic cell. Diagram (A) is adapted from ref. 93, and diagram (B) is as discussed by Lake (89).

explains the origin of all double-membrane organelles through a single mechanism rather than requiring two separate and different mechanisms. It has been suggested that the name urkaryote should also be applied to this organism (89), so that in either case one can use the concept of urkaryote to investigate the evolution of the archaebacterial, eubacterial, and urkaryotic lineages. However, consideration of these two alternatives will await a better understanding of the evolution of the three lineages.

C. Interlineage Ribosomal Alterations Suggest Steps in the Evolution of Lineages

The unusual stability of the archaebacterial bill and eukaryotic lobes over long time periods make them ideal markers to probe the creation of lineages. These two structures do not appear to have been significantly altered since lineages originated, possibly as long ago as the oldest (3.5 billion years) microfossils of bacteria (92). The topology of the formation of these three lineages can be represented by a single dendrogram, or tree. This tree, with ribosomal character assignments, is shown in Fig. 26. Because it is unrooted, no flow of time can be inferred. If we assume that the bill and the lobes represent unique evolutionary events—i.e., that each one was formed (or lost) only once—then there is only one character assignment for the central organism that fulfills this requirement. That choice is shown in Fig. 26. In general, the central character, referred to as a paleocyte, represents

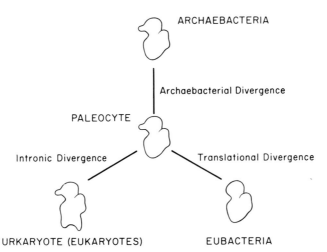

FIG. 26. Unrooted dendrogram representing the evolution of the three lineages. Ribosomal characters have been mapped on the tree. The central character, containing the bill and lacking the lobes, is the only solution that does not require multiple intro- duction of the bill or the lobes. Phylogenic data based on nucleotide differences (*1*) suggest that the divergences between any two of the three lineages are significantly deeper than they are within any single lineage. If this is true, then the characters labeled archaebacteria, eubacteria, and eukaryotes can be interpreted as corresponding to the single organisms that were ancestors to the three lineages. Adapted from Lake (89).

a now extinct organism that gave rise to two of the lineages. We cannot, however, predict which of the three ribosomal types is primitive, un- less we can root the dendrogram.

The unrooted tree clarifies some phylogenic relationships among the three lineages. Using the dendrogram as a guide, cellular proper- ties present in eubacteria but absent in archaebacteria and eukaryotes (urkaryotes) are interpreted as properties that were altered during the paleocyte-to-eubacterium transition. This branch of the dendrogram is referred to as the translational divergence because during this period the archaebacterial bill was modified. Similarly, features shared by archaebacteria and eubacteria, but not by urkaryotes, were altered dur- ing the paleocyte-to-urkaryote transition. This branch of the dendro- gram is referred to as the intronic divergence, because the lobes were modified during this period.

Understanding of ribosome structure has progressed in the last dec- ade. We now know the rudiments of ribosome structure and under- stand these for three cell types. We know where functional sites are, and we are starting to understand the domain structure of ribosomes. Furthermore, since our awareness of three distinct types of ribosomal architecture is increasing, workers in the field are in a position to start to decipher the events leading to the evolution of these alternative strategies of protein synthesis.

ACKNOWLEDGMENTS

I thank A. Kost, D. Williams, and J. Washizaki for excellent electron microscopy and photography. This work was supported by grants from the National Science Foundation and the National Institute of General Medical Sciences.

REFERENCES

1. J. A. Lake, *Sci. Am.* **245**, 84 (1981).
2a. H. E. Huxley and G. Zubay, *JMB* **2**, 10 (1960).
2b. C. E. Hall and H. S. Slayter, *JMB* **1**, 329 (1959).
3. J. A. Lake and H. S. Slayter, *Nature* **227**, 1032 (1970).
4. P. N. T. Unwin, *Nature* **269**, 118 (1977).
5. M. R. Wabl, *JMB* **84**, 241 (1974).
6. J. A. Lake, M. Pendergast, L. Kahan, and M. Nomura, *PNAS* **71**, 4688 (1974).
7. G. W. Tischendorf, M. Zeichardt, and G. Stöffler, *Mol. Gen. Genet.* **134**, 187 (1974).
8. J. A. Lake, D. D. Sabatini, and Y. Nonomura, *in* "Ribosomes" (M. Nomura, A. Tissieres, and P. Lengyel, eds.), p. 543. Cold Spring Harbor Laboratory, Cold Spring Harbor, New York, 1974.
9. J. A. Lake and L. Kahan, *JMB* **99**, 631 (1975).
10. V. D. Vasiliev, *Acta Biol. Med. Germ.* **33**, 779 (1974).
11. M. Boublik and W. Hellmann, *PNAS* **75**, 2829 (1978).
12. I. Emanuilov, D. D. Sabatini, J. A. Lake, and C. Freienstein, *PNAS* **75**, 1389 (1978).
13. D. G. Schindler, J. A. Langer, D. M. Engelman, and P. B. Moore, *JMB* **134**, 595 (1979).
14. J. A. Lake, *JMB* **105**, 131 (1976).
15. M. Boublik, W. Hellmann, and H. E. Roth, *JMB* **107**, 479 (1976).
16. I. N. Shatsky, A. G. Evstafieva, A. A. Bystrova, A. A. Bogdanov, and V. D. Vasiliev, *FEBS Lett.* **121**, 97 (1980).
17. E. R. Dabbs, R. Ehrlich, R. Hasenbank, B.-H. Schroeter, M. Stöffler-Meilicke, and G. Stöffler, *JMB* **149**, 553 (1981).
18. G. W. Tischendorf, H. Zeichhardt, and G. Stöffler, *PNAS* **72**, 4820 (1975).
19. M. Boublik, W. Hellmann, and H. E. Roth, *JMB* **107**, 479 (1976).
20. J. A. Lake, *JMB* **161**, 89 (1982).
21. C. Bernabeu and J. A. Lake, *JMB* **160**, 369 (1982).
22. B. Kastner, M. Stöffler-Meilicke, and G. Stöffler, *PNAS* **78**, 6652 (1981).
23. L. Kahan, D. A. Winkelmann, and J. A. Lake, *JMB* **145**, 193 (1981).
24. D. Winkelmann, L. Kahan, and J. A. Lake, *PNAS* **79**, 5189 (1982).
25. W. A. Strycharz, M. Nomura, and J. A. Lake, *JMB* **126**, 123 (1978).
26. J. A. Lake and W. A. Strycharz, *JMB* **153**, 979 (1981).
27. G. W. Tischendorf, H. Zeichhardt, and G. Stöffler, *PNAS* **72**, 4820 (1975).
28. P. B. Moore, D. M. Engelman, J. A. Langer, V. R. Ramakrishnan, D. G. Schindler, B. P. Schoenborn, I.-Y. Siller, and S. Yabuki, *in* "Brookhaven National Laboratories Neutron Symposium" (1982).
29. P. B. Moore, *in* "Ribosomes, Structure, Function and Genetics" (G. Chambliss, G. R.

Craven, J. Davies, K. Davis, L. Kahan, and M. Nomura, eds.), p. 111. Univ. Park Press, Baltimore, Maryland, 1979.
30. V. R. Ramakrishnan, S. Yabuki, I.-Y. Sillers, D. G. Schindler, D. M. Engelman, and P. B. Moore, *JMB* **153**, 739 (1981).
31. C. Bernabeu and J. A. Lake, *PNAS* **79**, 3111 (1982).
32. M. Nomura, S. Mizushima, M. Ozaki, P. Traub, and C. V. Lowry, *CSHSQB* **34**, 49 (1969).
33. H. F. Noller, C. Chang, G. Thomas, and J. Aldridge, *JMB* **61**, 669 (1971).
34. D. P. Rummel and H. F. Noller, *Nature NB* **245**, 72 (1973).
35. L. Gorini, *Nature NB* **234**, 261 (1971).
36. P. Anderson, J. Davies, and B. D. Davis, *JMB* **29**, 203 (1967).
37. L. C. Gorini, *CSHSQB* **34**, 101 (1969).
38. M. Kuwano, H. Endo, and Y. Ohrishi, *J. Bact.* **97**, 940 (1969).
39. J. A. Lake, *in* "Transfer RNA: Structure, Properties and Recognition" (J. Abelson *et al.*, eds.), p. 393. Cold Spring Harbor Laboratory, Cold Spring Harbor, New York, 1979.
40. B. S. Cooperman, *in* "Bioorganic Chemistry: A Treatise to Supplement *Bioorganic Chemistry*, an International Journal" (E. E. van Tamelen, ed.), Vol. 4, p. 81. Academic Press, New York, 1978.
41. J. Shine and L. Dalgarno, *Nature* **254**, 34 (1975).
42. S. M. Politz and D. G. Glitz, *PNAS* **74**, 1468 (1977).
43. M. Keren-Zur, M. Boublik, and J. Ofengand, *PNAS* **76**, 1054 (1979).
44. R. L. Heimark, L. Kahan, K. Johnston, J. W. B. Hershey and R. R. Traut, *JMB* **105**, 219 (1976).
45. J. Van Duin, C. G. Kurland, J. Dandon, and M. Grunberg-Manago, *FEBS Lett.* **59**, 287 (1975).
46. A. Bollen, R. L. Heimark, A. Cozzone, R. R. Traut, J. W. B. Hershey, and L. Kahan, *JBC* **250**, 4310 (1975).
47. S. Langberg, L. Kahan, R. R. Traut, and J. W. B. Hershey, *JMB* **117**, 307 (1977).
48. I. Schwartz and L. Kahan, personal communication.
49. W. Möller, *in* "Ribosomes" (M. Nomura, A. Tissieres, and P. Lengyel, eds.), p. 711. Cold Spring Harbor Laboratory, Cold Spring Harbor, New York, 1974.
50. H. Weissbach and S. Pestka, eds., "Molecular Mechanisms of Protein Biosynthesis." Academic Press, New York, 1977.
51. A. S. Girshovich, T. V. Kurtskhalia, Y. A. Ovchinnikov, and V. D. Vasiliev, *FEBS Lett.* **130**, 54 (1981).
52. A. S. Acharya, P. B. Moore, and F. M. Richards, *Bchem* **12**, 3108 (1973).
53. C. San Jose, C. G. Kurland, and G. Stöffler, *FEBS Lett.* **71**, 133 (1976).
54. D. Marquis, S. Fahnestock, E. Henderson, D. Woo, S. Schwinge, M. Clark, and J. A. Lake, *JMB* **150**, 121 (1981).
55. A. T. Matheson, R. N. Nazar, G. E. Willick, and M. Yaguchi, *in* "Genetics and Evolution of RNA Polymerases, tRNA and Ribosomes (S. Osawa, H. Ozeki, H. Uchida, and T. Yura, eds.), p. 625. Univ. of Tokyo Press, Tokyo, 1980.
56. J. A. Lake, *in* "Ribosomes, Structure, Function and Genetics" (G. Chambliss, G. R. Craven, J. Davies, K. Davis, L. Kahan, and M. Nomura, eds.), p. 207. Univ. Park Press, Baltimore, Maryland, 1979.
57. R. R. Traut, R. L. Heimark, T.-T. Sun, J. W. B. Hershey, and A. Bollen, *in* "Ribosomes" (M. Nomura, A. Tissieres, and P. Lengyel, eds.), p. 271. Cold Spring Harbor Laboratory, Cold Spring Harbor, New York, 1974.

58. B. S. Cooperman, *in* "Bioorganic Chemistry: A Treatise to Supplement *Bioorganic Chemistry*, an International Journal" (E. E. van Tamelen, ed.), Vol. 4, p. 81. Academic Press, New York, 1978.
59. H. M. Olson, P. G. Grant, B. S. Cooperman, and D. H. Glitz, *JBC* **257**, 2649 (1982).
60. M. Stöffler-Merlicke, G. Stöffler, O. W. Odom, A. Zinn, G. Kramer, and B. Hardesty, *PNAS* **78**, 5538 (1981).
61. M. Clark, Ph.D. Thesis, University of California, Los Angeles, 1982.
62. I. N. Shatsky, A. G. Evstafieva, T. F. Bystrova, A. A. Bogdanov, and V. D. Vasiliev, *FEBS Lett.* **121**, 97 (1980).
63. P. Leder, *Adv. Protein Chem.* **27**, 213 (1973).
64. Y. Kaziro, *BBA* **505**, 95 (1978).
65. J. A. Lake, *PNAS* **74**, 1903 (1977).
66. I. G. Wool, *ARB* **48**, 719 (1979).
67. H. Bielka and J. Stahl, *in* "International Review of Biochemistry Amino Acid and Protein Biosynthesis" (V. Arnstein, ed.), p. 79. Univ. Park Press, Baltimore, Maryland, 1978.
68. Y. Nonomura, G. Blobel, and D. D. Sabatini, *JMB* **60**, 303 (1971).
69. J. A. Lake and H. S. Slayter *JMB* **66**, 271 (1972).
70. M. Lubin, *PNAS* **61**, 1454 (1968).
71. M. Boublik and W. Hellmann, *PNAS* **75**, 2829 (1978).
72. G. Lutsch, F. Noll, H. Theise, G. Enzmann, and H. Bielka, *Mol. Gen. Genet.* **176**, 281 (1979).
73. C. Bernabeu, E. Tobin, A. Fowler, I. Zabin, and J. A. Lake, *J. Cell Biol.* **96**, 1471 (1983).
74. P. Siekevitz, and G. E. Palade, *J. Biophys. Biochem. Cytol.* **7**, 619 (1960).
75. C. M. Redman and D. D. Sabatini, *PNAS* **56**, 608 (1966).
76. M. R. Adelman, D. D. Sabatini, and G. Blobel, *J. Cell Biol.* **56**, 206 (1973).
77. D. D. Sabatini and G. Kreibich, *in* "The Enzymes of Biological Membranes" (A. Martonosi, ed.), Vol. 2, p. 531. Plenum, New York, 1976.
78. N. H. Chua, G. Blobel, P. Siekevitz, and G. E. Palade, *J. Cell Biol.* **71**, 497 (1976).
79. P. Walter and G. Blobel, *Nature* **299**, 691 (1982).
80. C. Taddei, *Exp. Cell Res.* **70**, 285 (1972).
81. P. N. T. Unwin and C. Taddei, *JMB* **114**, 491 (1977).
82. P. N. T. Unwin, *JMB* **132**, 69 (1979).
83. J. A. Lake, *in* "Electron Microscopy of Proteins" (J. R. Harris, ed.), Vol. 1, p. 167. Academic Press, New York, 1981.
84. C. R. Woese and G. E. Fox, *PNAS* **74**, 5088 (1977).
85. G. E. Fox, L. J. Magrumg, W. Balch, R. S. Wolfe, and C. R. Woese, *PNAS* **74**, 4537 (1977).
86. C. Sapienza and W. F. Doolittle, *Nature* **295**, 384 (1982).
87. C. R. Woese, *Sci. Am.* **244**, 98 (1981).
88. R. E. Dickerson, *Nature* **283**, 210 (1980).
89. J. A. Lake, E. Henderson, M. C. Clark, and A. Matheson, *PNAS* **79**, 5948 (1982).
90. U.-A. Bommerg, F. Noll, G. Lutsch, and H. Bielka, *FEBS Lett.* **111**, 171 (1980).
91. W. Kuhlbrandt and P. N. I. Unwin, *JMB* **156**, 431 (1982).
92. J. W. Shopf, *in* "Exobiology—Frontiers of Biology," Vol. 23, p. 16. Elsevier/North-Holland, Amsterdam, 1972.
93. W. F. Doolittle, *TIBS* **5**, 146 (1980).

Analysis of the Expression of Genes Encoding Animal mRNA by *in Vitro* Techniques

JAMES L. MANLEY

*Department of Biology,
Columbia University,
New York, New York*

Enormous progress in our understanding of eukaryotic gene expression has been made since 1977. In many cases, what we have learned has been quite surprising. For example, the genes that encode mRNAs, as well as many others, are frequently separated from one another by intervening sequences (*1–3*), and some genes (those transcribed by RNA polymerase III) contain internal promoters (*4, 5*), while others (those transcribed by RNA polymerases II and, probably, I) contain promoters that are more analogous to what we have come to expect from studies with prokaryotic systems; i.e., they are located in DNA sequences that lie in the 5′ direction from the transcribed region (*6–8*). However, even here, there are surprises. An example is the discovery, in several systems, of sequences called activators, or enhancers, which appear to increase the efficiency with which nearby promoters are utilized (*9–11*). The mechanism by which these elements function is unknown, but it is probably unlike anything uncovered in bacterial systems.

195

Progress in Nucleic Acid Research
and Molecular Biology, Vol. 30

Several factors are responsible for this sudden proliferation of knowledge. Perhaps not unexpectedly, the majority of these are technical advances bringing to eukaryotes methods that for many years have been of great use in studies of bacterial systems. For example, the ability to purify and amplify specific eukaryotic genes by recombinant DNA methodologies (12), and then to reintroduce these genes into cells (13, 14), has provided students of eukaryotic systems with a technique that is in many ways analogous to bacteriophage transduction. Likewise, site-specific *in vitro* mutagenesis techniques (4, 15, 16) have brought much of the power of molecular genetics to eukaryotic systems. Finally, the development of *in vitro* systems derived from mammalian cells that accurately reproduce many of the steps involved in RNA synthesis has begun to provide insights into the mechanisms and enzymology of gene expression and regulation (17–19). Similar systems from prokaryotes have been available for many years and have provided a wealth of information (20).

In this article, I discuss almost exclusively studies on genes that are transcribed by RNA polymerase II; i.e., genes that, for the most part, give rise to mRNAs. In the first part, I review what we know about the mechanisms and pathways of mRNA synthesis, concentrating on what has been learned from *in vitro* systems. Very little is known about the molecular mechanisms by which the expression of mammalian genes is regulated, but what little we have learned is also discussed here. The second part of the article deals with the genetics of mRNA synthesis; in particular, advances that have arisen from the application of *in vitro* mutagenesis technology will be emphasized. Studies on genes transcribed by other polymerases (e.g., nuclear RNA polymerases I and III, and various viral RNA polymerases) are discussed only to the extent that they complement or extend conclusions obtained from RNA polymerase II systems. Readers unfamiliar with the basic structure of nuclear RNA polymerases are referred to reviews by Roeder (21) and Chambon (22). In addition, several reviews that explore in greater detail some of the subjects described here have appeared (23–25).

I. The Mechanism of Gene Expression: Analysis Using *in Vitro* Transcription Systems

A. Initiation

In prokaryotes (and likewise with RNA polymerase III transcripts), the nucleotide at which transcription begins can be identified biochemically by the presence of a 5′ triphosphate group on the RNA chain. RNA polymerase II-catalyzed transcripts, however, are apparently without exception, "capped" at their 5' ends (26 see also 26a). Thus an important question has been whether such "caps" represent points of transcription initiation, or whether caps might be added posttranscriptionally, following endonuclytic cleavage of transcripts that had initiated further upstream. With one possible exception, the answer appears to be that caps correspond to points of initiation of transcription. The first strong support for this notion was provided by an examination of the 5' terminus of nuclear RNA synthesized from the adenovirus late transcription unit (27; see Fig. 1 for a map of the adenovirus genome). This study showed that, although an RNase T1-generated oligonucleotide corresponding to the capped 5' end of the RNA could be obtained in readily detectable yields after a three-hour pulse-label with [³²P]orthophosphate, RNase T1 oligonucleotides predicted from the DNA sequence that would be encoded *upstream* of the cap site could not be detected at all. This result strongly suggests that transcription begins at the nucleotide that ultimately becomes capped,

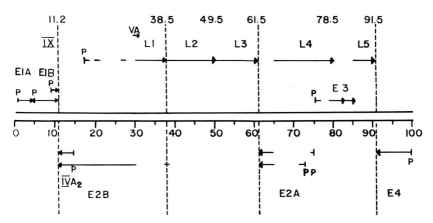

FIG. 1. Transcriptional map of human adenovirus. The adenovirus genome consists of a linear double-stranded DNA molecule approximately 36,000 base-pairs (nucleotides) in length. The map shown here is quite simplified and does not indicate the multiple mRNA species derived from many of the transcription units. P indicates a promoter site, and an arrowhead indicates an mRNA polyadenylylation site. Early regions are indicated E1 through E4. Two small genes, IX and IVA$_2$, are expressed at intermediate-to-late times. The promoter for the late transcription unit is located at 16.5 map units and directs transcription rightward. The common tripartite leader and the five mRNA families (L1–L5) are indicated. VA indicates the map position of the two small virus-associated RNAs, the syntheses of which are catalyzed by RNA polymerase III. The dashed vertical lines indicate where RNA processing signals are encoded in close proximity on each of the DNA strands. The genome is divided into 100 map units; 1 map unit = 360 base-pairs.

although very rapid turnover of a longer precursor could not be ruled out.

Similar results were obtained using DNA-dependent *in vitro* transcription systems (*28*). In particular, when a recombinant plasmid that contains the Ad2 late promoter was digested with a restriction enzyme that cleaves the DNA 52 base-pairs upstream from the apparent RNA initiation site (i.e., the cap site), normal levels of specific transcription were obtained, suggesting that, if a precursor does exist, it must initiate within about 50 pairs of the RNA cap site. Further, even after very short incubations, transcripts larger than those expected (i.e., if initiation had occurred upstream of the cap site) were not detected (*28*). Since no RNA processing was detected in this *in vitro* system (see Section I,C), these results strongly support the idea that, in this case at least, initiation occurs at the nucleotide that subsequently becomes capped.

A more direct means of addressing this question stems from the observation that nuclear caps (as opposed to those found at the 5′ ends of certain viral mRNAs that are synthesized by viral polymerases and capping enzymes) are formed by the condensation of the α-phosphate of GTP with the β-phosphate of the 5′ terminal residue of the RNA chain (*29*). This means that, in theory, the only way a β-phosphate can be incorporated into an RNA chain is at the initiation step, since a nuclear kinase that will transfer a β-phosphate to a 5′-OH or 5′-monophosphate RNA terminus has not been reported. Thus, using nuclei isolated from monkey cells infected with SV40, or infected cells that had been treated with lysolecithin to render them permeable to nucleotide triphosphates, it has been shown that both SV40 early and late mRNAs incorporate the β-phosphate from ribonucleotide triphosphate precursors almost exclusively into their 5′ cap structures (*30–32*). Similar studies using a soluble whole-cell DNA-dependent transcription system that had previously been shown to cap newly synthesized transcripts efficiently (*19, 33*) indicate that β-phosphate can be incorporated specifically into the 5′ cap structures of the Ad2 late and human β-globin transcripts (*34*).

Another line of evidence derives from the observation that, in at least several instances, the capped 5′ end of an mRNA can be heterogeneous (see below). Since this heterogeneity can be detected in the *in vitro* synthesized mRNAs, it is possible to ask if experimental manipulations that might be expected to alter transcription initiation frequencies can influence the distribution of capped 5′ ends. For example, since transcripts of adenovirus early region IV contain either A or U as the penultimate nucleoside (*35*), one can ask whether varying the concentrations of ATP and UTP added to *in vitro* reaction mixtures results in a change in the ratio of "A caps" to "U caps." When this experiment was done, it was apparent that increasing the ratio of ATP to UTP led to relatively more A caps, and vice versa (*36*). This result argues strongly that the cap sites are in fact the sites at which transcription initiation occurs. Similar results have been obtained in an analysis of *in vitro* transcription of the polyoma virus early region (*37*).

Very little is known about the actual mechanism by which transcription initiates. If we assume that the equivalence of cap site and transcription start site is a general one (the only possible exception detected to date, which may be a special case, is discussed in the following section), then it appears that, as is the case in prokaryotes, the predominant initiating nucleotides are purines, with adenosine by far the most common. However, both cytosine (*31, 37*) and uridine (*35*–*37*) starts have also been detected.

The 5′ termini of the transcripts of many genes, both viral and cellular, are heterogeneous; that is, transcription appears to begin not at just one nucleotide, but rather at several. The molecular mechanisms responsible for this phenomenon are not clear, nor is it known what function(s), if any, such heterogeneity might serve. The first and probably most common form of this is a microheterogeneity in which the start of transcription appears to occur at one of several adjacent, or clustered, nucleotides. Such microheterogeneity has been detected in SV40 (*31*) and polyoma (*37*) early-region transcripts, a variety of adenoviral transcripts (*35, 38*), and several cellular transcripts, including those from chicken ovalbumin (*39*) and lysozyme genes (*40*). A possible explanation for this type of heterogeneity is that RNA polymerase, bound to the DNA at a promotor site (see Section II,A), "measures" a distance along the DNA, after which transcription begins. This distance is probably not completely precise, and at exactly which nucleotide transcription begins most likely depends, in ways not completely clear, on the nucleotide sequence around the start site.

An interesting observation was made during analysis of the microheterogeneity of the polyoma virus early-region transcripts (*37*): nucleotide sequence analysis showed that several of the mRNA 5′ ends were not colinear with the viral DNA sequence. A model consistent with the explanation for heterogeneity just described was presented. It suggests that, after polymerization of the first three or four nucleotides, elongation can be aborted, and polymerase, still bound to the promoter, can "slip" backward on the DNA. At this point, another attempt at initiation is made. The previously synthesized oligonucleotide is not released from the polymerase, but, rather, is used as a primer for this second start. The nucleotide sequences obtained are consistent with this model.

Another type of heterogeneity cannot be explained by the mechanism described above. Some mRNAs contain 5′ heterogeneity extending over a region of considerably more than several nucleotides. This structure was first, and most dramatically, observed in transcripts of the SV40 late region (41–43). The capped 5′ ends of late viral mRNAs (of which there appear to be as many as a dozen) extend over a distance of nearly 300 nucleotides. Similar results have been obtained with polyoma virus late transcripts (44), as well as with at least two cellular mRNAs (40, 45); however, in both these cases, the heterogeneity is limited to a region of about 50 nucleotides. As mentioned above, both the mechanism of synthesis and the significance of this macroheterogeneity are unknown. At least two types of models exist that can explain these results. In one, it is proposed that multiple, perhaps overlapping, promoters direct transcription initiation at different start sites (46). An alternative model suggests that there is only one promoter, or, more precisely, only one RNA polymerase binding site, located upstream from the RNA start sites. For reasons unclear, transcription in these cases does not begin a set number of nucleotides downstream. Rather, the polymerase may "wander," or "scan" the downstream DNA for acceptable initiation sites. Note that this would require migration of the polymerase along the DNA in the absence of RNA polymerization. Genetic evidence that might bear on these models is discussed below.

Readers familiar with prokaryotic transcription studies (e.g., 47) will note that many basic and important questions are not addressed in the above discussion. No mention is made, for example, of open or closed promoter complexes, of the existence of specificity factors analogous to σ, or of a description of the DNA sequences with which RNA polymerase interacts during initiation. The reasons are that experiments addressing these questions are not yet really feasible. Two factors are primarily responsible for this. First, specific *in vitro* transcription is very inefficient. Even with the strongest promoters, at most about 10% of the DNA templates are transcribed once. This makes experiments such as DNA "footprinting" extremely difficult to perform. Second, to obtain specific transcription requires a complex mixture of factors, since purified eukaryotic RNA polymerases are incapable of specific initiation (e.g., 47, 47a). However, several groups are making significant progress in fractionation and identification of the factors required for transcription initiation (48–50). It is thus likely that questions similar to those just mentioned, if not answered, will at least be testable within a few years.

B. Capping and Methylation

The 5' ends of all RNA polymerase II products studied to date contain cap structures (general structure: ^{7}mGpppNm-Nm); see 26, 26a for review). Caps play an important role in determining the translation efficiencies of mRNAs as well as contributing to mRNA stability. In this section, I do not deal with the function of caps on mature mRNAs. Rather, I consider experiments that address such questions as: When does capping occur during the course of mRNA synthesis? and What role does capping play during transcription initiation? In addition to methylations at their 5' ends (which are considered here as part of the cap structure), mRNAs also contain internal methylated residues (at the N^6 position of some adenosine residues; e.g., 51, 52). What little is known about the significance of these modifications is also discussed here.

All indications suggest that capping occurs very early during mRNA synthesis. Analysis of pulse-labeled, size-fractionated hnRNA molecules from Chinese hamster ovary cells revealed that short (less than 750 nucleotides in length) transcripts contained cap structures (53). No label was incorporated into the caps of longer RNA species, consistent with the idea that such molecules had already been capped. Although pppG and pppA structures could be detected in the short RNAs, these are probably derived from the 5' ends of RNAs transcribed by RNA polymerase III, such as 5 S RNA. This assumption is supported by a separate study (54) that used similar techniques to analyze short adenovirus-specific transcripts. In this work, short, nascent transcripts initiated from the major late promoter were first purified by hybridization to a promoter-proximal DNA restriction fragment. Subsequent analysis of the RNA 5' ends revealed that even the smallest RNAs detected (approximately 70 nucleotides long) are quantitatively capped.

Similar conclusions were reached from an analysis of RNA synthesized *in vitro* in nuclei that had been isolated from Ad2-infected HeLa cells (55). Equimolar amounts of label were incorporated into the m^{7}G cap and into each of the first dozen or so nucleotides in the major late transcript. Since 80–90% of the transcription that occurs in this isolated-nuclei system is elongation of nascent chains that had been initiated *in vivo*, this result also argues that capping occurs very early during transcription. (If long nascent chains, or completed transcripts, could be capped, a greater than equimolar amount of label would have been detected in m^{7}G.) In addition, uncapped 5' ends have not been detected in RNA synthesized from the Ad2 major late promoter in soluble DNA-dependent *in vitro* transcription systems (e.g., 18, 19).

Finally, a study of *in vitro* transcripts obtained from cytoplasmic polyhedrosis virus (a double-stranded RNA virus that encodes its own RNA polymerase and capping enzymes) indicates that, in this system, capping is actually a "pretranscriptional" event; i.e., GTP is condensed onto the initiating A residue to form GpppA before transcription commences, and this event is in fact necessary for transcription to proceed (56).

These results have led to speculation that perhaps transcription initiation by RNA polymerase II is linked to cap formation. Consistent with this idea are results that show that transcription initiation on exogenously added DNA by RNA polymerase II contained in a whole-cell extract is specifically inhibited by S-adenosylhomocysteine (57). Since this compound is an inhibitor of methyl group transfer reactions, such as methylations of mRNA caps, these results suggest that RNA polymerase II forms an initiation complex with the enzymes involved in cap formation, and that capping and initiation are linked. However, this finding does not necessarily suggest that these events are obligatorily linked. In fact, it appears that, in at least one case, transcription initiation *in vitro* can occur in the absence of capping. Transcripts from one early region on the Ad2 genome (early region IV) can initiate *in vitro* (36) and *in vivo* (35) at any nucleotide in the sequence 5'-TTTTTTA-3'. In contrast to all other 5' termini that have been studied, a fraction of the transcripts produced *in vitro* are not capped [based on the observation that these RNAs can be labeled by treatment with alkaline phosphatase and polynucleotide kinase without prior decapping (36)]. This observation suggests that these transcripts are initiated without being capped, although the possibility that, for some reason, initially capped RNAs are decapped during the transcription reaction cannot be excluded.

Direct evidence that initiation can occur in the oligo(T)-stretch without capping was obtained in another study that examined the 5' end structure of EIV RNA (see Fig. 1) synthesized *in vitro* in the presence of a nonhydrolyzable analog of UTP, (β,γ imido)UTP (58). This analog can serve as a precursor for RNA synthesis, but should be "uncappable," owing to the nature of the β-γ linkage. As expected, if capping and initiation are not obligatorily coupled, uncapped, triphosphorylated 5' ends were detected. However, one caveat must be raised concerning the generality of this finding: The DNA sequence at the initiation site for EIV transcription is so unusual that the possibility that initiation occurs here by a different mechanism than is used at other sites cannot be discounted.

As discussed in the preceding section, cap sites appear to correspond to transcription initiation sites. One possible exception to this rule is a class of small nuclear RNAs, the U1 RNAs (59).[1] These RNAs (164 nucleotides in length; 60) are produced by RNA polymerase II transcription. Unlike all other known RNA polymerase II products, these transcripts do not encode protein. The RNA does not contain a poly(A) segment at its 3' end, but does contain a capped 5' end. However, instead of the usual N^7-methylguanosine cap, these RNAs contain N^2,N^2,N^7-trimethylguanosine caps. Recent results (61) suggest that this cap may not represent the point of transcription initiation in these genes. When a cloned human U1 RNA gene was microinjected into *Xenopus laevis* nuclei, authentic U1 RNA was produced. However, when the same cloned gene was transcribed *in vitro* in a HeLa whole-cell extract, an RNA species that had initiated 183 nucleotides upstream of the authentic 5' end was the only species detected. Transcription initiation from this site was relatively efficient, and the product contained a normal m^7G cap. One explanation of these results is that transcription begins at the site utilized *in vitro*, but *in vivo* this RNA is efficiently processed (by cleavage and recapping). However, a precursor–product relationship must be established in order to prove this model.

In addition to cap methylations, mammalian mRNAs contain internal methylated bases. In particular, approximately 1–2% of adenosine residues are methylated at the N^6 position. One study has followed the fate of such methylations during biogenesis of Ad2 late mRNAs (62). The results showed that these methylations are introduced early during mRNA synthesis and that they are conserved between nucleus and cytoplasm. These findings suggest that methylations occur primarily in RNA exons, at least in this system. There is no evidence at all as to what the function of this type of methylation might be. However, the fact that N^6 methylation can affect base-pairing by the modified residue raises the possibility that the translatability of the RNA may be affected.

The above discussion has emphasized experiments suggesting that capping occurs concomitantly with, or very shortly after, transcription initiation. Several arguments can be advanced to rationalize such a linkage. First, it may be necessary to protect the 5' ends of mRNA precursors from nuclear exonucleases that could conceivably act on even nascent RNA chains. That such nucleases exist is strongly suggested by the fact that much uncapped nuclear RNA appears to be very rapidly degraded. This includes excised exons, as well as RNA that lies

---

[1] See article by Reddy and Busch in this volume. [Eds.]

distal to mRNA 3′ end sites. (This is discussed in Section I,D.) Nothing
is known, however, about these hypothetical nucleases, primarily because suitable *in vitro* assays are not yet available. Another function
that early capping might serve is to prevent RNA species not destined
to receive caps from becoming capped. For example, transcripts produced by RNA polymerase III (e.g., tRNAs and 5 S RNA) do not become capped. Since, as far as we know, the site of synthesis of these
RNAs is not separated from the site of synthesis of RNA polymerase II
products, and since there does not appear to be a sequence of nucleotides at the end of an RNA that signals whether or not it should be
capped, the idea that capping enzymes form a complex with RNA
polymerase II, and that capping is thereby coupled to transcription
initiation, provides an attractive explanation for why only RNA
polymerase II products become capped. Finally, an intimate association between cap formation and transcription initiation could perhaps
provide an additional mechanism for regulating gene expression. Although no examples of this type of control have yet been described,
precedent suggests that wherever control can be effected, it is. Thus it
will not be surprising if examples of control of gene expression by
regulation of cap formation are uncovered.

C. Splicing

The phenomenon of mRNA splicing was discovered in the late
1970s (*1–3*).[2] The fact that most eukaryotic genes are "split" was at
first quite surprising and has revolutionized the way we think about
gene organization and expression. To obtain an understanding of the
molecular mechanism of RNA splicing has therefore been a goal of
many laboratories. It is thus somewhat surprising that virtually nothing
is known about the enzymology of mRNA splicing. This is in striking
contrast to the situation with tRNA splicing. In yeast, the enzymology
has been worked out in some detail (*63–66*). Two enzyme activities
have been identified and characterized. One, an endonuclease, is apparently associated with the nuclear membrane, as its purification requires that a nonionic detergent be present during extraction and fractionation. The other, a ligase, is in the particulate fraction, and requires
a high salt concentration for solubilization. The reaction mechanism
involves the formation of an unusual 2′-phosphate, 3′-5′ diester intermediate (*66*). While it is not yet clear whether higher eukaryotes splice
tRNA precursors by a similar mechanism, the observation that yeast
pre-tRNAs are accurately spliced in lysates of both *X. laevis* (*67*)

[2] See article by Aloni in Volume 25 (1981) of this series. [Eds.]

and HeLa (68) cells suggests that the enzymology is at least very similar.

In one species, the protozoan *Tetrahymena thermophilia,* the mechanism by which an rRNA precursor is spliced *in vitro* has been elucidated in some detail (69–71). Amazingly, the reaction is autocatalytic: neither ATP nor protein is required. The only requirements are mono- and divalent cations, and guanosine. Whether splicing of rRNA precursors in other organisms occurs in a similar fashion is not clear. Given the diversity of mRNAs in a cell, splicing of pre-mRNAs is unlikely to occur by this simple (and unprecedented) mechanism.

A first step in the above experiments was to establish conditions under which the splicing reaction could easily be detected *in vitro.* Studies on the mechanism of mRNA splicing remain at this first step: conditions yielding efficient and reproducible splicing of pre-mRNAs in cell lysates have not yet been described.

The earliest studies utilized isolated, intact nuclei to synthesize RNA, because soluble transcription systems were not available at the time. Most of this work involved the use of adenovirus as a model system, since this is where splicing was first detected, and, in the days before cloning, the fact that large amounts of DNA could be obtained was important. Two studies followed the fate of adenovirus-specific RNA (from early region II; 72) that had been pulse-labeled *in vivo* before isolation of nuclei (73, 74). During incubation of the isolated nuclei, the labeled pre-mRNA is apparently converted to mRNA by RNA splicing, as judged by size and hybridization analyses.

One other study suggests that splicing can occur in nuclei isolated from adenovirus-infected cells (75, 76). In this case, RNA synthesized (at least in part) *in vitro* was separated from endogenous RNA by the use of mercurated ribonucleoside triphosphate precursors. These precursors can be incorporated into RNA efficiently by RNA polymerase II, and the resultant RNA can then be separated from endogenous RNA by affinity chromatography on resins containing sulfhydryl groups. (That RNA so isolated is the product of RNA polymerase II transcription is suggested by the observation that mercurated RNA does not accumulate in the presence of low concentrations of α-amanitin.) Nuclease S1 analysis using ^{32}P-labeled DNA probes indicated that a substantial fraction of the newly synthesized RNA was spliced. Note that this method cannot differentiate between RNAs initiated *in vivo* and only elongated *in vitro,* and RNAs completely synthesized *in vitro.* Thus, if splicing of adenovirus mRNAs occurs primarily on nascent RNA chains, all the observed splicing may have taken place *in vivo*. Although such a result would indeed be of interest (see below), it is likely that a good deal of the observed splicing did in fact occur *in vitro*. However, reaction conditions that preferentially inhibit splicing, i.e., that allow uncoupling of transcription and splicing, have not been found.

This problem has largely prevented any progress being made with this system toward obtaining an understanding of the mechanism of mRNA splicing, with one important exception: the first evidence suggesting that U1 RNA might be involved in mRNA splicing came from studies with this system (77). The notion that this might be so originally arose from a comparison of nucleotide sequences. The five nucleotides at the 5' end of introns in higher eukaryotes are highly conserved, as are a similar number of nucleotides at the 3' end of introns (78–80). The nucleotide sequence at the 5' end of U1 RNA is such that base-pairs can be formed that would serve to bring together the 5' and 3' ends of introns to form a loop. Such base-pairing could serve to align adjacent exons for subsequent splicing (81, 82). Some individuals with the autoimmune disease systemic lupus erythematosus produce antibodies that will precipitate U1 RNA when it is contained in a ribonucleoprotein particle (snRNP). When anti-snRNP antibodies were added to the isolated nuclei system mentioned above, the accumulation of spliced RNAs (transcribed from the Ad2 early region IA) was prevented, while having little effect on the synthesis of primary transcripts. Also, it has been shown that splicing of RNA transcribed from SV40 DNA microinjected into *X. laevis* oocytes is inhibited by coinjection of anti-snRNP antibodies (82a). These results are particularly striking because, in the absence of antibody, the SV40 RNA was nearly quantitatively spliced, but in its presence, splicing was almost completely blocked. Only uncleaved precursor RNA was detectable, and the total amount of SV40 RNA that accumulated was not altered.

These studies suggest an involvement of U1 RNA in splicing. However, since the antibody used was total IgG, the possibility that the observed inhibition was due to another unrelated antibody cannot at this time be rigorously excluded. An experiment using monoclonal antibodies could overcome this objection, as would a demonstration that the inhibition could be blocked by addition of purified snRNP particles.

Another series of experiments has also examined the structure of adenovirus specific RNA synthesized in isolated nuclei (55, 83, 84). In particular, these studies showed that transcripts from the late transcription unit can accurately be initiated, capped, and methylated *in vitro.* In addition, RNA 3′ ends were efficiently created, in some cases by a specific endonucleolytic cleavage followed by polyadenylylation (see next section). However, no evidence was obtained suggesting that RNA splicing could occur in the isolated nuclei. It remains unclear why some studies with isolated nuclei found that splicing continues efficiently *in vitro,* whereas others found that splicing is blocked upon cell lysis. One obvious explanation is a difference in the preparation of nuclei. However, this is probably not the cause of the discrepancy, since attempts by the later authors to produce "splicing" nuclei by adhering to the procedures of Yang and Flint (76, 77) only produced "nonsplicing" nuclei (J. L. M., unpublished data). The only consistent difference appears to be the method used for RNA analysis. In contrast to the previously discussed work, the experiments of Manley *et al.* (83, 84) analyzed the structure of the *in vitro* synthesized RNA directly: newly synthesized RNA was labeled by the use of ribonucleoside [^{32}P]triphosphates, and the structure of the RNA was determined by nuclease S1 analysis using unlabeled DNA probes.

Even though mRNA splicing does not appear to occur in this system (83, 84), an important observation concerning the mechanism of splicing was nonetheless made. A large fraction (approximately 50%) of the RNA synthesized *in vitro* from the late transcription unit has, in fact, undergone a splice, the one that joins the first, promoter proximal leader segment to the second segment of the tripartite leader (see Fig. 1). However, no evidence could be obtained that this splice occurred *in vitro* (i.e., kinetic or pulse–chase analysis did not reveal any increase in the relative concentration of this species). These observations suggest that the splice may have taken place *in vivo* on nascent RNA chains, which were subsequently elongated *in vitro* to produce the labeled molecules. In support of this idea are the observations that this species has been detected in poly(A)$^-$ as well as poly(A)$^+$ RNA, and that the amount of the spliced species was apparently greatly reduced, relative to primary transcript, when small DNA probes were used. (This portion of the RNA would not be labeled had it been synthesized *in vivo.*)

Thus these results strongly suggest that mRNA splicing, at least in one instance, can occur not only before polyadenylylation, but actually on nascent RNA chains. This view is in contrast to earlier ideas suggesting that polyadenylylation precedes splicing (e.g., 85, 86). The simplest explanation is one based on kinetics: if we assume that splicing is slow relative to transcription or 3′-end formation, then the probability of whether a particular splice will occur on a nascent RNA chain will be a function of the length of the transcription unit and whether the splice to be made involves squences at the 5' or 3' end of the RNA. In addition, the "strength" of the recognition signal for the presumptive splicing enzymes will also be important. [No evidence is yet available that addresses the question of whether some splice sites are intrinsically more efficiently utilized, or "stronger," than others. However, all previous examples in which a particular protein recognizes a conserved nucleotide sequence (e.g., RNA polymerase promoter sequences) provide precedents that suggest that this will be the case.] Thus, the first-to-second leader splice in Ad2 late RNA is at the 5' end of a relatively long (25000-base) transcription unit. If the splice-site sequence is "strong," then these facts would be sufficient to explain why this splice, but not others in this primary transcript, occurs on nascent chains. In support of this notion that splicing can precede polyadenylylation, and in fact occurs on nascent chains, are experiments showing that splicing proceeds unabated *in vivo* in the presence of cordycepin, an adenosine analog that inhibits polyadenylylation (87). Also, electron micrographs of actively transcribed chromatin show breaks and loops in the classical "Christmas tree" structure, which can be interpreted as sites at which splicing occurs (88).

As should by now be apparent, isolated nuclei are of limited value in deciphering the mechanism of mRNA splicing. The reactions all still occur in membrane-delimited space and are dependent on transcription of endogenous DNA. It was thus obvious that conditions under which pre-mRNAs could be spliced in a soluble cell-extract would have to be found. However, before this could even be attempted, a source of suitable precursors was required. Pre-mRNAs are so rapidly processed *in vivo* that it is extremely difficult to obtain sufficient amounts of precursor by purifying nuclear RNAs from cells. It was thus very promising when soluble, DNA-dependent transcription systems were developed that would accurately and specifically initiate transcription of mRNA-encoding genes, cap and methylate the RNA 5' ends, and elongate the RNA chains for considerable distances (18, 19). Although the RNA synthesized under conditions optimized for transcription initiation was not modified to detectable levels by RNA splicing (e.g., 89), it was felt that either alternative conditions of extract preparation or incubation could be found that would bring about splicing in a coupled transcription-splicing system, or else the unspliced RNA could be purified and used as a substrate in a second *in vitro* reaction. Unfortunately, despite some preliminary successes, progress toward fulfilling these expectations has been disappointingly slow.

To date, three reports present evidence that mRNA splicing can occur in soluble cell-lysates. In all three, the conditions of extract preparation and *in vitro* incubation were very similar to those used to obtain DNA-dependent transcription (*19*). In one (*90*), concentrated whole-cell lysates prepared from HeLa cells were used to transcribe cloned adenovirus genes. When a plasmid containing early region III was used as the DNA template, a high fraction of the RNA synthesized had a structure consistent with that of correctly spliced RNA. However, the assay used (S1 analysis with 5' end-labeled DNA and alkaline agarose gels) is by itself at best able only to suggest that the RNA had been cleaved at or near the 3' splice acceptor site. Additional data that would confirm whether or not splicing had occurred have not yet been presented.

In another series of experiments (*91*), whole-cell lysates were prepared from mouse myeloma cells, rather than HeLa cells, and data were obtained suggesting that such lysates can splice mRNA precursors. (The authors stated that, although active extracts could be obtained from HeLa cells, the splicing activity was more stable if myeloma cells were used.) In this case, the precursor used was obtained from the nuclei of adenovirus-infected HeLa cells; specifically, transcripts of early region II, which encodes the 72-kDa DNA-binding protein, were used. Evidence that splicing had occurred was based on size and S1 analyses. Although the evidence presented was, for the most part, convincing, it has proved to be difficult to pursue this line of study. This is because, as mentioned above, it is very difficult to obtain sufficient amounts of precursors synthesized *in vivo*. In the experiments described, it was often necessary to use the RNA obtained from 1 liter of infected cells (5×10^8 cells) in a single experiment.

Finally, there is evidence suggesting that the coupled transcription-splicing of human β-globin RNA can occur *in vitro* (*92*). Again, concentrated HeLa whole-cell lysates were used. Although the level of splicing was quite low (much less than 10% of the transcribed RNA appeared to be spliced), the evidence that splicing had occurred was the most convincing that has been presented to date: the sequence of the RNA across the splice junction was determined and was shown to be identical with that of authentic globin mRNA.

The above experiments show that, although some promising first steps have been taken, the study of mRNA splicing remains in its infancy. It is appropriate to conclude this section by asking why it has been so difficult to obtain mRNA splicing *in vitro*.

Several explanations, not mutually exclusive, can be advanced to explain why mRNA splicing has been so intractable to experimental analysis. First, it is possible that some protein or factor is being lost or destroyed during cell lysis and fractionation. Although the extracts currently in use are very crude and designed to retain a maximum number of components, a number of steps are involved in their preparation. It is easy to imagine, that, if a particular enzyme is, for example, membrane-associated (as is the yeast tRNA splicing endonuclease, see above), it could be easily lost. Another possibility is that the splicing enzymes are tightly associated with the nuclear matrix (93), which is discarded in conventional protocols. Second, the pre-mRNA may have to be incorporated into ribonuclear-protein complexes (hnRNP). The formation of such particles *in vitro* might have totally different requirements than either transcription or splicing.

Finally, it is possible that the correct set of conditions have not yet been uncovered. Some commonly used ion may be inhibitory, for example, or an uncommon one may be required. At first glance, this idea might seem unlikely because of the large number of laboratories studying this problem. However, several examples may be relevant. For example, the demonstration that initiation of DNA replication at the *Escherichia coli* chromosomal origin can occur *in vitro* (94) was the result of extremely careful adjustments in experimental conditions. Closer to home, it has been shown that the RNA polymerase III contained in a HeLa whole-cell lysate will initiate transcription at some promoter sites only under conditions drastically different than those required for initiation by RNA polymerase II (95). Finally, the poly(A) sequences can be specifically and efficiently added to the 3' ends of mRNA precursors in a soluble HeLa cell extract (95a). Again, the requirements for this reaction are precise, and they are dramatically different than those required for transcription initiation. It is therefore anticipated that careful and precise manipulations of experimental conditions will soon lead to the definition of *in vitro* conditions that will result in the accurate and efficient splicing of pre-mRNAs.

D. 3' End Formation and Polyadenylylation

It is probably safe to say that even less is known about the enzymology and mechanism of mRNA 3' end formation and polyadenylylation than is known about mRNA splicing. One point that appears likely to be general is that the 3' ends of most mRNAs are not created by transcription termination, but rather by an RNA processing reaction, most likely an endonucleolytic cleavage.

The first evidence in support of this notion was obtained from analysis of the adenovirus late transcription unit (86). RNA from this transcription unit is processed to give rise to five families of mRNAs (L1 through L5), which are defined by the location of their 3' end sites (see Fig. 1). Analysis of pulse-labeled nuclear RNA by hybridization to purified DNA restriction fragments showed approximately equimolar hybridization across the entire transcription unit. This result suggests that RNA polymerase II transcribes the entire length of the transcription unit, and that the 3' ends of mRNAs are created by endonucleolytic cleavage. However, it is impossible by this method to rule out completely the possibility that a small percentage of polymerases do, in fact, terminate at each of the five 3' end sites, and that these are the molecules that give rise to mRNA. Alternatively, a type of transcription termination in which a newly synthesized RNA chain is released, but the polymerase remains bound to the DNA and continues transcription of downstream sequences, is consistent with the above results. Similar results have been obtained in papovavirus systems (85, 96), adenovirus early transcripts (97) as well as with transcription of the β-major mouse globin gene (98). It should be noted that analysis of steady-state nuclear RNA will most likely fail to reveal any transcription past the poly(A) addition site. For example, an analysis of rabbit β-globin RNA by sensitive S1 analysis gave no indication of transcription past the poly(A) addition site (99). This is most likely indicative of extremely rapid degradation of RNA transcribed downstream from the poly(A) addition site (84).

A direct demonstration of cleavage of a larger precursor to produce an mRNA 3' end has been demonstrated in only two cases: the L3 and L4 family adenovirus late mRNAs (84, 100). These experiments utilized isolated nuclei previously shown to be capable of producing mRNA precursors with polyadenylylated 3' termini located at the correct sites. Advantage was taken of the permeability of isolated nuclei to nucleoside triphosphates in order to carry out pulse–chase experiments. The results showed that these two 3' ends were efficiently created in the absence of any ongoing transcription, thereby demonstrating that they are formed by cleavage of a larger precursor. A discrete precursor was not identified, suggesting that RNAs extending varying distances past the 3' end site (perhaps all the way to the end of the genome; see Fig. 1) could serve as substrate for the cleavage. If the cleavage is endonucleolytic, then an RNA with a 5' end at the site of cleavage should be detected. Such species were in fact found, using S1-nuclease mapping. However, they were never seen at equimolar levels with the newly created mRNA and could not be observed at all in steady-state nuclear RNA. Once the 3' ends are formed by cleavage, they are polyadenylylated very rapidly; in fact, no cleaved, non-polyadenylylated RNA was detected. This suggests that, at least in isolated nuclei, the cleavage and polyadenylylation reactions are tightly coupled, perhaps carried out by one enzyme or enzyme complex. This coupling does not appear to be obligatory, since another 3′ end site in the adenovirus late transcription unit (L1) gives rise to both poly(A)$^+$ and poly(A)$^-$ RNAs (83).

The study of 3′ end formation and polyadenylylation of mRNA in isolated nuclei is subject to the same limitations that were mentioned above in the discussion of mRNA splicing: the reactions occur in a membrane-delimited space and are entirely dependent on endogenous transcription. Thus, it has again been an important goal to obtain conditions allowing specific and efficient 3′ end formation in soluble DNA- (or, preferably, RNA-) dependent *in vitro* systems. One important step in this direction has been the demonstration that transcription complexes isolated from HeLa cells during the late phase of adenovirus infection are capable of forming polyadenylylated 3′ ends (*101*). It remains to be seen, however, how useful this system will be. Although all membranes have been removed from the active components, RNA processing is still dependent upon transcription of endogenous chromatin. To date, it has not been possible to separate, or uncouple, transcription from the 3′ end formation and polyadenylylation reactions. This will be required if this system is to be used to study the enzymology of these reactions.

Enzymes from mammalian cells capable of the primer-dependent synthesis of poly(A) have been studied for over 20 years (*102*), and, in fact, purified nearly to homogeneity (see *103, 104* for reviews). However, these studies have been somewhat disappointing: no specificity is shown by the partially purified enzyme in the utilization of primers (tRNA and 5 S RNA work best; larger RNAs function poorly, if at all), the size of the product does not correspond to the approximately 250-nucleotide length of nuclear RNAs, and the rate of elongation is invariably extremely slow (two nucleotides per minute). These results are strikingly analogous to those that were (and are) obtained when purified RNA polymerase II is used to transcribe double-stranded DNA: no specificity is shown by this enzyme during initiation (except that nicks and ends are preferred), and the efficiency of transcription is very low. The finding that accurate and relatively efficient initiation can be obtained when purified RNA polymerase II is supplemented with a cell extract (*18*), or present in a crude whole-cell lysate (*19*), strongly suggests that additional factors are required to obtain accurate initiation. The same situation probably obtains with the synthesis of poly(A) by poly(A) polymerase.

The systems of Weil *et al.* (*18*) and Manley *et al.* (*19*) do not form 3′ ends or poly(A) tails on mRNA at detectable levels. However, conditions have been developed that result in the specific and efficient polyadenylylation of pre-mRNAs (*95a*). RNA was first synthesized in a whole-cell lysate under standard conditions (*19*), using DNA templates from recombinant plasmids containing SV40 or adenovirus genes and linearized by a restriction endonuclease. When this RNA was isolated and subsequently incubated in another aliquot of whole-cell lysate, the transcripts were found to be efficiently polyadenylylated if the proper conditions had been fulfilled. These included salt, extract, and RNA concentrations. Under suboptimal conditions, both the fraction of transcripts polyadenylylated, as well as the length of poly(A) added, are reduced. Under optimal conditions, the length of the poly(A) segment is approximately 200–300 nucleotides, and it appears to be synthesized processively, at a rate of at least 20–50 nucleotides per minute. The reaction is extremely specific: tRNA and 5 S, 18 S, and 28 S rRNAs are not detectably polyadenylylated. In addition, transcripts synthesized *in vitro* from DNA templates linearized at sites upstream from the poly(A) addition site utilized *in vivo* are polyadenylylated very inefficiently, if at all. Again, both the efficiency and the length of poly(A) added are reduced. These results suggest that factors in addition to the poly(A) polymerase are required to obtain specific and efficient polyadenylylation. In addition, they suggest that a nucleotide sequence at the 3′ end of pre-mRNA functions as a recognition site, or "promoter," for the poly(A) polymerase. (A likely candidate is the highly conserved sequence 5′-AAUAAA-3′; this is discussed in Section II,B,2.) Thus, the strength of this "promoter" coupled with the concentration of specificity factors could determine how efficiently a pre-mRNA is polyadenylylated, and the length of the poly(A) tract added. The ability of a cell to modulate the efficiency of polyadenylylation could provide an important way to control gene expression. Pre-mRNAs that do not receive poly(A) might be unable to leave the nucleus, while the length of poly(A) added may contribute to determining the half-life of the mRNA in the cytoplasm (see *105, 106* for reviews).

With the availability of *in vitro* systems that accurately polyadenylylate mRNA precursors, it should only be a short time before the enzymology and mechanism of the reaction are understood. However, an assay for the endonuclease required for 3′ end formation *in vivo* has not yet been obtained. It is likely, though, that further manipulation of *in vitro* conditions will soon reveal this enzyme.

E. Termination

In this section we consider two questions: Are the 3' ends of mRNA ever created by transcription termination, as opposed to endonuclytic cleavage? Second, in systems where transcription continues past the poly(A) addition site, where does termination occur?

One example in which transcription termination may occur at or near the 3' end sites of mRNA is the histone genes. The transcripts from these genes differ from other mRNAs in that they lack poly(A) segments at their 3' ends. These mRNAs do not contain the conserved 5'-AAUAAA-3' sequence, but instead contain a highly conserved 23-nucleotide sequence at their 3' end (107). This sequence contains a 16-nucleotide interrupted inverted repeat, suggesting an analogy to prokaryotic terminators, all of which appear to contain a stem-loop structure as part of the terminator signal (see 108 for review). While genetic evidence suggests that this sequence is necessary for the formation of histone mRNA 3' ends (see Section II,B,3), the only support for the idea that this is a termination rather than a processing signal is the negative evidence that larger species do not accumulate to significant levels (109, 110), and the analogy to prokaryotic termination signals.

Some progress in understanding the biochemistry of 3' end formation in histone mRNA has already been made (111). When cloned sea urchin histone genes are microinjected into the nuclei of X. laevis oocytes, apparently authentic H2A and H2B mRNAs are synthesized in readily detectable yields. However, although initiation of histone H3 mRNA synthesis occurs at comparable levels, the mature message is not detected, owing to a failure to create a properly terminated molecule. However, simultaneous injection of a partially purified protein factor, isolated by salt extraction of sea urchin embryo chromatin, results in the appearance of H3 mRNA. A reasonable conclusion is that this factor is required for transcription termination of H3, but not H2A or H2B, mRNAs.

It has also been suggested that transcription termination plays a role in generating adenovirus-specific mRNAs. It is now known that the adenovirus late promoter, originally thought to be active only at times late after infection (i.e., after the onset of viral DNA replication), is in fact active at early times (112–114). However, only mRNA from the most proximal promoter family (L1) can be detected (see Fig. 1). It appears that, at early times, transcription terminates at, or shortly beyond, the L1 poly(A) addition site. The activation of the remainder of the late transcription unit might then be mediated by control of transcription termination. Some support for the idea that 3' end formation of the L1 mRNAs is due to transcription termination rather than to RNA cleavage comes from studies with isolated nuclei obtained from infected HeLa cells (84). Although pre-mRNAs with 3' ends mapping at the correct site for L1 mRNAs are detected, the synthesis of such molecules requires ongoing transcription. This is in contrast to the 3' ends of the L3 and L4 families, which are created efficiently during a chase in which transcription is totally blocked. An attractive explanation for this result is that, unlike the L3 and L4 family 3' ends, which are created by endonucleolytic cleavage of larger precursors, the L1 family 3' ends are created by transcription termination.

The above two instances provide the best evidence to date that mRNA 3' end formation may occur by transcription termination in some instances. However, even in these cases, it cannot yet be ruled out that the 3' ends are actually created by RNA processing. A final resolution of this question will require the use of reconstituted *in vitro* transcription systems that accurately form 3' ends on mRNAs.

It was argued in Section I,D that the 3' ends of some (perhaps most) mRNAs are created by endonucleolytic cleavage. An important question then arises: Where does transcription in fact terminate? This question has not yet been answered with certainty for any system. Perhaps the strongest evidence that termination can occur at specific downstream sites again comes from studies on the adenovirus late transcription unit (115). It appears that transcription past even the last polyadenylylation site (L5; see Fig. 1) occurs efficiently. However, it also seems that transcription terminates before reaching the very end of the genome, since RNA complementary to DNA restriction fragments obtained from this part of the genome was not detected. These conclusions were obtained from "fingerprint" analysis of ^{32}P-labeled nuclear poly(A)⁻ RNA (these terminal sequences apparently do not become polyadenylylated), as well as hybridization analysis of RNA pulse-labeled [3H]adenosine. The simplest interpretation of these observations is that transcription terminates at one or more sites downstream from the last poly(A) addition site but before the end of the genome. However, the possibility that transcription does not terminate at a particular site, but instead continues to the end of the genome, and that the RNAs detected are the product of nuclease digestion, cannot be rigorously excluded.

The DNA tumor viruses SV40 and polyoma have also yielded some important facts that may be relevant to the problem of transcription termination. As discussed above, it appears that transcription continues well beyond the mRNA 3' end site, at least at late times (and probably early times as well; e.g., *116*). Nuclear RNAs three to four times the size of the genome have been detected in cells infected with polyoma virus (*117*). These transcripts represent tandem copies of the entire late strand of the viral genome (*118*) and probably result from multiple rounds of transcription of the circular DNA molecule. The existence of these relatively abundant giant transcripts suggests that there is no termination site on polyoma virus DNA, at least for late transcription. Such giant transcripts have not been detected in cells infected by the very similar virus SV40, although transcripts roughly the size of one genome equivalent have been found (*119, 120*). This result suggests that there is a transcription termination signal on SV40 DNA [although the possibility that the difference between the two viruses is in the cell type they infect (mouse cells vs monkey cells) rather than in the viruses themselves cannot be excluded].

Evidence for the existence of a specific termination signal on SV40 DNA has been obtained (*120a*). Transcription in whole-cell lysates of recombinant plasmids containing the strong adenovirus late promoter inserted into SV40 sequences just to the late side of the origin-SV40 promoter region reveals that approximately 75% of the transcripts terminate at specific sites within the origin region. Since these are the only examples to date of specific transcription termination *in vitro* by RNA polymerase II, the possibility that they are physiologically relevant is strengthened. The orientation of the adenovirus insert in the plasmid used as template is such that the early strand is transcribed. Thus, the results suggest that at early times of infection by SV40, genome-length transcripts might also be produced *in vivo*. The precise sites at which termination occurs have not yet been determined. However, the origin region contains several palindromic sequences, and the size of terminated transcripts (four or five discrete species are detected) is such that these structures may be important (the structure of the SV40 origin, as well as the possibility that it may be involved in transcription termination, have been discussed in ref. *23*). These results suggest that the SV40 origin region may be even more complex than previously thought. In addition to containing the signals required for initiation of DNA replication, and promoters for early and late transcription, it may also contain the signals required for termination of both early and late transcription.

F. Regulation

One of the most important uses of prokaryotic *in vitro* transcription systems has been in studies of regulation of gene expression. The ability to reproduce regulatory events *in vitro* has led, in many cases, to detailed understanding of the diverse ways in which bacterial genes are regulated (e.g., *121*). The newly developed eukaryotic RNA polymerase II transcription systems have begun to be used with some success to study questions dealing with regulation of transcription initiation.

The most information obtained to date has been on the mechanism by which the SV40 large T antigen is able to autoregulate its own synthesis. That such autoregulation occurs was strongly suggested from *in vivo* measurements of early RNA synthesis in cells infected with mutant viruses encoding temperature-sensitive T antigens (*122*–*123a*). Direct confirmation that autoregulation is brought about by the binding of T antigen to sites near the viral origin of DNA replication (*124*), thereby blocking initiation of early transcription, was obtained by showing that addition of purified T antigen (or, more accurately, an analogous protein, D2, that is produced by a defective SV40-adenovirus hybrid virus) to HeLa whole-cell lysates resulted in specific inhibition of SV40 early transcription (*125*). It was later shown that authentic SV40 T antigen will also specifically repress transcription initiation *in vitro*, and that this inhibition probably occurs as a result of a direct competition between T antigen and RNA polymerase II for overlapping sites, rather than from bound T antigen blocking elongation by RNA polymerase (*126*). In fact, specifically bound T antigen will not block elongation by RNA polymerase II that had initiated transcription from an upstream promoter (*126*). Further studies revealed that this repression is probably quite complex. However, a slight digression into the nature of transcription initiation from the SV40 early promoter region is required in order that these complexities can be appreciated. At early times after infection the 5' termini of early mRNA are located near the origin of DNA replication. As the infection proceeds, these termini are no longer detected, but rather 5' termini that map 40–50 base-pairs upstream are observed (*127*). All these transcription starts are detected *in vitro* as well as *in vivo* (*127*, *128*). T antigen binds to three distinct sites on the viral DNA that overlap these transcription start sites. Site I, downstream from the origin, is the highest-affinity site. Sites II and III are located within a 100-base-pair distance upstream, relative to the direction of early transcription, from site I, and have progressively lower affinities for T antigen (*124*).

In vitro transcription experiments shed light on how this complex array of regulatory elements might control early gene expression (*128*). At low concentrations of T antigen, binding site I is filled, and this binding blocks transcription initiation from the downstream start sites, probably by sterically hindering binding of RNA polymerase (or an initiation factor), as discussed above. At higher T antigen concentrations, binding site II is also filled, and this inhibits transcription initiation from the upstream start sites. (Binding site III is apparently not involved.) This series of events is analogous to what occurs in the infected cell: as the infection proceeds, the concentration of T antigen rises, eventually becoming sufficiently high so that binding site I is occupied and early transcription is blocked. Binding of T antigen induces DNA replication, and the late phase of infection commences. This process, by an unknown mechanism and for reasons that are unclear, results in the utilization of the upstream start sites mentioned above. This results in a further increase in the concentration of T antigen, which ultimately becomes high enough to fill sites II (and III) quantitatively, thereby (presumably) greatly reducing the amount of early transcription.

The late promoter of SV40 becomes active only after the onset of DNA replication. While the nature of the regulatory events involved remains obscure, one observation from *in vitro* transcription analyses may be relevant. As the concentration of SV40 DNA in reaction mixtures is increased, the efficiency with which the late promoter is utilized relative to the early promoter increases significantly (*125*). This mirrors the situation in the infected cell, where the concentration of viral DNA increases dramatically during the course of infection. Perhaps transcription initiation from the late promoter can occur in the absence of some factor required for initiation from other promoters, including the early promoter. If this factor is present at limiting concentrations, either *in vitro* or *in vivo*, it could in effect be titrated out as the concentration of promoters increases, thus explaining the preferential utilization of the late promoter. However, it is likely that this is an oversimplification and that other factors are required to modulate the expression of the SV40 late promoter *in vivo*.

A strikingly analogous set of findings has been obtained concerning control of transcription initiation from several adenovirus promoters. For example, as was again suggested by *in vivo* experiments with temperature-sensitive mutants (*129*), addition of the purified 72-kDa DNA binding protein (a product of early region II) to *in vitro* reaction mixtures specifically represses transcription initiation from the early region IV promoter (*129a*). A detailed analysis of transcription initiation efficiencies *in vitro* from several adenovirus promoters (*36*) has revealed two points that are relevant to the question of how viral gene expression is regulated. First, both the late promoter and also a so-called intermediate promoter (the one giving rise to transcription of the gene that encodes the viral polypeptide IX; see Fig. 1) are preferentially utilized over all early promoters as the DNA concentration in *in vitro* transcription reactions is raised. This result, which is analogous to the findings obtained with SV40, again reflects the course of events during the infectious cycle. Second, the efficiencies with which these same two promoters are utilized relative to early promoters dramatically increases when they are transcribed in extracts prepared from late adenovirus-infected cells as opposed to uninfected or early-infected cells. These results imply that some factor is induced during the late phase of viral infection that results in inhibition of early transcription and/or enhancement of late transcription. The nature of this factor and the mechanism by which it functions remain to be determined.

One important question in eukaryotic molecular biology is to learn how gene expression is regulated during development and differentiation. To date, there is only one indication that *in vitro* transcription systems currently in use will be valuable in studying this problem (*130*). The *Bombyx mori* silk fibroin gene is accurately expressed in HeLa cell extracts. However, in extracts prepared from *B. mori* posterior silk glands, which is the only tissue in which the gene is expressed, the efficiency with which the gene is transcribed is greatly increased (relative to the adenovirus late and mouse β-globin promoters). Hopefully, it will be possible to identify the factor(s) required, and to determine the mechanism of this specific activation.

The HeLa cell transcription sytems are quite promiscuous: a variety of genes such as the α- and β-like globin genes that are not expressed *in vivo* in these cells are expressed relatively efficiently *in vitro* (*131, 132*). At least two factors might be relevant. First, the number of copies of a gene added to *in vitro* reaction mixtures is invariably immense, corresponding to roughly 10^5 copies per cell equivalent. Thus, one could easily imagine that, if specificity *in vivo* is brought about by the action of specific repressor-like molecules, it is likely that these factors are titrated out, allowing for expression of the gene. On the other hand, if specific gene activation is mediated by positive regulatory elements, it could be that the observed *in vitro* expression is the result of a low level of "escape" or background transcription that would not be detected *in vivo*.

The second factor is that, although a fraction of the DNA added to *in vitro* transcription lysates can be incorporated into nucleosomes (*133*), the template for *in vitro* transcription is undoubtedly "naked," relaxed DNA (discussed in *134*). Thus, any controls that are mediated at the level of chromatin structure or DNA supercoiling will not be operative *in vitro*. One likely example of this comes from studies of specific DNA methylation. When cloned genes are methylated *in vitro* with bacterial methylases and then introduced into animal cells, their expression can be drastically reduced relative to unmethylated controls (*135–137*). (Although the molecular mechanism by which this inactivation is mediated is unknown, a likely explanation is that chromatin structure is somehow affected.) When these types of experiments are repeated using *in vitro* transcription as an assay, no effect of methylation has ever been detected (e.g., *137a*).

The above discussion suggests two lines of study that might improve the utility of *in vitro* transcription systems for studies of gene regulation. One approach would be to lower the requirements for such high concentrations of DNA. Some progress has, in fact, already been made in this regard (*128*). Another approach that might be fruitful would be the development of conditions that allow the purification of significant quantities of specific chromatin for *in vitro* transcription analysis. Cell systems that allow the replication of cloned genes as exogenous plasmid-like elements, such as COS monkey cells (*138*) or bovine papilloma virus-transformed mouse cells (*139*) merit consideration.

II. The Genetics of Gene Expression: Analysis Using *in Vitro* Mutagenesis

The development of enzymatic and chemical techniques that allow the site-specific mutagenesis of cloned genes has resulted in an explosion in our knowledge of the genetic signals that affect gene expression. Even though this field is only about 3 years old, a huge amount of data has been obtained. In this last half of the article, I concentrate on genetic studies that have already provided some insights into the mechanisms by which mRNA-encoding genes are expressed and regulated.

A. Promoters

As recently as 1979, experimental evidence that there are nucleotide sequences that bring about the specific initiation of transcription by RNA polymerase II was completely lacking. In fact, in the absence of any genetics, and in light of the unusual cap structure found on mRNA 5' ends, one could not readily refute an idea put forth by some skeptics to explain the observed inability of purified RNA polymerase II to initiate transcription specifically, namely, that transcription begins randomly, and that mRNA 5' ends are created by specific processing.

Our ability to do genetic studies with mammalian cells stems from four important technical advances: first, the ability to purify and amplify specific genes from animal cells by recombinant DNA technology (e.g., 12); second, the ability to introduce mutations *in vitro* into such genes (e.g., 4, 15); third, DNA sequencing methodologies, which allow the rapid determination of precisely what mutagenic changes has been effected (140, 141); and fourth, the development of assay systems that allow the consequences of mutagenesis to be readily determined (e.g., 14, 19).

The nature of the assay used to determine the effects of promoter mutations must be considered in a discussion of promoter structure and function. Somewhat different results have been obtained when mutated DNAs are transcribed *in vitro* in soluble transcription systems and when the same genes are expressed *in vivo* after their introduction into living cells. Although in all cases transcription appears to initiate accurately, additional nucleotide sequences are, in some cases, required to obtain efficient expression *in vivo* and are not required *in vitro*. In this section, therefore, results obtained for *in vitro* and *in vivo* assays are discussed separately; at the end, possible explanations for the differences are presented.

1. ANALYSIS OF RNA POLYMERASE II PROMOTERS
in Vitro

The earliest experiments painted a deceivingly simple picture of what the nucleotide sequences that constitute a eukaryotic RNA polymerase II promoter might be. It had previously been pointed out, based originally on DNA sequence analysis of *Drosophila* histone genes (142), that a nucleotide sequence for the prototype 5'-TATAAA-3' is located 25–30 nucleotides upstream from the transcription start site of most protein encoding genes. This sequence is similar to the promoter element found in bacteria, the so-called "Pribnow box," which is a highly conserved nucleotide sequence (consensus: 5'-TAT (G/A)AT(G/A)-3') located approximately ten nucleotides upstream from the start point of transcription of virtually all prokaryotic genes (143, 144). Thus, it was a possibility that the "TATA box" might constitute part, if not all, of the eukaryotic RNA polymerase II promoter.

The first experiments aimed at determining what sequences were required to bring about accurate and efficient transcription initiation by RNA polymerase II confirmed that the TATA box is indeed part of the eukaryotic promoter, and, in fact, suggested that perhaps only a few additional nucleotides, lying on either side of the element, were required for promoter function. These experiments all utilized *in vitro* transcription as an assay for promoter function and, for the most part, analyzed deletion mutants that were constructed by site-specific *in vitro* mutagenesis techniques (e.g., *4*). The TATA-box region is necessary and sufficient to bring about accurate and relatively efficient transcription initiation *in vitro* of the cloned adenovirus late (*6, 7*), chicken conalbumen (*6*), chicken ovalbumin (*145*), and rabbit β-globin (*146*) genes. Note that genes from a wide variety of organisms are transcribed accurately in extracts prepared from human tissue-culture cells. This appears to be a general rule, and it suggests that the basic transcriptional machinery and signals have been highly conserved throughout the animal kingdom. Confirming the important role of the TATA sequence on *in vitro* transcription are experiments that analyzed the consequences of single base mutations (T→G and T→A transversions in the second T of the TATA box), which were again constructed using site-specific techniques (e.g., *16*). Transcription initiation of the conalbumin (*147, 148*) and sea urchin histone H2A (*149*) genes was reduced approximately by a factor of 10 as a result of these single base changes. In all the above examples, the actual start site of transcription could be deleted without dramatically reducing the rate of initiation. In fact, in at least one case (*7*), deletions removing nucleotides near the RNA start site actually *increased* the levels of transcription initiation obtained.

As additional genes were analyzed, it soon became apparent that sequences other than the TATA box are important for obtaining high levels of transcription initiation. The first suggestions that this is so again came from DNA sequencing studies: some genes do not contain TATA-like sequence located upstream of apparent transcription start sites. The best-studied example of this is the SV40 late region. Accurate initiation of transcription of these genes occurs *in vitro* [at least in the whole-cell lysate system (*19*)] at readily detectable levels (*89, 125*). As mentioned in Section I,A, the 5′ ends of SV40 late RNAs are extremely heterogeneous, *in vivo* as well as *in vitro* (U. Hansen, personal communication). The heterogeneity in start sites may be related to the absence of a TATA box (see below), although this remains to be demonstrated. In addition, the adenovirus early region II also lack a TATA box in the region upstream from the transcription start site. This promoter is also active *in vitro* (*36, 150*), although at barely detectable levels. The 5′ ends of early region II RNA, both *in vitro* and *in vivo* and in contrast to SV40 late RNA, display only a limited micro-heterogeneity, suggesting that a TATA box is not essential, in this case at least, for "fixing" the site at which initiation occurs. Exactly what nucleotide sequences constitute promoters for these genes is not yet known.

At least two genes (SV40 early and sea urchin histones) studied extensively by *in vitro* transcription appear to require, for efficient initiation, sequences that lie further upstream than the TATA box and, in one case, may not require the TATA box at all. Using deletion mutagenesis techniques, one group defined the sequences required for accurate initiation of transcription as lying between -70 and -150 nucleotides from the SV40 major early start site (*126*). The results, based on analysis of runoff transcripts approximately 500 nucleotides long, showed that deletion of the TATA box did not have a detectable effect on transcription initiation. Another study analyzed a separate set of deletions, and also found that deletion of the TATA box did not result in a significant decrease in the *amount* of early transcription *in vitro* (*151*). However, qualitatively, a dramatic change was observed: the RNA 5' ends became extremely heterogeneous, extending over a region up to approximately 200 nucleotides downstream from the wild-type start site.

The reasons for the qualitative difference between the results of these two groups is not clear, although differences in methods of RNA analysis cannot be excluded. Likewise, it is not clear why deletion of the TATA box for this gene apparently does not affect transcription quantitatively, whereas for all other genes that have been tested *in vitro*, such deletions greatly reduce the levels of initiation. One explanation is related to the complex structure of this promoter region (see Section I,F on regulation; also *152*). It is possible that this region actually consists of two promoters. One, the more downstream of the two, might be similar to the other TATA box containing promoters discussed above. The other, located somewhat upstream, could be analogous to the SV40 late promoter. (In fact, it is not inconsistent with available data that these promoters are overlapping, directing early and late transcription in opposite directions on the circular viral DNA molecule.) Then one could imagine that the TATA box deletions do, in fact, inactivate the downstream promoter, but do not affect the second, upstream promoter. This promoter, especially in the absence of the downstream TATA box, gives rise to heterogeneous initiations, as does the SV40 late promoter. Consistent with this model is the fact that the authentic late promoter and the upstream early promoter hypothesized here are both active *in vivo* at the same time, i.e., after the onset of viral

DNA replication. Further mutagenesis experiments, coupled with precise RNA analysis, should resolve this question.

Another gene in which it appears that upstream sequences are required for *in vitro* transcription initiation is the sea urchin histone H2A gene (153). Deletion of sequences between −111 and −139 nucleotides from the transcription start site results in a fivefold reduction in transcription initiation in a HeLa whole-cell lysate. (Unlike the SV40 early genes, deletion of the TATA box resulted in a similar reduction in rate of transcription initiation. The 5′ ends of the RNA synthesized are, however, heterogeneous.) This result was obtained when covalently closed circular DNAs were used as templates for transcription, but not with the more commonly used linearized DNAs that are utilized to generate readily assayable runoff transcripts. The authors suggest that the upstream sequences may function as an entry site for RNA polymerase II, and that the effects of these sequences might be mimicked by DNA free ends, although results from other systems (see below) are not consistent with this idea, at least as a general rule.

The whole-cell lysate system (19) may be better suited for revealing the effects of upstream deletions than the system that utilizes purified RNA polymerase II supplemented with a cytoplasmic extract (18). For example, an approximately 75% reduction in transcription initiation only in a HeLa whole-cell lysate, but not in an RNA-polymerase-II-supplemented system, was reported when sequences 62 nucleotides upstream from the adenovirus late RNA start site were deleted (154). Similar results have been obtained with the adenovirus early region III promoter (P. Sassone Corsi, personal communication). These are similar to the results obtained when these promoters were tested *in vivo* (see Section II,A,2). However, in another study (7), when similar mutants of the adenovirus late promoter (such as an upstream deletion with an end point at −66) were transcribed in a HeLa whole-cell lysate, very little, if any, effect on transcription was detected. In addition, *in vitro* transcription in a whole-cell lysate from a promoter contained in the long terminal repeat of cloned avian sarcoma virus is not detectably affected by deletion of all sequences 55 nucleotides upstream from the RNA start site, even though these sequences appear to be absolutely required *in vivo* (155). At the moment, it is not clear whether these differences can be attributed to differences in the promoters tested, experimental conditions, or some other factor. One possibility that must be considered whenever the effects of deletion mutations are being analyzed is that foreign sequences (often plasmid DNA) are by necessity introduced at the deletion end-point. The effects of such sequences need not always be neutral, and it is conceivable that alterations in transcriptional efficiency (or lack thereof) attributed to deletions may in fact, be the result of substitutions. While it is possible to allow for these effects (by ensuring that the same sequence always abuts the deletion end point, for example), this possibility must always be kept in mind when analyzing deletion mutants.

An interesting effect of DNA concentration and free DNA ends on the function of the adenovirus late promoter has been observed (155a). At high DNA concentrations, transcription initiation from an upstream deletion terminated at −47 is only slightly reduced to about one-half relative to the −66 deletion (or wild-type, which behaves the same), as previously observed (7). However, at lower DNA concentrations, initiation from the −47 deletion mutant is reduced more dramatically (to less than 20%), relative to the −66 deletion. Since construction of these mutations involved the use of DNA linkers, DNA free-ends near the site of the deletion end point can be readily created by restriction endonuclease digestion. Cleavage of the −47 deletion mutant had little, if any, effect on transcription initiation, relative to the uncleaved DNA. However, cleavage of the −66 deletion mutant drastically reduced the efficiency of transcription initiation, such that roughly the same levels of transcription were obtained from both mutants. These results suggest that a DNA sequence between −47 and −66 base-pairs from the RNA start site is required to obtain efficient transcription initiation in a HeLa whole-cell lysate. Although *specific* sequences upstream of −66 appear not to be required, it appears that nonspecific DNA sequences are required, perhaps to stabilize binding of RNA polymerase or a factor to the specific sequences located downstream.

In vitro transcription of virtually all the genes discussed above is unaffected (or only slightly so) by deletions that remove the transcription start site. However, analysis of several genes suggests that sequences around the start site may be required in order to obtain efficient *in vitro* transcription. These include the silk fibroin gene (156), adenovirus early regions I (T. Shenk, personal communication) and III (157), and the avian sarcoma virus promoter (155). These results may define a distinct type of promoter, in which interaction between specific nucleotides at the RNA start site and RNA polymerase II (or an associated factor) are required to obtain efficient transcription initiation. An alternative view is that in no case is a specific nucleotide sequence in the DNA required at the transcription start site. However, some sequences, such as those created by the above deletions, may actually be deleterious to obtaining efficient initiation. A further resolution of this question will require analysis of additional mutated genes.

A full understanding of RNA polymerase II promoter structure and function will ultimately require, among other things, an analysis of the effects of large numbers of point mutants. Such mutations exclude the possible artifact discussed above, as well as allow for precise determinations of the nucleotides required to bring about accurate transcription initiation. With *in vitro* techniques now available (e.g., *15, 158*), it is possible to "saturate" defined segments of DNA with point mutations. Although such studies are just getting underway, they should be of great value in the future. One study (*159*) has analyzed the effects on *in vitro* transcription of fourteen different single-base transition mutations in the silk fibroin promoter region (between nucleotides -30 and $+1$). Mutations in the TATA box resulted in 50–70% inhibition of transcription, as did mutations between -21 and -17. One point mutation in the TATA box resulted in the generation of considerable microheterogeneity in the RNA 5' ends. However, mutations near the start site of transcription did not appear to result in either quantitative or qualitative changes in transcription initiation.

2. ANALYSIS OF RNA POLYMERASE II PROMOTERS *in Vivo*

The effects of mutations constructed *in vitro* in cloned genes can also be determined by introducing these genes into living animal cells and analyzing the transcripts produced. Several different methods of gene transfer are available. The most common method is transfection into animal cells, which is usually accomplished by coprecipitation with calcium phosphate. Although stably transformed cells can be obtained by this procedure, the results discussed here are based on "transient expression" experiments, in which the transfected DNA is expressed efficiently for only two or three days, at which time the cells are harvested. Usually DNA replication does not occur, although systems are available that allow for replication of the unintegrated DNA (e.g., *138*). Another method for introducing genes into cells is to inject the DNA into the cell nucleus. Owing to its large size, the most commonly used cell for this type of transfer is *X. laevis* oocytes (see *176* for review). Although it is certainly possible that the method of gene transfer used might affect the results obtained, this question has not received detailed study, and for the purpose of this discussion, it will be assumed that all methods are equivalent. In addition, with one exception (see below), there is no evidence that differences in species or cell type influence expression, and this possibility is not considered further.

The results obtained from *in vivo* analysis are, in many respects, similar to those obtained with *in vitro* assays, but in other respects they are quite different. One important similarity is that deletion of nucleotides lying downstream from the transcription start site, almost without exception, fails to affect transcription initiation significantly.

The TATA box appears to play very similar roles *in vivo* and *in vitro*. Thus, deletions of the SV40 early region TATA box that leave upstream sequences intact have only very small quantitative effects on transcription initiation, but result in the creation of mRNAs with heterogeneous 5' ends (*160, 161*). Similarly, detetions that remove the sea urchin histone TATA box reduce the level of transcription initiation and also bring about heterogeneity in the positioning of mRNA 5' ends (*162*).

A similar situation appears to exist with adenovirus early region IA transcription (*163*). Deletions that remove the TATA box region result in an 80 to 90% reduction in the amount of EIA-specific RNA synthesized. The residual transcription again results in heterogeneous mRNA 5' ends. However, in this case, the 5' ends of the new RNAs are spread over a region of approximately 200 nucleotides *upstream* of the wild-type start site. Interestingly, these upstream starts become readily detectable in infections with wild-type virus after the onset of viral DNA replication (*164*). Furthermore, at least one is detectable as a product of *in vitro* transcription (*36*). This situation is strikingly analogous to that observed when transcripts from the SV40 early region are analyzed (see above), and raises the possibility that the EIA "promoter" may actually consist of two functionally distinct promoters.

Most of the promoters that have been analyzed by *in vitro* transcription show dramatic (an order of magnitude) decreases in the efficiency of transcription initiation when the TATA box is deleted. To date, only with one of these, the rabbit β-globin gene, have experiments been done that would reveal the effects of such deletions *in vivo* (*165, 166*). The results show that deletions removing the TATA box, but leaving upstream, as well as downstream, sequences intact, virtually eliminate transcription initiation *in vivo* as well as *in vitro*.

One gene that appears to behave somewhat anomalously is the herpes virus thymidine kinase gene. Deletions that remove the TATA box and downstream sequences have very little effect on transcription initiation *in vivo* either quantitatively or qualitatively (*167*). This is the only example to date of a gene containing a TATA box that does not seem to be required to obtain accurate and/or efficient transcription initiation. This gene is transcribed extremely inefficiently *in vitro* (*168*), and it has not yet been determined whether the TATA box is also dispensable for *in vitro* transcription.

The major difference between *in vitro* and *in vivo* expression assays is that DNA sequences that lie significantly upstream of the TATA box region play, in most instances, a much more important role in the latter system than in the former. These sequences appear to affect transcription initiation only quantitatively. The magnitude of the effect that genetic manipulations with these sequences can bring about varies greatly, from less than threefold to one-hundredfold or greater. How "upstream sequences" function to enhance transcription efficiency is not known, although it is clear that there is more than one class of sequence and that they probably affect transcription in diverse ways.

A sequence that lies more than 110 nucleotides upstream of the sea urchin histone H2A gene transcription start site plays an important role in modulating initiation (169). Deletion of an approximately 340-base-pair segment that extends from approximately -110 to -450 results in a 95% inhibition of transcription initiation *in vivo*. (As mentioned above, this effect can be partially reproduced *in vitro*.) Interestingly, inversion of this segment *increases* the rate of transcription initiation *in vivo* about fivefold. (A slight reduction is observed *in vitro*.) What nucleotide sequence within this segment is responsible for this effect is not yet known. The fragment does, however, contain an extremely A,T-rich "spacer region" that separates the histone H2A and H3 genes.

The SV40 early promoter is the only promoter examined to date that appears to have an absolute requirement for sequences that lie far upstream (i.e., -70 to -150) from the major mRNA start site to obtain transcription initiation *in vitro*. Sequences within this upstream region are also required for expression *in vivo* (160, 170). Comparison of the nucleotide sequences within this region does not reveal any striking homologies with similarly located sequences in other genes. However, the region contains two tandem copies of a perfect 21-base-pair repeat. In addition, an imperfect copy of this repeat is located from approximately -50 to -70 nucleotides from the major RNA start site. The region contains six copies of the sequence 5'-CCGCCC-3' between -50 and -110. It appears that these repeated sequences constitute part (or perhaps all) of the SV40 early promoter. Recall that not only is the SV40 early promoter itself very complicated, but this region also contains signals required for the initiation of DNA replication and (possibly) elements of the SV40 late promoter and transcription termination signals. This complexity raises the possibility that the structure of the SV40 early (and late) promoter may be quite different than that of other promoters.

Transcription initiation from the SV40 early promoter *in vivo* (but not *in vitro*) requires additional sequence elements that lie even farther upstream (*160, 171*). In this region are two tandemly repeated copies of a 72-base-pair sequence, located between position -110 and -250. At least approximately one copy of this sequence is required to obtain efficient transcription initiation (*171*). Interestingly, this sequence, like the far upstream sequence of the histone H2a gene, can function in either orientation relative to the RNA start site (*11*). In addition, the sequence can enhance transcription even when far removed from its original location and distant from other promoter elements (*9, 11*). (It will, however, only function if present in *cis*). Furthermore, it can enhance transcription from heterologous promoters, such as rabbit β-globin (*9*) and the adenovirus late (*154*) promoters. Sequences with similar properties have been found in the long terminal repeat of murine sacoma virus (*172*), in polyoma virus (*173, 174*), and in monkey cell chromosomal DNA (*10*). Finally, there appears to be some cell specificity in the action of enhancer sequences: the SV40 enhancer works better in monkey cells than in mouse cells, while the reverse is true with the murine sarcoma virus enhancer (*175*). There is no strong sequence homology between the enhancer elements that have been analyzed to date. How these intriguing elements function is not known, although some possibilities are discussed in Section II,A,3).

The globin genes also require an upstream sequence to be efficiently expressed *in vivo* (*138, 165, 166*). The important sequence appears to be located between about -70 and -80 nucleotides upstream of the RNA start site, and consists of, at least in part, the sequence 5'-CCAAT-3'. This sequence is highly conserved in all globin genes (*177*) as well as several other eukaryotic genes (*178*). However, it is not common to all (or perhaps even most) eukaryotic genes, and in some cases where it is present, it can be deleted without significantly affecting transcription initiation (*162*). Globin genes do not have enhancer type sequences located nearby.

A detailed analysis of a number of small deletion mutants in the herpes virus thymidine kinase gene has defined precisely two upstream sequence elements required for efficient expression of this gene (*179*). These elements lie between nucleotides -47 and -61 and -80 and -105. Again, no highly conserved sequences are detectable, although the sequence 5'-CCGCCC-3', thought to be important in SV40 early expression, is located in the far-upstream element. The sequence elements can be separated by 20–30 base-pairs from each other, or from the RNA start site, without impairing their effectiveness, although further separation inactivates transcription of the gene.

Deletion of sequences upstream of -62 from the adenovirus late promoter decreases its transcriptional efficiency when recombinant plasmids containing this promoter are introduced into human or monkey cells. However, the effect is rather small (to one-third). Sequences upstream of −97 do not appear to be important for transcription initiation from this promoter.

3. A HYPOTEHTICAL RNA POLYMERASE II PROMOTER

The above discussion illustrates both that our understanding of the eukaryotic RNA polymerase II promoter is very primitive and also that it is likely to be quite complex. Thus, it is probably premature, and perhaps inappropriate, to suggest a "general model" for an RNA polymerase II promoter. However, such a speculative model might serve to tie together the results presented above and to suggest areas of future study.

One can imagine that the eukaryotic RNA polymerase II promoter consists of three elements: a "far-upstream" sequence located 100 or more nucleotides upstream of the RNA start site, an "upstream sequence" located between roughly −50 and −80 nucleotides from the start site, and the "TATA box," which precedes the initiation site by 25 to 35 nucleotides. The far-upstream element might be typified by the SV40 72-base-pair "enhancer" sequence. Since this sequence can function in a position- and orientation-independent fashion, it may be that such sequences should not really be considered as part of the promoter, i.e., it may not interact at all with RNA polymerase II or associated factors. Three possible functions for this sequence are (i) a recognition signal for a hypothetical site-specific topoisomerase that could affect the superhelicity of a domain of DNA; (ii) a site at which nucleosome phasing is controlled (a variation of this idea (11) is that enhancers might result in the formation of sites in chromatin that serve as bidirectional "entry sites" for RNA polymerase II); and (iii) a site that "directs" a region of DNA to a site within the nucleus, where transcription takes place.

The upstream element, perhaps best exemplified by the globin 5'-CAATT-3' sequence, may be envisioned as having two possible functions. First, this sequence may play a role similar to the bacterial "−35 homology." This is a conserved (although rather imprecisely) sequence lying 35 nucleotides upstream of the mRNA start site (reviewed in 180, 181). The initiating RNA polymerase contacts this region, as well as the Pribnow box. It is thought that this region may represent an *initial* RNA polymerase-DNA contact point (i.e., "closed-complex") that is required for subsequent formation of an "open complex" in which the two DNA strands are locally melted. This involves RNA polymerase-DNA contact at the Pribnow box. However, it is unlikely that this analogy is correct in its strictest sense: in bacteria, the distance between the Pribnow box and −35 homology cannot vary without destroying promoter function (182). In eukaryotes, it appears that the distance between the TATA box and upstream element can vary by as much as 30 base-pairs without affecting promoter function (165, 179).

Another possible role of upstream sequences is that they might represent sites at which hypothetical "initiation factors" or "activating" proteins interact with DNA. Although evidence for such factors is sparse, a bacterial analogy may again be relevant: to obtain high levels of expression of certain operons, the action of a positive regulatory protein, the catabolite activator protein (CAP), is required. CAP, in the presence of 3′,5′-cAMP, binds to promoter regions and facilitates the binding of RNA polymerase and, subsequently, transcription initiation. The DNA sequence with which CAP interacts has been well studied in several cases (e.g., *lac*, reviewed in 181). The "CAP site" is a region located upstream of the Pribnow box and −35 homology, roughly between −50 and −70 nucleotides from the mRNA start site. It is conceivable that the upstream elements of eukaryotic RNA polymerase II promoters serve similar functions. This would raise the exciting possibility that different classes of proteins may positively regulate the expression of mammalian genes. In fact, two genes that are inducible—the herpes virus thymidine kinase gene, which is induced by an early viral protein, and the mouse mammary tumor virus, which is induced by glucocorticoid hormones—require sequences upstream of −50 for induction (183, 184). Additionally, as discussed above, the silk fibroin gene is more efficiently expressed *in vitro* in lysates prepared from homologous (i.e., *B. mori* posterior silk-gland) cells than it is in heterologous (i.e., HeLa) cell lysates (130). Interestingly, sequences in the −70 region (i.e., "upstream sequences") are required for this enhanced expression.

The third element of the eukaryotic promoter, the TATA box, is almost certainly a point with which RNA polymerase II makes contact in the process of initiating transcription. It appears that interaction between RNA polymerase II and a region of DNA containing the TATA box "fixes" the site at which transcription initiates, so that RNA synthesis begins, almost invariably, 25–30 nucleotides downstream of the TATA box. The sequence at the start site is probably of little importance, except that adenosine starts are preferred, perhaps simply because ATP is the most abundant nucleotide in the cell [with *E. coli*

RNA polymerase, the K_m for the first nucleotide is approximately ten times the K_m for subsequent nucleotides (see 185)].

The above model, if nothing else, offers explanations for why additional sequences are required for obtaining maximal efficiency of transcription initiation in vivo than are required in vitro. For example, far-upstream sequences (i.e., enhancers) may not be required because the template is "naked," relaxed (or linear) DNA, and transcription occurs in a soluble lysate. Thus factors that affect DNA supercoiling, nucleosome phasing, or nuclear localization would likely be of no importance in vitro. If upstream sequences are indeed sites with which positive regulatory factors interact, it is certainly possible that such factors are lost or destroyed during extract preparation, or that a required cofactor is missing. Consistent with this notion is the fact that transcription in vivo is 10- to 100-fold more efficient than in vitro.

To conclude this section, I speculate on what determines promoter "strength." In vitro, the answer is clear: the TATA box, and surrounding nucleotides, are the predominant factor. (More than just the sequence 5'-TATA-3' is required: the sequence 5'-TATAAAA-3', which is the sequence of the strong adenovirus late TATA box, occurs at sites other than in promoters. However, these "TATA boxes" direct RNA synthesis in vitro very inefficiently at best.)

In vivo, both the TATA box and the upstream sequence element probably contribute directly to promoter strength. Promoters that have "good" TATA boxes may be less dependent on upstream sequences, while the strength of promoters that have "poor" TATA boxes may depend more on upstream sequences. This appears to be the case in prokaryotes: the well-studied lac promoter mutant UV5 has two base changes that alter the Pribnow box so that it exactly matches the consensus sequence. The consequences of this mutation are that in vivo, although the maximal rate of transcription initiation is not significantly altered, transcription is now essentially independent of CAP; i.e., the "upstream sequences" are no longer required to obtain high levels of expression. Also, in vitro, where CAP protein is a limiting factor, the UV5 promoter is ten times "stronger" than the wild-type promoter (see 181). However, whether this prokaryotic analogy applies to eukaryotes is not yet clear. In fact, it is difficult to say at the moment whether a particular promoter is strong or weak in vivo, owing, at least in part, to problems arising from possible differential rates of RNA processing and/or turnover. Further experiments are required to answer this question, as well as many others dealing with the structure and function of the RNA polymerase II promoter.

B. mRNA Processing

Genetic analysis of the signals that control mRNA processing in mammalian cells is quite a new field. Therefore, mutations that affect mRNA splicing, 3' end formation, polyadenylylation and termination are all discussed in this section.

1. SPLICING

As with RNA polymerase II promoters, the first clues as to what nucleotide sequences in pre-mRNA might be important in directing splicing came from DNA sequence analysis of cloned genes. When the sequences of genomic clones are compared with cDNA clones, not only can the exon–intron boundaries be deduced, but also, sequences from different splice sites can be compared to determine whether a particular nucleotide sequence is conserved. In fact, such an analysis led to "Chambon's rule": all introns start at the 5' end with G-U and end at the 3' end with A-G (78). Further analysis of nucleotide sequences (e.g., 79, 80, 186) led to a longer "consensus splice sequence":

$$5'\text{-}(C/A)AG|GU(A/G)A\ GU\ldots(C/U)_3N(C/U)AG|G\text{-}3'$$

Exon   Intron   Exon

This consensus sequence was derived by examination of over 130 splice sites (186). Interestingly, Chambon's rule (G-U . . . A-G) was never violated. The other positions are filled with the indicated nucleotide(s) roughly 60 to 95% of the time.

Genetic analysis has thus been directed toward establishing that this consensus sequence is of functional importance, as well as determining what role (if any) the remainder of the intron plays in splicing. One early study examined naturally occurring deletion mutants of SV40 and found that large deletions, as long as they did not remove a splice junction, had no effect on the accumulation in infected cells of correctly spliced T antigen mRNA (187). Another study created a hybrid gene by fusing the first exon of the SV40 early region with the third exon of the mouse β-globin gene, in the process also forming a hybrid intron (188). Despite the fact that the two exons were from such different sources, the RNA produced when this plasmid was transfected into monkey cells was efficiently spliced. This suggests that splicing can occur between a wide range of donor and acceptor splice sites, and again implies that sequences within the intron, away from the intron–exon boundary, are not important for splicing. Finally, deletions constructed *in vitro* that remove up to 77% of a rabbit β-globin intron do not affect splicing of this RNA (165).

Several studies have examined the effects of point mutations on splicing. In one (*189*), a fragment of adenovirus DNA containing the E1A region (see Fig. 1) was purified and mutagenized with nitrous acid. Intact viral DNA molecules were reconstructed and screened for defects in E1A function. One mutant was shown to be defective in splicing. DNA sequence analysis revealed that the mutant had two transversions in the 5′ consensus sequence, at positions 5 and 6 following the splice site. Further experiments strongly suggested that these two mutational changes were responsible for the almost total lack of splicing of the affected RNA. In another study, a number of single-base transition mutations were introduced by site-specific techniques into the cloned rabbit β-globin gene (*190*). Mutagenized DNAs were separated by recloning, and nucleotide changes were ascertained by DNA sequence analysis. The effects of single-base changes at six different positions in the 5′ consensus sequence were determined after transfection into HeLa cells. The only mutation that had a detectable effect on splicing was one that changed the first nucleotide of the intron from G to A. (This is one of the highly conserved nucleotides that make up Chambon's rule; see above.) This change completely eliminated splicing at that site. Finally, using oligonucleotide-directed site-specific mutagenesis (e.g., *16*), a single T-to-G transversion was constructed so that the second "Chambon's rule" nucleotide in the adenovirus E1A 5′ splice site was altered (*191*). This mutation also resulted in drastically reduced splicing. These results suggest that, at least at the 5′ splice site, the "Chambon's rule" nucleotides must remain inviolate, but alteration of the other nucleotides may or may not affect splicing.

In the above-mentioned study, which showed that a base change in the first nucleotide of the rabbit β-globin large intron abolished correct splicing, an interesting additional observation was made: inactivation of the normal 5′ splice site resulted in the utilization by the splicing machinery of three different sites. These sequences are apparently never utilized when the normal 5′ splice site is functional. While two of these "cryptic" splice sites show reasonable agreement with the "consensus" sequence, one displays only, at best, very limited homology: 5′-TAAA|GCTGAG-3′. Note that this sequence, in fact, even violates Chambon's rule.

Several other examples of the activation of cryptic splice sites by mutation have been observed. One particularly interesting class consists of natural mutations in the human globin genes that result in β-(or α)thalassemia. In one case, a single point mutation within the first intron of the β-globin gene gives rise to a nucleotide sequence that fits the 3′ splice site consensus sequence very precisely (*192*). In fact, when this gene is introduced into animal cells, high levels of the improperly spliced RNA are detected, while only low levels of correctly spliced RNA are produced (*193, 194*). Another β-thalassemic gene contains a single base-change at the first nucleotide of the large intron (*195*). In this case, no authentic β-globin mRNA is detected, although two incorrectly spliced speces are produced. Finally, a small (five base-pair) deletion in the first intron of a human α-globin gene that abuts the 5' exon–intron junction results in the inactivation of the normal 5' splices site and the utilization of an upstream cryptic splice site (*196*).

In summary, it appears that only nucleotide sequences at or very near splice junction are required for splicing. Further, except for the "Chambon rule" nucleotide, these sequences are by no means invariant. When a normal splice-site is destroyed, other nearby sequences that resemble the consensus sequence are sometimes utilized as splice donors or acceptors, often with high efficiencies. Why some "cryptic" splice sites are used and others are not, and why these sites are not normally utilized, is not clear. Two factors are probably relevant. First, pre-mRNA undoubtedly forms complex secondary and tertiary structures and is most likely associated with a variety of proteins. Such structures may mask certain splice sites that might otherwise be utilized. Second, factors (nucleotide sequences or specific proteins) that we have not yet identified may make some splice sites much "better" than others. However, no adequate methods currently exist for measuring whether one splice site is stronger than another. Since the concentration of pre-mRNAs in cells is extremely low, it is virtually impossible to follow the kinetics of RNA splicing *in vivo*. Therefore, it is likely that measurements of splice site "strength" will require the development of *in vitro* systems capable of efficient splicing. The answers to many other important questions, such as whether there is any polarity to the splicing process, and whether the reaction is processive, are not known and will require additional work.

2. 3' END FORMATION AND POLYADENYLYLATION

Genetic analysis of RNA polymerase II promoters and mRNA splice sites was preceeded by DNA sequence analysis that identified certain conserved nucleotide sequences as candidates for controlling elements. Subsequent mutagenesis experiments have confirmed the role of such sequences in these processes and have also provided insights into the mechanisms by which these important reactions are carried out. A strikingly similar approach is beginning to yield information about how the 3' ends of mRNAs are created. It was first observed that the nucleotide sequence 5'-AAUAAA-3' is found approximately twenty nucleotides upstream from the 3' ends of several different mRNAs (197). This sequence, or a closely related derivative, has since been found within ten to thirty nucleotides from the 3' end of virtually every animal mRNA studied to date. (An exception is the histone mRNAs. However, these mRNAs are not polyadenylylated, and, as discussed elsewhere in this article, their 3' ends are probably created by a different mechanism than is used with most mRNAs.)

This analysis strongly suggests that this highly conserved sequence is important in the creation of mRNA 3' ends. Two genetic analyses support this notion. In one, deletion mutations were constructed *in vitro* in SV40 DNA in the region that encodes the 3' end of SV40 late mRNAs, and the consequences of these mutations on the synthesis of polyadenylylated late mRNAs were determined (198). Three different types of effects were observed. First, small deletions that remove DNA segments between the AATAAA sequence and the normal mRNA 3' end site (a distance of 12 nucleotides in the wild type) gave rise to normal quantities of polyadenylylated mRNA. However, the mRNA now extends to sequences slightly downstream (always 11–19 nucleotides downstream from the AAUAAA sequence). This result is consistent with the notion that the AAUAAA sequence serves as a recognition signal for an enzyme or enzyme complex that catalyzes RNA cleavage and polyadenylylation a set distance downstream from this sequence. Another mutant analyzed had 12 base-pairs of DNA deleted just upstream of this site. This mutant also gave rise to normal amounts of steady-state cytoplasmic mRNA. However the mRNAs produced now had at least two different 3' ends, one of which was only two nucleotides downstream of the AAUAAA sequence. Finally, a sixteen base-pair deletion that removed the AAUAAA sequence completely prevented 3' end formation. These results confirm that the AAUAAA sequence constitutes a part of the signal required for proper formation of polyadenylylated mRNA 3' ends.

Another study utilized oligonucleotide-directed site-specific mutagenesis to change the AATAAA sequence at the 3' end of the adenovirus early region 1A to AAGAAA. The effects of this mutation were then determined by analysis of E1A-specific RNA produced following infection of HeLa cells with the mutant virus (C. Montell, E. Fisher, M. Caruthers, and A. J. Berk, manuscript in preparation). The results show that the concentration of E1A-specific mRNA in the cytoplasm is reduced to 10–20% of that in wild-type infected cells. The concentration of nuclear RNAs, though, was unaltered. However, new nuclear RNA species were observed: about 90% of the RNA extended well beyond the wild-type 3′ end site (in fact, as far as the 3′ end site for the adjacent E1B region; see Fig. 1). The 3′ ends of the remaining 10% were at the normal 3′ end site. While all of these latter RNAs were polyadenylylated, only about 50% of the remainder of the RNA was polyadenylylated (although this RNA may consist exclusively of nascent chains). These results again emphasize the important role of the AAUAAA sequence in mRNA 3′ end formation. Of particular interest is the finding that a substantial fraction of the RNAs that read through into the E1B region are improperly spliced, such that sequences at the 3′ end of E1A now function as 5′ splice sites, and sequences at the 5′ end of E1B serve as 3′ splice sites. This result is consistent with the idea that the utilization of an mRNA 3′ end site may influence RNA splicing. This mechanism was previously implicated in the expression of immunoglobulin genes (*199, 200*).

Finally, it should be pointed out that the sequence AAUAAA cannot constitute the entire recognition signal, since this sequence occurs at sites within genes, where it is apparently not utilized. Whether the remainder of the signal consists of additional nucleotide sequences or a specific RNA secondary or tertiary structure is not yet clear. Also not known is whether the poly(A) polymerase or endonuclease recognizes this signal. However, as discussed in Section I,D, these enzymes are probably part of a single enzyme complex. The development of *in vitro* systems that carry out these reactions should allow the resolution of this and related questions in the near future.

3. TERMINATION

It remains to be shown conclusively that the 3′ end of any mRNA is formed by transcription termination. However, for reasons already discussed in this article, it is very likely that transcription terminates at the 3′ end of histone genes. Thus, it is appropriate to discuss here experiments that define sequences required to create his tone mRNA 3′ ends.

As mentioned above, a highly conserved 23-base-pair DNA sequence is found at the 3′ end of all animal histone genes (e.g., *107*). This sequence contains within it a sixteen-base-pair interrupted inverted repeat and ends in 5′-ACCA-3′. This tetranucleotide immediately follows the hyphenated repeat and also coincides precisely with the histone mRNA 3′ end.

The conserved sequence, as well as sequences downstream from it, are required for the generation of histone H2A mRNA 3′ ends (*201*). This conclusion is based on analysis of a variety of deletion mutants constructed *in vitro*. The results show that deletion of either a segment of DNA containing the entire conserved sequence or a twelve-base-pair fragment that destroys the inverted repeat suffices to prevent transcription termination when the mutated genes are injected into *X. laevis* oocytes. Transcription initiation and RNA stability are, however, not affected. Although sequences upstream from the conserved sequence are probably not required for termination, sequences that lie downstream from the gene appear to be: insertion of an approximately 60-base-pair fragment containing the conserved sequence and four nucleotides downstream from it into the histone H2B gene does not bring about transcription termination of that gene. More precise mapping of this downstream element is not yet available. Further studies will thus be required to define exactly what sequences are required to bring about transcription termination, as well as to learn about the mechanism of the reaction.

The 3' ends of most mRNAs are probably created by cleavage rather than termination. Therefore, transcription must terminate at sites downstream from the gene. However, as discussed above, the sites at which transcription does indeed terminate, with one possible exception, have not been identified. Thus, important goals in this area will be to identify such sites, to learn how they function and what the role, if any, of this downstream transcription might be.

III. Summary

How, then, is a messenger RNA synthesized in the nucleus of an animal cell, and how might this synthesis be regulated? While it is not yet possible to answer all parts of this question in great detail, the experiments discussed here indicate that significant progress toward this goal has been made. In fact, it is now possible to outline a pathway by which a "typical" mammalian mRNA might be synthesized. While such an outline must, by necessity, be quite vague and, in some parts, speculative, this approach offers a good way to summarize this article.

Transcription begins by an interaction between RNA polymerase II, as part of a larger enzyme complex, with DNA sequences upstream of the transcription start site that extend over a region of about 100 base-pairs. DNA sequences even farther upstream are in fact required for the expression of many genes, but it may be that RNA polymerase does not interact directly with this region. Very shortly after transcription initiation, or perhaps concomitantly with it, the RNA 5' end is "capped" by enzymes associated with RNA polymerase. As transcription proceeds, the nascent RNA is subject to further modification, such as internal methylation and splicing. Whether a given splice occurs before transcription is completed is a function of both the length of the transcription unit and also the affinity of the splicing enzyme complex for the nucleotide sequences at that particular splice site. RNA polymerase continues transcription past the 3' end of the gene and terminates transcription at a site a considerable distance downstream. The mRNA 3' end is created by endonucleolytic cleavage, followed by polyadenylylation. After completion of splicing, synthesis of the mRNA is complete, and the mRNA is transported to the cytoplasm. Regulation of gene expression can certainly occur at the transcription initiation step and very likely at many, if not all, of the latter steps as well. The development of *in vitro* systems to study the enzymology of transcription, as well as *in vitro* mutagenesis techniques to study the genetics of transcription, are, to a large degree, responsible for the progress that has been made in the last few years. It is likely that these methods will be of increasing value during the upcoming years, which promise to be exciting ones indeed for the field of eukaryotic molecular biology.

ACKNOWLEDGMENTS

I thank many colleagues who supplied me with the details of their work prior to publication, C. Prives and R. Jove for their thoughtful comments, and M. Hatch for preparing the manuscript. Work cited from the author's laboratory was supported by National Institutes of Health Grant GM 28983.

REFERENCES

1. S. M. Berget, C. Moore, and P. A. Sharp, *PNAS* **74**, 3171 (1977).
2. L. T. Chow, R. E. Gelinas, T. R. Broker, and R. J. Roberts, *Cell* **12**, (1977).
3. D. F. Klessig, *Cell* **12**, 9 (1977).
4. S. Sakonju, D. F. Bogenhagen, and D. D. Brown, *Cell* **19**, 13 (1980).
5. D. F. Bogenhagen, S. Sakonju, and D. D. Brown, *Cell* **19**, 27 (1980).
6. J. Corden, B. Wasylyk, A. Buchwalder, P. Sassone-Corsi, C. Kedinger, and P. Chambon, *Science* **209**, 1406 (1980).
7. S.-L. Hu and J. L. Manley, *PNAS* **78**, 820 (1981).
8. C. Benoist and P. Chambon, *Nature* **290**, 304 (1981).
9. J. Banerji, S. Rusconi, and W. Schaffner, *Cell* **27**, 299 (1981).
10. S. E. Conrad and M. R. Botchan, *Mol. Cell Biol.* **2**, 949 (1982).
11. P. Moreau, R. Hen, B. Wasylyk, R. Everett, M. P. Gaub, and P. Chambon, *NARes* **9**, 6047 (1981).
12. T. Maniatis, R. Hardison, E. Lacy, J. Lauer, C. O'Connell, D. Quon, G.-K. Sim, and A. Efstradiatis, *Cell* **15**, 687 (1978).
13. F. L. Graham and A. J. van der Eb, *Virology* **52**, 456 (1973).
14. M. Wigler, S. Silverstein, L. S. Lee, A. Pellicier, Y. C. Cheng, and R. Axel, *Cell* **11**, 223 (1977).
15. D. Shortle and D. Nathans, *PNAS* **75**, 2170 (1978).

16. S. Gillam and M. Smith, *Gene* **8**, 81 (1979).
17. G.-J. Wu, *PNAS* **75**, 21,55 (1978).
18. P. A. Weil, D. S. Luse, J. Segal, and R. G. Roeder, *Cell* **18**, 469 (1979).
19. J. L. Manley, A. Fire, A. Cano, P. A. Sharp, and M. L. Gefter, *PNAS* **77**, 3855 (1980).
20. G. Zubay, D. Chambers, and L. Cheong, *in* "The Lactose Operon" (J. Beckwith and D. Zipser, eds.), p. 375. Cold Spring Harbor Laboratory, Cold Spring Harbor, New York, 1970.
21. R. G. Roeder, *in* "RNA Polymerase" (R. Losick and M. Chamberlin, p. 285. Cold Spring Harbor Laboratory, Cold Spring Harbor, New York, 1976.
22. P. Chambon, *ARB* **44**, 613 (1975).
23. P. Lebowitz and S. M. Weissman, *Curr. Top. Microbiol. Immunol.* **87**, 43 (1979).
24. R. Breathnach and P. Chambon, *ARB* **50**, 349 (1981).
24a. S. J. Flint, *CRC Crit. Rev. Biochem*, in press.
25. T. Shenk, *Curr. Top. Microbiol. Immunol.* **93**, 25 (1981).
26. A. J. Shatkin, *Cell* **9**, 645 (1976).
26a. Symposium on mRNA: The Relation of Structure to Function, This Series **19** (1976).
27. E. Ziff and R. Evans, *Cell* **15**, 1463 (1978).
28. J. L. Manley, S.-L. Hu, P. A. Sharp, and M. L. Gefter, *ICN-UCLA Symp.* **18**, 353 (1980).
29. L.-M. Wei and B. Moss, *PNAS* **74**, 3758 (1977).
30. Y. Groner, E. Gilboa, and H. Aviv, *Bchem* **17**, 977 (1978).
31. D. Gidoni, C. Kahara, D. Canaani, and Y. Groner, *PNAS* **78**, 2174 (1981).
32. R. Contreras and W. Fiers, *NARes* **9**, 215 (1981).
33. T. Yamamoto, B. de Crombrugghe, and I. Pastan, *Cell* **22**, 787 (1980).
34. O. Hagenbuchle and U. Schibler, *PNAS* **78**, 2283 (1981).
35. C. Baker and E. Ziff, *JMB* **149**, 189 (1981).
36. A. Fire, C. C. Baker, J. L. Manley, E. B. Ziff, and P. A. Sharp, *J. Virol.* **40**, 703 (1981).
37. A. Cowie, P. Jat, and R. Kamen, *JMB* **159**, 225 (1982).
38. C. Baker, J. Herisse, G. Courtois, R. Galibert, and E. Ziff, *Cell* **18**, 569 (1979).
39. L. T. Malek, W. H. Eshenfedt, T. W. Munns, and R. E. Rhoads, *NARes* **9**, 1657 (1981).
40. M. Grez, H. Land, K. Giesecke, G. Schutz, A. Jung, and A. Sippel, *Cell* **25**, 743 (1981).
41. D. Canaani, C. Kahana, A. Mukamel, and Y. Groner, *PNAS* **76**, 3078 (1979).
42. P. K. Ghosh, V. B. Reddy, J. Swinscoe, P. Lebowitz, and S. M. Wiessman, *JMB* **126**, 813 (1978).
43. G. Haegeman and W. Fiers, *J. Virol.* **25**, 824 (1978).
44. A. J. Flavell, A. Cowie, S. Legon, and R. Kamen, *Cell* **16**, 357 (1979).
45. O. Hagenbuchle, M. Tosi, U. Schibler, R. Bovey, P. K. Wellauer, and R. A. Young, *Nature* **289**, 643 (1981).
46. P. K. Ghosh, M. Piatak, J. E. Mertz, S. M. Wiessman, and P. Lebowitz, *J. Virol.* **44**, 610 (1982).
47. R. Losick and M. Chamberlin, eds. "RNA Polymerase." Cold Spring Harbor Laboratory, Cold Spring Harbor, New York, 1976.
47a. M. K. Lewis and R. R. Burgess, *JBC* **255**, 4928 (1980).
48. T. Matsui, J. Segall, and R. G. Roeder, *JBC* **255**, 11992 (1980).
49. W. S. Dynan and R. Tjian, *ICN–UCLA Symp.* **23**, 401 (1981).
50. M. Samuels, A. Fire, and P. A. Sharp, *JBC* **257**, 14019 (1982).

51. S. M. Sommer, M. Salditt-Gorgieff, S. Bachenheimer, J. E. Darnell, Y. Furuichi, M. Morgan, and A. J. Shatkin, *NARes* **3**, 749 (1976).
52. B. Moss and F. Koczot, *J. Virol.* **17**, 305 (1976).
53. M. Salditt-Georgieff, M. Harpold, S. Chen-Kiang and J. E. Darnell, *Cell* **19**, 69 (1980).
54. A. Babich, J. R. Nevins, and J. E. Darnell, Jr., *Nature* **287**, 246 (1980).
55. J. L. Manley, P. A. Sharp, and M. L. Gefter, *PNAS* **76**, 160 (1979).
56. Y. Furuichi, *PNAS* **75**, 1086 (1978).
57. R. Jove and J. L. Manley, *PNAS* **79**, 5842 (1982).
58. D. Bunick, R. Zandomeni, S. Ackerman, and R. Weinmann, *Cell* **29**, 877 (1982).
59. R. Reddy and H. Busch, *in* "The Cell Nucleus" (H. Busch, ed.), p. 261. Academic Press, New York, 1981. Also in this volume.
60. C. Branlant, A. Krol, J. P. Ebel, E. Lazer, H. Gallinoro, M. Jacob, J. Sri-Widada, and P. Jenateur, *NARes* **8**, 4143 (1980).
61. J. T. Murphy, R. R. Burgess, J. E. Dahlberg, and E. Lund, *Cell* **29**, 265 (1982).
62. S. Chen-Kiang, J. R. Nevins, and J. E. Darnell, *JMB* **135**, 733 (1979).
63. C. L. Peebles, R. C. Ogden, G. Knapp, and J. Abelson, *Cell* **18**, 27 (1979).
64. G. Knapp, R. C. Ogden, C. L. Peebles, and J. Abelson, *Cell* **18**, 37 (1979).
65. C. L. Peebles, P. Gegenhiemer, and J. Abelson, *Cell* **32**, 525 (1983).
66. C. L. Greer, C. L. Peebles, P. Gegenheimer, and J. Abelson, *Cell* **32**, 537 (1983).
67. R. C. Ogden, J. S. Beckman, J. Abelson, H. S. Kang, D. Söll, and O. Schmidt, *Cell* **17**, 399 (1979).
68. D. N. Standring, A. Venegas, and W. J. Rutter, *PNAS* **78**, 5963 (1981).
69. A. J. Zaug and T. R. Cech, *NARes* **10**, 2823 (1982).
70. T. R. Cech, A. J. Zaug, and P. J. Grabowski, *Cell* **27**, 487 (1982).
71. K. Kruger, P. J. Grabowski, A. J. Zaug, J. Sands, D. E. Gottschling, and T. R. Cech, *Cell* **31**, 147 (1982).
72. S. J. Flint and T. R. Broker, *in* "The DNA Tumor Viruses (J. Tooze, ed.), p. 443. Cold Spring Harbor Laboratory, Cold Spring Harbor, New York, 1981.
73. J.-M. Blanchard, J. Weber, W. J. Jelinek, and J. E. Darnell, *PNAS* **75**, 5344 (1978).
74. C. J. Goldenberg and H. J. Raskas, *Bchem* **19**, 2719 (1980).
75. V.-W. Yang and S. J. Flint, *J. Virol.* **32**, 394 (1979).
76. V.-W. Yang, M. H. Binger, and S. J. Flint, *JBC* **255**, 2097 (1980).
77. V.-W. Yang, M. R. Lerner, J. A. Steitz, and S. J. Flint, *PNAS* **78**, 1371 (1981).
78. R. Breathnach, C. Benoist, K. O'Hare, F. Gannon, and P. Chambon, *PNAS* **75**, 4853 (1978).
79. I. Seif, G. Khoury, and R. Dhar, *NARes* **6**, 3387 (1979).
80. P. A. Sharp, *Cell* **23**, 643 (1981).
81. M. R. Lerner, J. A. Boyle, S. M. Mount, S. L. Wolin, and J. A. Steitz, *Nature* **283**, 220 (1980).
82. J. Rodgers and R. Wall, *PNAS* **77**, 1877 (1980).
82a. A. Fradin, R. Jove, C. Hemenway, J. L. Manley, and C. Prives, unpublished.
83. J. L. Manley, P. A. Sharp, and M. L. Gefter, *JMB* **135**, 171 (1979).
84. J. L. Manley, P. A. Sharp, and M. L. Gefter, *JMB* **159**, 581 (1982).
85. L.-J. Lai, R. Dhar, and G. Khoury, *Cell* **14**, 971 (1978).
86. J. R. Nevins and J. E. Darnell, *Cell* **15**, 1477 (1979).
87. M. Zeevi, J. R. Nevins, and J. E. Darnell, *Cell* **26**, 39 (1981).
88. A. L. Beyer, A. H. Bouton, and O. L. Miller, Jr. *Cell* **26**, 155 (1981).
89. H. Handa, R. Kaufman, J. L. Manley, M. L. Gefter, and P. A. Sharp, *JBC* **256**, 478 (1981).

90. B. Weingartner and W. Keller, *PNAS* **78**, 4092 (1981).
91. C. J. Goldenerg and H. J. Raskas, *PNAS* **78**, 5430 (1981).
92. R. Kole and S. Weissman, *NARes* **10**, 5429 (1982).
93. R. Berezney and D. S. Coffey, *J. Cell Biol.* **73**, 616 (1977).
94. R. S. Fuller, J. M. Kaguni, and A. Kornberg, *PNAS* **78**, 7370 (1981).
95. J. L. Manley and M. Colozzo, *Nature* **300**, 376 (1982).
95a. J. L. Manley, *Cell* **33**, 595 (1983).
96. J. P. Ford and M.-T. Hsu, *J. Virol.* **28**, 795 (1978).
97. J. R. Nevins, J.-M. Blanchard, and J. E. Darnell, *JMB* **144**, 377 (1980).
98. E. Hofer and J. E. Darnell, *Cell* **23**, 585 (1981).
99. G. C. Grosveld, A. Koster, and R. A. Flavell, *Cell* **23**, 573 (1981).
100. J. L. Manley, M. L. Gefter, and P. A. Sharp, *ICN–UCLA Symp.* **14**, 595 (1979).
101. S. Chen-Kiang, D. J. Wolgemuth, M.-T. Hsu, and J. E. Darnell, *Cell* **28**, 575 (1982).
102. M. Edmonds and R. Abrams, *JBC* **237**, 1008 (1962).
103. M. Edmonds and M. A. Winters, This Series **17**, 149 (1976).
104. G. Brawerman, This Series **17**, 117 (1976).
105. G. Brawerman, *CRC Crit. Rev. Biochem.* **10**, 1 (1981).
106. U. Z. Littauer and H. Soreq, This Series **27**, 53 (1982).
107. M. Buslinger, R. Portmann, and M. L. Birnsteil, *NARes* **6**, 2997 (1979).
108. M. Rosenberg and D. Court, *Annu. Rev. Genet.* **13**, 319 (1979).
109. A. Mauron, S. Levy, G. Childs, and L. Kedes, *Mol. Cell. Biol.* **1**, 661 (1981).
110. A. Seiler-Tuyns and M. L. Birnsteil, *JMB* **151**, 607 (1981).
111. H. G. Stunnenberg and M. L. Birnsteil, *PNAS* **79**, 6201 (1982).
112. A. R. Shaw and E. B. Ziff, *Cell* **20**, 905 (1980).
113. G. Akusjarvi and H. Persson, *Nature* **292**, 420 (1981).
114. J. B. Lewis and M. B. Mathews, *Cell* **21**, 303 (1980).
115. N. W. Frazer, J. R. Nevins, E. Ziff, and J. E. Darnell, *JMB* **129**, 643 (1979).
116. N. H. Acheson and F. Mieville, *J. Virol.* **28**, 885 (1978).
117. N. H. Acheson, E. Buetti, K. Scherrer, and R. Weil, *PNAS* **68**, 2231 (1971).
118. N. H. Acheson, *PNAS* **75**, 4754 (1978).
119. S. Tonegawa, G. Walter, A. Bernardini, and R. Dulbecco, *CSHSQB* **35**, 823 (1971).
120. R. A. Weinberg, S. O. Warnaar, and E. Winocour, *J. Virol.* **13**, 1263 (1972).
120a. D. Grass and J. L. Manley, unpublished.
121. G. Zubay, *Annu. Rev. Genet.* **7**, 267 (1978).
122. P. M. Tegtmeyer, J. K. Schwartz, J. K. Collins, and K. Rundell, *J. Virol.* **16**, 168 (1975).
123. S. I. Reed, G. R. Stark, and J. C. Alwine, *PNAS* **73**, 3083 (1976).
123a. G. Khoury and E. May, *J. Virol.* **23**, 167 (1977).
124. R. Tjian, *Cell* **13**, 165 (1978).
125. D. Rio, A. Robbins, R. Myers, and R. Tjian, *PNAS* **77**, 5706 (1980).
126. R. M. Myers, D. C. Rio, A. K. Robbins, and R. Tjian, *Cell* **25**, 373 (1981).
127. P. K. Ghosh and P. Lebowitz, *J. Virol.* **40**, 224 (1981).
128. U. Hansen, D. G. Tenen, D. M. Livingston, and P. A. Sharp, *Cell* **27**, 603 (1981).
129. T. H. Carter and R. A. Blanton, *J. Virol.* **25**, 664 (1978).
129a. H. Handa and P. Sharp, unpublished.
130. M. Tsuda and Y. Suzuki, *Cell* **27**, 175 (1981).
131. N. J. Proudfoot, M. H. M. Shander, J. L. Manley, M. L. Gefter, and T. Maniatis, *Science* **209**, 1329 (1980).
132. D. S. Luse and R. G. Roeder, *Cell* **20**, 691 (1980).

133. P. U. C. Hough, I. A. Mastrangelo, J. S. Wall, J. F. Hainfield, M. N. Simon, and J. L. Manley, *JMB* **160**, 375 (1982).
134. J. L. Manley, *in* "Genetic Engineering" (J. K. Setlow and A. Hollaender, eds.), Vol. 4, p. 37. Plenum, New York, 1982.
135. L. Vardimon, A. Kressman, H. Cedar, M. Muechler, and W. Doerfler, *PNAS* **79**, 1073 (1982).
136. A. Fradin, J. L. Manley, and C. Prives, *PNAS* **79**, 5142 (1982).
137. R. Stein, A. Razin, and H. Cedar, *PNAS* **79**, 3418 (1982).
137a. R. Jove and J. L. Manley, unpublished.
138. P. Mellon, U. Parker, Y. Gluzman, and T. Maniatis, *Cell* **27**, 279 (1981).
139. M.-F. Law, D. R. Lowy, I. Dvoretzky, and P. M. Howley, *PNAS* **78**, 2727 (1981).
140. A. Maxam and W. Gilbert, *PNAS* **74**, (1977).
141. F. Sanger, S. Nicklen, and A. R. Coulson, *PNAS* **74**, 5463 (1977).
142. M. Goldberg, Ph.D. Thesis, Stanford Univ., Palo Alto, California, 1979.
143. D. Pribnow, *PNAS* **72**, 784 (1975).
144. H. Schaller, C. Gray, and K. Hermann, *PNAS* **72**, 737 (1975).
145. S. T. Tsai, M. J. Tsai, and B. W. O'Malley, *PNAS* **78**, 879 (1981).
146. G. C. Grosveld, C. K. Shewmaker, P. Jat, and R. A. Flavell, *Cell* **25**, (1981).
147. B. Wasylyk, R. Derbyshire, A. Guy, D. Molko, A. Roget, R. Teoule, and P. Chambon, *PNAS* **77**, 7024 (1980).
148. B. Wasylyk and P. Chambon, *NARes* **9**, 1813 (1981).
149. R. Grosschedl, B. Wasylyk, P. Chambon, and M. L. Birnstiel, *Nature* **294**, 178 (1981).
150. D. C. Lee and R. G. Roeder, *Mol. Cell. Biol.* **1**, 635 (1981).
151. D. Mathis and P. Chambon, *Nature* **290**, 310 (1981).
152. P. Lebowitz and P. K. Ghosh, *J. Virol.* **41**, 449 (1982).
153. R. Grosschedl and M. L. Birnstiel, *PNAS* **79**, 297 (1982).
154. R. Hen, P. Sassone-Corsi, J. Corden, M. P. Gaub, and P. Chambon, *PNAS* **79**, 7132 (1982).
155. A. S. Mitsialis, J. L. Manley, and R. V. Guntaka *Mol. Cell. Biol.* **3**, 811 (1983).
155a. R. Jove and J. L. Manley, *JBC*, in press.
156. Y. Tsujimoto, S. Hirose, M. Tsuda, and Y. Suzuki, *PNAS* **78**, 4838 (1981).
157. D. C. Lee, R. G. Roeder, and W. S. M. Wold, *PNAS* **79**, 41 (1982).
158. D. Shortle, D. Koshland, G. M. Weinstock, and D. Botstein, *PNAS* **77**, 5375 (1980).
159. S. Hirose, K. Takeuchi, and Y. Suzuki, *PNAS* **79**, 7258 (1982).
160. C. Benoist and P. Chambon, *Nature* **290**, 304 (1981).
161. P. Ghosh, P. Lebowitz, J. Frisque, and Y. Gluzman, *PNAS* **78**, 100 (1981).
162. R. Grosschedl and M. Birnstiel, *PNAS* **77**, 1432 (1980).
163. T. F. Osborne, R. B. Gaynor, and A. J. Berk, *Cell* **29**, 139 (1982).
164. T. F. Osborne and A. J. Berk, *J. Virol.* in press.
165. P. Dierks, B. Wieringa, D. Marti, J. Reiser, A. van Ooyen, F. Meyer, H. Weber, and C. Weissman, *ICN–UCLA Symp.* **23**, 347 (1981).
166. G. C. Grosveld, E. de Boer, C. K. Shewmaker, and R. Flavell, *Nature* **295**, 120 (1982).
167. S. L. McKnight, E. R. Gavis, R. Kingsbury, R. Axel, *Cell* **25**, 385 (1981).
168. S. G. Read and W. C. Summers, *PNAS* **79**, 5215 (1982).
169. R. Groscheldl and M. L. Birnstiel, *PNAS* **77**, 7102 (1980).
170. B. J. Byrne, M. S. Davis, J. Yamaguchi, D. J. Bergsma, and K. N. Subramanian, *PNAS*, in press.

171. P. Gruss, R. Dhar, and G. Khoury, *PNAS* **78**, 943 (1981).
172. B. Levinson, G. Khoury, G. Vande Woude, and P. Gruss, *Nature* **295**, 568 (1982).
173. J. de Villiers, and W. Schaffner, *NARes* **9**, 6252 (1981).
174. C. Tyndall, G. La Mantia, C. Thacker, J. Favaloro, and R. Kamen, *NARes* **9**, 6231 (1981).
175. L. A. Laimins, G. Khoury, C. Gorman, B. Howard, and P. Gruss, *PNAS* **79**, 6453 (1982).
176. J. B. Gurdon and D. A. Melton, *Annu. Rev. Genet.* **15**, 189 (1981).
177. A. Efstradiatis, J. W. Posakony, T. Maniatis, R. M. Lawn, C. O'Connell, R. A. Spritz, J. K. DeRiel, B. G. Forget, S. M. Weissman, C. C. Slighton, and N. J. Proudfoot, *Cell* **21**, 653 (1980).
178. C. Benoist, K. O'Hare, R. Breathnach, and P. Chambon, *NARes* **8**, 127 (1980).
179. S. L. McKnight, *Cell* **31**, 355 (1982).
180. U. Siebenlist, R. B. Simpson, and W. Gilbert, *Cell* **20**, 269 (1980).
181. W. S. Reznikoff and J. N. Abelson, *in* "The Operon" (J. H. Miller and W. S. Reznikoff, eds.), p. 221. Cold Spring Harbor Laboratory, Cold Spring Harbor, New York, 1978.
182. J. E. Stefano and J. D. Gralla, *PNAS* **79**, 1069 (1982).
183. D. Zipser, L. Lipsich and J. Kwoh, *PNAS* **78**, 6276 (1981).
184. F. Lee, R. Mulligan, P. Berg, and G. Ringold, *Nature* **294**, 228 (1981).
185. M. J. Chamberlin, *in* "RNA Polymerase" (R. Losick and M. Chamberlin, eds.), p. 159. Cold Spring Harbor Laboratory, Cold Spring Harbor, New York, 1976.
186. S. M. Mount, *NARes* **10**, 459 (1982).
187. G. Khoury, P. Gruss, R. Dhar, and C.-J. Lai, *Cell* **18**, 85 (1979).
188. G. Chu and P. A. Sharp, *Nature* **289**, 378 (1981).
189. D. Solnick, Nature **291**, 508 (1981).
190. B. Wieringa, F. Meyer, J. Reiser, and C. Weissmann, *Nature* **301**, 38 (1983).
191. C. Montell, E. F. Fisher, M. H. Caruthers, and A. J. Berk, *Nature* **295**, 380 (1982).
192. R. A. Spritz, P. Jagadeeswaran, P. U. Choudary, P. A. Biro, J. T. Elder, J. K. de Riel, J. L. Manley, M. L. Gefter, B. G. Forget, and S. M. Weissman, *PNAS* **78**, 2455 (1981).
193. M. Busslinger, N. Moschonas, and R. A. Flavell, *Cell* **27**, 289 (1981).
194. Y. Fukumaki, P. K. Ghosh, E. J. Benz, Jr., V. B. Reddy, P. Lebowitz, B. G. Forget, and S. M. Weissman, *Cell* **28**, 585 (1982).
195. R. Treisman, N. J. Proudfoot, M. Shander, and T. Maniatis, *Cell* **29**, 903 (1982).
196. B. K. Felber, S. H. Orkin, and D. H. Hamer, *Cell* **29**, 895 (1982).
197. N. J. Proudfoot and G. G. Brownlee, *Nature* **263**, 211 (1976).
198. M. Fitzgerald and T. Shenk, *Cell* **24**, 251 (1976).
199. P. Early, J. Rogers, M. Davis, K. Calame, M. Band, R. Wall, and L. Hood, *Cell* **20**, 313 (1980).
200. R. Maki, W. Roeder, A. Traunecker, C. Sidman, M. Wabi, W. Raschke, and S. Tonegawa, *Cell* **24**, 353 (1981).
201. C. Birchmeier, R. Grosschedl, and M. L. Birnstiel, *Cell* **28**, 739 (1982).

Synthesis, Processing, and Gene Structure of Vasopressin and Oxytocin

DIETMAR RICHTER

*Institut für Physiologische Chemie,
Abteilung Zellbiochemie
Universität Hamburg,
Hamburg, Federal Republic of
Germany*

In recent years, several neuropeptide hormones have attracted attention as models for studying gene expression and regulation. These peptides have a number of interesting features. First, they are often multifunctional and may serve as neurotransmitters or neuromodulators. The nonapeptide hormone arginine vasopressin[1] (Table I), for example, increases blood pressure and controls water resorption in the distal kidney tubuli (reviewed in *1*). It is also considered to be involved in some step of the adrenocorticotropin-releasing process (*2*), and behavioral studies suggest that it may play a role in memory as well (*3*). Second, neuropeptides are not restricted to the central nervous system, being found also in the gastrointestinal tract and in other organs. The enkephalins, known to raise the threshold to pain, can be detected in brain as well as in the adrenal gland (*4*). Third, neuropeptides are synthesized as considerably larger, but biologically inactive,

---

[1] Also known as argininevasopressin and argipressin (International Nonproprietary Name, British Adopted Name, United States Adopted Name), analogous to lypressin, which is also a U.S. Adopted Name and an FDA Name. Abbreviated AVP. Other abbreviations are Np for neurophysin; OT for oxytocin. [Ed.]

245

Progress in Nucleic Acid Research
and Molecular Biology, Vol. 30

TABLE I

AMINO-ACID SEQUENCES OF HYPOTHALAMIC NEUROPEPTIDES[a]

Thyroliberin	Z H P *
Arginine vasopressin	C Y F Q N C P R G*
Oxytocin	C Y I Q N C P L G*
Luliberin	Z H W S Y G L R P G*
Somatostatin	A G C K N F F W K T F T S C
Corticoliberin	S Q E P P I S L D L T F H L L R E V L E M T K A
	D Q L A Q Q A H S N R K L L D I A*
Met-enkephalin	Y G G F M
Leu-enkephalin	Y G G F L
Neo-endorphin	Y G G F L R K Y P
Dynorphin	Y G G F L R R I R P K L K W D N Q

[a] An asterisk (*) indicates an NH_2 group at the C terminus.

precursors, which quite often contain the sequences of other neuropeptides or of repetitive units (4). The biological entities within such a composite precursor are flanked by basic amino acids, which serve as signals for posttranslational conversion of the precursor into the mature peptides. In analogy to composite viral precursors obtained after virus infection, the neuropeptide precursors have been called "cellular polyproteins" (4, 5). Examples are the precursors to adrenocorticotropin, the enkephalins, arginine vasopressin, and oxytocin (6–10) (Fig. 1).

The two hormones arginine vasopressin[1] and oxytocin are synthesized in the supraoptic and paraventricular nuclei of the hypothalamus with their corresponding "carrier" proteins, the neurophysins (11). Within these nuclei, oxytocin and arginine vasopressin appear to be produced in different populations of magnocellular neurons, where they are packaged into neurosecretory vesicles and axonally transported into the neurohypophysis to be stored in the nerve endings or released on appropriate stimuli into the blood stream (12).

Sachs and co-workers proposed that AVP is synthesized as an inactive precursor molecule that is converted into the active hormone (13). Studies of hereditary hypothalamic diabetes insipidus in Brattleboro rats suggested that AVP is synthesized in close context with its particular carrier protein (reviewed in 1). These animals, with an impaired resorption of water, lack biologically active AVP as well as its neurophysin carrier. Later experiments demonstrated the in vivo synthesis of a longer neurophysin precursor in rodents (14, 15) that gave rise to a vasopressin-like oligopeptide upon tryptic digestion.

Oxytocin (OT), primarily responsible for the milk-ejection reflex in female mammals following parturition and uterine contractions, differs

Prepro –

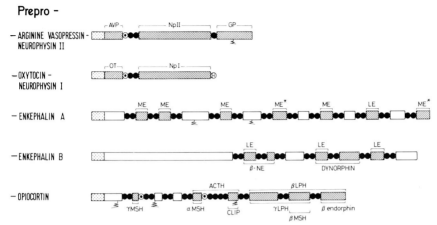

FIG. 1. Structures of precursors of some neuropeptide hormones. Stippled bars, pre-sequence; hatched bars, *in vivo* isolated neuropeptides; open bars, "spacer" sequences (the bars are not drawn to scale); filled circles, basic amino acids; open circles with dots, glycine residues; zig-zag lines, glycosylation site; H, histidine residue. AVP, arginine vasopressin; NpII, bovine neurophysin-II; OT, oxytocin; NpI, bovine neurophysin-I; ME, methionine-enkephalin; ME*, C-terminally extended methionine-enkephalin; LE, leucine-enkephalin; β-NE, β-neoendorphin; β- or γ-LPH, β- or γ-lipotropin; MSH, melanotropin-stimulating hormone; CLIP, corticotropin-like intermediate-lobe peptide; ACTH, adrenocorticotropin. The precursor scheme was deduced from the following publications: AVP-NpII (6); OT-NpI (7); enkephalin A (8, 9); enkephalin B (10), opiocortin (4).

from AVP by only two amino acids. Like AVP, OT was thought to be synthesized together with its neurophysin carrier (12). The two neurophysin carriers in general consist of 93 and 95 amino-acid residues, respectively, are cysteine-rich, and, significantly, share a sequence of 74 amino-acid residues that is identical in both carrier proteins (11). Both peptides bind to the two hormones; however, *in vivo*, one is associated with OT (in the following referred to as bovine neurophysin-I), the other with AVP (referred to as bovine neurophysin-II).

The present report summarizes our attempts to resolve the structural organization of the two hormone precursors as well as the rat AVP gene. We approached this aim from three directions: firstly, *in vitro* translation of hypothalamic mRNA and identification of the specific products by immunoprecipitation; second, tryptic peptide mapping of the precursors synthesized *in vitro*; third, analysis of the primary structure of the precursors and the rat AVP gene using cDNA recombinant techniques.

I. Biosynthesis, Processing, and Modification

Routinely, hypothalamic mRNA was translated in the presence of [^{35}S]methionine, [^{35}S]cysteine, or [^{3}H]leucine in a reticulocyte lysate system (16). The translation products were identified by immunological means, using specific antibodies, electrophoresed in dodecyl sulfate on polyacrylamide gels, and were visualized by autoradiography. In order to study processing and glycosylation of the synthesized precursors, the reticulocyte lysate system was complemented with microsomal membranes from dog pancreas. These membranes are known to contain a proteolytic activity that removes the N-terminal signal- or "pre" sequence as the nascent peptide is transported across the membrane, thus converting a "prepro"- into a "pro"-hormone (17). In addition, these membranes contain glycolipid precursors, a prerequisite for core-glycosylation of potential glycoproteins. Another approach taken to study glycosylation and processing steps was use of the oocyte cell (*Xenopus laevis*) injected with mRNA. This system allows the study of glycosylation and processing as well as secretory events under quasi *in vivo* conditions (18).

A. Arginine Vasopressin

A high-molecular-weight precursor (M_r of 21,000; mass of 21 kDa) of AVP was identified immunologically, using a specific anti-AVP serum; this antiserum did not discriminate between AVP and its deamidated form, an essential prerequisite for identifying any potential AVP precursor (19). Sequential immunoprecipitation experiments showed that the 21-kDa precursor also cross-reacted with anti-bovine-NpII sera, strongly suggesting the existence of a common precursor composed of AVP and NpII (20).

Translation experiments in the presence of the tritiated amino acids leucine, phenylalanine, lysine, proline, and tyrosine indicated that about 1% of the radioactivity incorporated was present in material immunoreactive with antibodies against bovine NpII. On the basis of these data, the specific mRNA was calculated to represent not more than 1% of the poly(A)-containing RNA, or about 0.03% of the total RNA of the tissue. This estimate was later confirmed when recombinant colonies were screened with a labeled vasopressin-specific cDNA probe (6).

When studying cell-free translation of bovine hypothalamic mRNA, another translation product of 18 kDa cross-reacted with anti-NpII sera, but not with anti-AVP sera (20). Further analysis by chromatography of a trypsin digest of the 18-kDa product confirmed the presence of the NpII-derived peptides and the absence of the AVP(1–8) peptide (21, 22). Since N-formyl[^{35}S]methionine was incorporated into the 18-kDa precursor, an intact N terminus was assumed (19).

At present, it is not possible to decide whether the 18-kDa protein is the product of an independent mRNA, akin to the neurophysin-III found in rats (12), or an artifact of the in vitro translation system. The latter may be more likely, as the 18-kDa product was found preferentially in the reticulocyte lysate, not in the injected oocyte system. The earlier hypothesis, that it may be the product of a pretermination event (16), is no longer justified, as the sequence data show that AVP is adjacent to the pre sequence (outlined in detail in Section II,B and Fig. 7). Alternatively, owing to less stringent constraints, the 18-kDa precursor may be synthesized from the 21-kDa-specific mRNA, but initiated at a later position, thus eliminating the AVP sequence. Examples for such a second initiation site within a given mRNA are known only from viral "polyproteins." According to the hypothesis of Kozak (23), ribosomes bind at the "cap" region of the 5'-noncodon region and scan the mRNA until they "detect" the first AUG initiation codon. In the case of the 18-kDa precursor, initiation at the first AUG codon (position −43 in Fig. 7) could be suppressed, e.g., by formation of double-stranded RNA stem(s) at the 5' region. The second AUG codon would be available only at position +40, corresponding to the second amino acid on the NpII sequence (see Fig. 7). Thus the 18-kDa product should lack the first 32 amino acids of the 21-kDa prepro-hormone. In preliminary experiments, [^{35}S]cysteine-labeled 21- and 18-kDa products were isolated from dodecyl sulfate/polyacrylamide gels and subjected to cyanogen bromide cleavages. As expected from the amino-acid sequence of the 21-kDa precursor (details in Fig. 7), this cleavage reaction gave rise to two [^{35}S]cysteine-labeled products of 3 and 18 kDa (22). The latter comigrated with the 18-kDa product synthesized in vitro. No molecular-weight shift was observed with the cyanogen bromide-treated 18-kDa precursor. Direct sequence analysis of the labeled 18-kDa precursor is required to resolve the nature of this precursor.

That the 21-kDa precursor represents the prepro form of the hormone was supported by experiments where N-formyl[^{35}S]methionine was incorporated exclusively into the N-terminal position of the synthesized prepro-hormone, but not of the pro-hormone (19). For further characterization of the hormone precursor, the hypothalamic mRNA-directed reticulocyte lysate system was complemented with microsomal membranes, and the synthesized product was identified by immunoprecipitation. The 21-kDa prepro-hormone was now converted into the pro-hormone with an apparent higher molecular weight (23 kDa). The apparent increase in the mass of the hormone precursor when synthesized in the presence of microsomal membranes (from 21 to 23 kDa) suggested that the latter carried a carbohydrate chain (see below).

In order to determine the size of the "signal peptide" cleaved off by the membrane fraction, translation was performed in the presence of membranes derived from ascites tumor cells treated *in vivo* with tunicamycin. This antibiotic eliminates the glycosylation capability, but not the "signal peptidase" activity of the membranes. A single product of 19 kDa was the result, reacting with both anti-AVP and anti-NpII sera, implying the loss of a signal peptide of about 20 amino acids (*20*). Sequencing of the cloned cDNA encoding the AVP-NpII precursor (together with H. Land and G. Schütz) as well as comparison with sequencing data obtained with the [³H]leucine-labeled *in vitro* products (together with J. Spiess) showed that the signal sequence comprises 19 amino acids.

That the 23-kDa pro form was a glycoprotein was confirmed by (a) its affinity to bind specifically to concanavalin-A/Sepharose; (b) its sensitivity toward treatment with α-mannosidase, which converts the 23-kDa into a 19-kDa product (Fig. 2); and (c) its ability to be labeled by mannose, glucosamine, and fucose in the oocyte system (*24*). As indicated by the amino-acid sequence, the carbohydrate chain is located at the C terminus of the precursor (see Fig. 7); neither the AVP nor NpII amino-acid sequence contains a typical glycosylation site (Asn-Xaa-Ser or Asn-Xaa-Thr).

Whether glycosylation plays a role in specifying posttranslational modification steps, such as exposing or masking a cleavage site, remains to be elucidated. Although the precursors to AVP and OT are remarkably homologous molecules structurally, only the AVP pro-hormone carries a carbohydrate chain.

When *Xenopus laevis* oocytes were injected with hypothalamic mRNA, glycosylated polypeptides of 23 and 25 kDa, and a smaller unglycosylated product of 14 kDa, were identified with anti-AVP and anti-NpII sera (Fig. 3). The 25-kDa product most likely contained a more complete carbohydrate chain than the 23-kDa pro-hormone (*25*). Pulse–chase experiments indicated that the 14-kDa peptide was an intermediate product derived from the larger precursors. Because the 14-kDa peptide showed antigenic reactivity toward both antisera, it was regarded as the immediate precursor to AVP (M_r 1200) and NpII (M_r 10,000) (*21*). This assumption was later confirmed by sequencing (*6*).

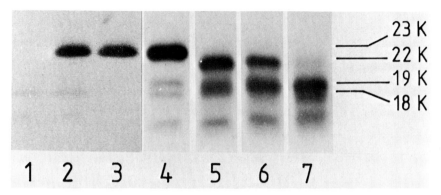

FIG. 2. Bovine 23-kDa pro-arginine-vasopressin—Neurophysin-II precursor analyzed by concanavalin-A affinity chromatography (lanes 1–3) or by α-mannosidase digestion (lanes 4–7). For experimental details see Ivell *et al.* (*24*). ^{35}S-labeled 23-kDa material was mixed with a concanavalin-A/Sepharose suspension in the absence of 0.4 M
α-methylmannosidase and centrifuged; the supernatant fraction was analyzed on sodium
dodecyl sulfate/polyacrylamide gels (lane 1); the remaining concanavalin-A/Sepharose
beads were then washed with 0.4 M α-methylmannoside, and the released material was
subjected to the dodecyl sulfate/polyacrylamide gel separation (lane 2). In lane 3 the
23-kDa material was absorbed to the beads in the presence of 0.4 M α-methylmannoside;
the glycosylated material was no longer absorbed, but immediately released into the first
wash. Lanes 4–7 show the kinetics of the conversion of the ^{35}S-labeled 23-kDa material
into a 19-kDa product by treatment with α-mannosidase and its analysis on dodecyl
sulfate/polyacrylamide gels (*24*). Incubation was carried out at 37°C for 0 (lane 4), 1
(lane 5), 2 (lane 6), and 3 hours (lane 7). The discrete band migrating at 22 kDa accumulated first and diminished later, giving place to the final 19-kDa product.

Besides being a useful "one-cell test-tube," the oocyte is also a
potent system for studying secretory events, such as the export of
heterologous pro-hormones (*18, 25*). The major products secreted into
the incubation medium were the 25-kDa precursor and the 14-kDa
intermediate. Cosecretion of these suggested that proteolytic cleavage
between NpII and the glycoprotein region at the C terminus occurred
within the secretory vesicles of the oocyte. It also indicated that this
cleavage site is readily accessible and recognizable by heterologous
proteolytic enzyme(s). Neither authentic NpII nor the hormone itself
were found in the oocyte or in the incubation medium. Most likely this
process (proteolysis and amidation of the hormone) requires a tissue-
specific set of processing enzymes, with trypsin- and carboxypeptidase
B-like specificities. Whether the sequence of processing events
observed is comparable to those taking place in the hypo-
thalamoneurohypophysial system also remains to be established.
Neither a 14-kDa product nor other possible intermediate candidates,

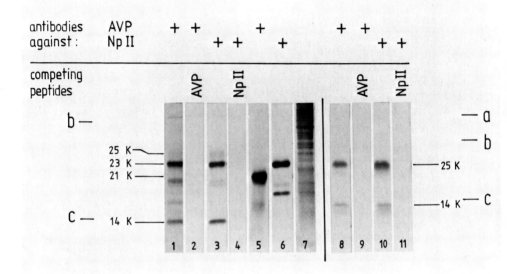

FIG. 3. Synthesis, processing, and secretion of the AVP-NpII precursor in the oocyte (*Xenopus laevis*) programmed with hypothalamic mRNA (*21*). Lanes 1 and 3 show the different products synthesized in the oocyte and immunoprecipitated with anti-AVP or anti-NpII, respectively. The specificity of the reaction is demonstrated with the indicated competing peptides (lanes 2 and 4). As shown in lanes 8 and 10, two of the AVP-Np II-containing proteins synthesized in the oocyte, the 25- and 14-kDa products, are exported into the oocyte incubation medium and could be identified with anti-AVP-(lanes 8 and 9) or anti-NpII sera (lanes 10 and 11). Lane 7 represents 5 μl of an oocyte homogenate after translation of bovine hypothalamic mRNA prior to immunoprecipitation. Lanes 5 and 6 show the different products synthesized in the reticulocyte lysate system in the absence (lane 5) and the presence (lane 6) of microsomal membranes, and immunoprecipitated with the indicated antibodies. For further details see Schmale and Richter (*21*).

e.g., a neurophysin glycoprotein, have yet been isolated from brain tissues.

A direct comparison of the rat and bovine AVP-Np precursors synthesized by *in vitro* translation of the respective mRNAs showed minor differences in the molecular weights: 21,000 for the bovine compared to 19,000 for the rat prepro form (*26*). Cotranslational addition of microsomal membranes from dog pancreas yielded glycosylated products with M_r's of 23,000 for the bovine and 22,000 for the rat pro-hormone. The rat precursor of M_r 22,000 comigrated roughly with the one extracted from rat hypothalami.

B. Oxytocin

Studies similar to those described above for the AVP–NpII precursor were carried out on the OT–NpI polyprotein, using the respective antisera (25). The prepro-hormone showed an M_r of 16,500. In the presence of microsomal membranes, an unglycosylated pro-hormone of M_r 15,500 was immunoprecipitated. Competition experiments using oligopeptides related to OT indicated that anti-OT serum specifically recognized amino-acid sequences within the hormone precursor that are at least immunologically identical to OT (19). The only slight cross-competition observed was with arginine vasopressin and the tripeptide Pro-Leu-Gly-OH, whereas Pro-Leu-Gly-NH$_2$ did not compete. Oocytes-injected with hypothalamic mRNA produced the 15.5-kDa prohormone identified with either anti-OT or anti-NpI sera. This product was detected not only in the oocyte cell, but also in the incubation medium (Fig. 4). Kinetic experiments indicated that the secretory process started after a lag phase of about 16 hours. No further processing into authentic NpI or OT was observed.

II. Structural Analysis

To confirm the common-precursor model by means independent of antisera, the elucidation of the structure was approached from two directions, (a) tryptic peptide "mapping" of the immunoprecipitated products, and (b) cloning and sequencing of cDNAs encoding the respective precursors.

A. Tryptic Peptide Mapping

The precursors were labeled with [35S]cysteine in the reticulocyte lysate or oocyte system directed by bovine hypothalamic mRNA. The products were immunoprecipitated and separated in dodecyl sulfate on polyacrylamide gels. Radioactive bands corresponding to the precursors were eluted, oxidized in performic acid, and trypsinized (21); internal standards included the respective peptide to be analyzed. The resulting peptides were separated by two-dimensional electrophoresis and chromatography on thin-layer cellulose plates and located by ninhydrin staining and autoradiography.

When the [35S]cysteine-labeled 21-kDa prepro-hormone is thus treated, four radioactive spots comigrate with four cysteine-containing spots of the peptides obtained by tryptic digestion and visualized by ninhydrin staining (Fig. 5) A fifth radioactive spot could not be related to either arginine vasopressin itself or AVP (1–8), although the material cross-reacted with anti-AVP sera.

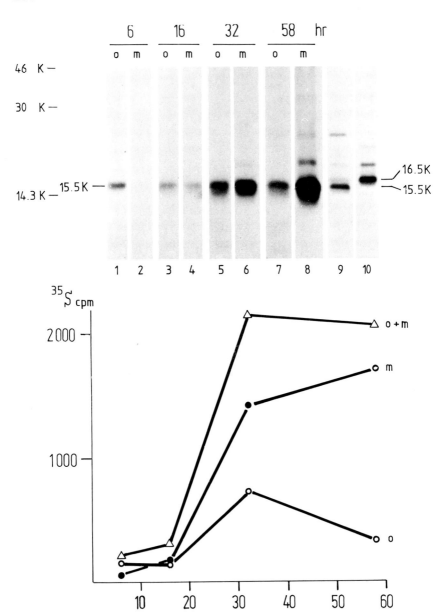

Tryptic digests similarly chromatographed, prepared from the 14-kDa intermediate (Fig. 5) and the glycosylated 23-kDa pro-hormone, also gave rise to the four NpII-specific peptides. An additional radioactive spot comigrated with AVP(1–8). The main difference between the 21-, 23-, and 14-kDa products was that the two precursors (23 and 14 kDa) without the "signal" sequence gave rise to the AVP(1–8) peptide, whereas the prepro-hormone (21 kDa), containing the signal sequence, yielded an AVP-like peptide. Signal sequences, in general, are not separated from their pro-hormones by basic amino acids and consequently are not accessible to trypsin. The AVP-like peptide (spot 5) identified by its cross-reactivity with anti-AVP sera would represent AVP(1–8) with an N-terminal extension comprising all of the signal sequence (see Fig. 7). Because of its size, the 14-kDa intermediate form implies a neighbor relationship of the hormone and NpII in which the latter would be C-terminal to AVP. Based on these observations, a single unambiguous model for the AVP-NpII precursor has been proposed (21). In this model, the signal sequence is followed by AVP, NpII, and a protein with a glycosylation site. Experiments with the rat AVP-Np pro-hormone cleaved by cyanogen bromide predicted a similar arrangement (27). Our model of the hormone precursor was later confirmed by the sequence data (6, 7).

B. Primary Sequence Analysis

Conclusive proof of the intramolecular organization of the composite precursors was obtained by sequence analysis of cloned cDNAs encoding the respective precursors (6, 7). Starting material was

---

FIG. 4. Kinetic studies of oxytocin-neurophysin-I precursor synthesis and export in the *Xenopus laevis* oocyte translation system. Batches of 8–10 oocytes (stages V to VI) were injected with ~50 ng of bovine hypothalamic mRNA per oocyte and incubated in modified Barth's medium including ~400 μCi of [^{35}S]cysteine per milliliter as described in (25). At the indicated times, oocytes were removed from the radioactive medium, washed, and extracted. The OT-NpI-specific polypeptides were immunoprecipitated from both the cell extracts and the media, using specific antisera, electrophoresed on 15% polyacrylamide/dodecyl sulfate gels, and fluorographed (upper panel). The 15.5-kDa OT-NpI-specific bands were excised from the gel and counted (lower panel). Lanes 9 and 10 (upper panel) represent the NpI-specific product synthesized in a rabbit reticulocyte lysate translation system in the presence (lane 9) or the absence (lane 10) of dog pancreas microsomal membranes. The translation products with molecular weights above 15,500 (lane 9) and 16,500 (lane 10) contain NpII antigenic determinants and are coprecipitated because of a slight cross-reactivity exhibited by the anti-NpI serum. o, oocyte; m, medium; 43K, 30K and 14.3K are marker proteins: ovalbumin, carbonic anhydrase, and α-lactalbumin, respectively.

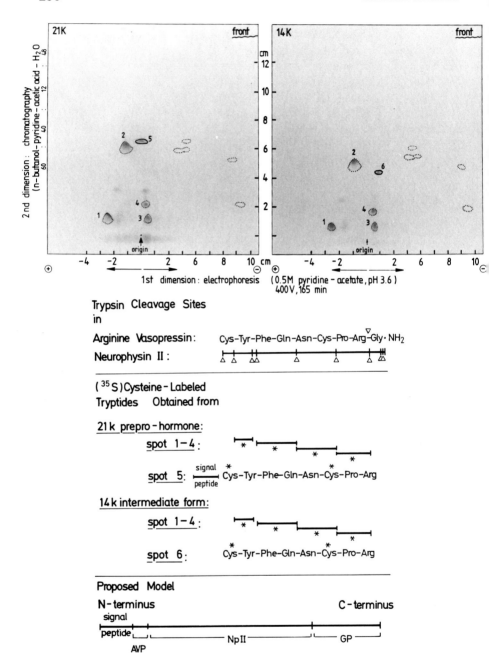

Trypsin Cleavage Sites
in

Arginine Vasopressin: Cys-Tyr-Phe-Gln-Asn-Cys-Pro-Arg-Gly·NH₂

Neurophysin II :

(^{35}S)Cysteine - Labeled
Tryptides   Obtained from

21 k prepro - hormone:

      spot 1-4 :

      spot 5: signal / peptide Cys-Tyr-Phe-Gln-Asn-Cys-Pro-Arg

14 k intermediate form:

      spot 1-4 :

      spot 6 : Cys-Tyr-Phe-Gln-Asn-Cys-Pro-Arg

Proposed Model

N-terminus   C-terminus
  signal

peptide   NpII   GP

AVP

poly(A)-containing RNA from membrane-bound polysomes of bovine hypothalami, which was used for constructing the single-stranded cDNA in the presence of reverse transcriptase. cDNA was "dC-tailed" (extended with dC residues at the 3' end) with terminal deoxyribonucleotidyl transferase. Oligo(dG) was used to prime the formation of the second cDNA strand. The ds-cDNA was inserted into the *Pst*I site of plasmid pBR322, and a bovine hypothalamic cDNA "library" was constructed using strain 5 K of *Escherichia coli*. Screening for tetracycline-resistant cells yielded 200 colonies per nanogram of dscDNA. This library was used initially for screening clones specific for AVP-NpII precursor sequences. In later experiments this library was extended and screened primarily for clones specific for OT-NpI sequences. To identify the plasmids carrying hormone-specific mRNA sequences, plasmid DNAs from 550 colonies were hybridized to labeled bovine hypothalamic mRNA that was enriched approximately 10-fold for AVP-NpII precursor-mRNA by sucrose-gradient centrifugation.

Of the 550 initial colonies, 55 were positive at this first screening. Initial attempts to hybridize mRNA to the plasmid cDNA and to identify the specifically bound mRNA in a translation assay failed for unknown reasons. Therefore, an approach was taken in which endonuclease restriction sites in an unknown DNA can be unambiguously predicted from the known sequence of a protein. One of these restriction endonucleases is *Sau*96I with the recognition site GGNCC; it cuts DNA at positions coding for the sequence Gly-Pro, which occurs twice in the amino-acid sequence of neurophysin (at positions 14–15 and 23–24) (Fig. 6). Consequently, DNA coding for neurophysin and digested with *Sau*96I should yield a 27-base-pair fragment. The analysis was in full agreement with this approach and revealed that, altogether, seven positive clones were identified, five of which carried sequences homologous to the bovine AVP-Np precursor; two were specific for the oxytocin-neurophysin-I precursor.

FIG. 5. Chromatography of tryptic peptides from performic acid-oxidized AVP-NpII precursors. (For experimental details see ref. 21). The [^{35}S]cysteine-labeled 21- or 14-kDa products were isolated from dodecyl sulfate/polyacrylamide gels and trypsinized in the presence of the unlabeled reference peptides bovine NpII and AVP. The peptides were separated on cellulose thin-layer plates, and the reference peptides from NpII (dotted circles) and AVP (AVP$_{1-8}$, filled circle) were visualized with ninhydrin; the chromatograms were exposed to films for a week (upper panels). The lower panel shows schematically the expected peptides, the results of the two-dimensional chromatography as well as a model based on the tryptic digest experiments.

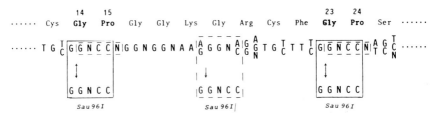

FIG. 6. Part of the bovine neurophysin-II amino-acid sequence (residues 13–25) and the possible nucleotides coding for it. Corresponding to amino acids 14,15 and 23,24 are recognition sequences (solid boxes) specific for the restriction endonuclease Sau96I. A third, less probable restriction site is also indicated in the dashed box.

C. Structure and Comparison of the Bovine Precursors to Arginine-Vasopressin and Oxytocin

The bovine AVP-NpII prepro-hormone is composed of 166 amino-acid residues with a calculated M_r of 17,310 (Figs. 7 and 8). This value is smaller than that of the estimated prepro-hormone (M_r 21,000) obtained by cell-free translation of mRNA (20). The difference may be explained in a way similar to that of the mature neurophysins, the M_r's of which were overestimated by dodecyl sulfate/polyacrylamide gel electrophoresis. A putative signal sequence of 19 amino acids was confirmed by sequencing radioactively labeled hormone precursors. Arginine vasopressin, being adjacent to the signal sequence, is followed by a glycine and two basic amino-acid residues, lysine and arginine, and then by the bovine neurophysin-II sequence. The latter is separated by a single arginine residue from a polypeptide of 39 amino acids, which contains a single glycosylation site (Asn-Ala-Thr at residues 114–116). The glycoprotein located at the C terminus of the precursor is completely homologous with a protein isolated and sequenced from pituitaries of several species (28, 29). The function of this glycoprotein is not known, nor is its target organ, though several processed fragments have been isolated from pituitary extracts (28).

The amino-acid sequence of the OT-Np precursor deduced from the nucleotide sequence of cloned cDNA shows remarkable homologies to its AVP-Np counterpart (Figs. 7 and 8). The OT-Np pro-hormone (Figs. 7 and 8) consists of 106 amino-acid residues with a calculated M_r of 10,889. The yet incomplete signal sequence is again directly followed by the hormone. Neurophysin-I adjacent to oxytocin is separated from the hormone by the sequence Gly-Lys-Arg. The C terminus of neurophysin-I is extended by one amino acid, histidine, which immediately precedes the stop codon. At present the significance of the extended neurophysin-I molecule is not known; it should

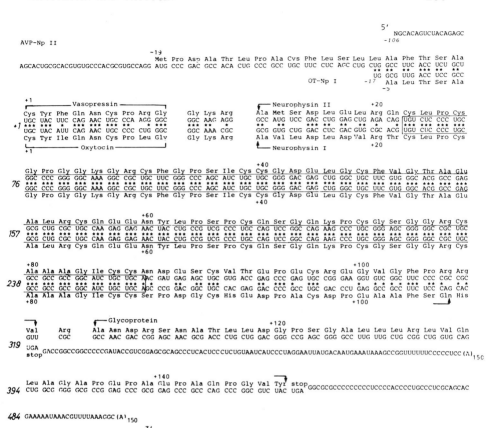

FIG. 7. Comparison of the nucleotide sequences of AVP-NpII and OT-NpI mRNA from bovine hypothalamus. The italic numbers indicate the positions of the nucleotides; the others indicate the amino-acid sequences; identical nucleotides in both sequences are shown by asterisks (*). The boxed area indicates a precise homology of 197 successive nucleotides identical to both precursors. The nucleotides upstream from residue 1 and the amino-acid residues representing the putative signal sequences are indicated by negative numbers.

be noted, however, that the mRNA of the γ2b heavy-chain immuno-globulin family (30) also predicts a supernumerary amino acid at the C terminus, in this case a lysine residue. It seems probable that the primary translation product includes the extra residue, which is removed during the subsequent posttranslational processing steps accompanying the separation of the oxytocin and neurophysin-I peptides

Hybridization experiments indicate a length of about 690 nu-

260   DIETMAR RICHTER

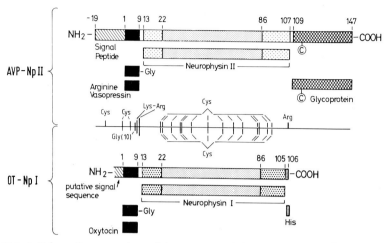

FIG. 8. Schematic comparison of the prepro-argininevasopressin, and oxytocin precursors. The negative number shows the beginning of the signal sequence; the positive numbers refer to the amino-acid residues of the pro-hormones and indicate significant amino acids within the precursors. The internal amino-acid homology of the two neurophysins are shown as a dark-stippled area. C, carbohydrate chain; His, histidine. The cysteine residues and the basic amino acids including the glycine are presented in the middle part of the scheme.

cleotides for the OT-NpI precursor-mRNA as compared to 750 nucleotides for the AVP-NpII counterpart. Comparison of the two cDNAs surprisingly reveals a long region of precise homology of 197 successive nucleotides. This region codes for the highly conserved central part of the neurophysins. Comparison of oxytocin and arginine-vasopressin, and their respective neurophysins from different species leads to the conclusion that both hormones emerged by gene duplication from a common ancestor about 450 million years ago (31). Thus, it appears to be very unlikely that the observed homology in the nucleotide sequence was achieved by conservation of the protosequence. Alternate splicing as an explanation for this finding seems to be excluded, because in some species (pig and rat) differences in amino-acid sequences are found within the conserved part of the neurophysins. Whether this sequence homology can be explained by a recent gene conversion event (32) requires sequence data on the two hormone genes from various species.

There appears to be no standard glycosylation site in the precursor polypeptide sequence, as was predicted from studies of the OT-NpI precursor (25). The glycosylation in the related AVP-NpII common precursor was shown to reside in the C-terminal glycopolypeptide moiety (14, 15, 24), which has no homology in the OT-NpI precursor

TABLE II
PARTIAL AMINO-ACID SEQUENCE OF PRECURSORS TO OLIGOPEPTIDES
AMIDATED AT THE CARBOXY TERMINUS[a]

Melittin	-Arg	-Lys	-Arg	-Gln	-Gln	-Gly	-COOH
α-Melanotropin (α-MSH)	-Trp	-Gly	-Lys	-Pro	-Val	-Gly	-Lys -Lys -
γ-Melanotropin (γ-MSH)	-Arg	-Trp	-Asp	-Arg	-Phe	-Gly	-Arg -Arg -
Vasopressin	-Asn	-Cys	-Pro	-Arg	-Gly	-Gly	-Lys -Arg -
Oxytocin	-Asn	-Cys	-Pro	-Leu	-Gly	-Gly	-Lys -Arg -
Caerulein	-Gly	-Trp	-Met	-Asp	-Phe	-Gly	-Arg -Arg -
Gastrin	-Gly	-Trp	-Met	-Asp	-Phe	-Gly	-Arg -Arg -
Calcitonin	-Gly	-Val	-Glu	-Ala	-Pro	-Gly	-Lys -Lys -
"Human joining peptide"[b]	-Pro	-Gly	-Pro	-Arg	-Glu	-Gly	-Lys -Arg -
"Egg-laying hormone"[c]	-Arg	-Leu	-Glu	-Lys	-Lys	-Gly	-Lys -Arg -
Corticoliberin[d]	-Leu	-Leu	-Asp	-Ile	-Ala	-Gly	-Lys

[a] Reviewed by Richter (33).
[b] Seldah et al. BBRC **102**, 710 (1980).
[c] Schaller et al. Cell **28**, 707 (1982).
[d] From Furutani et al., Nature **301**, 537 (1983).

structure. The finding of a glycine residue adjacent to the carboxy terminus of the two hormones is consistent with other amidated oligopeptides. A survey of various amidated oligopeptides (Table II) suggests that the glycine residue serves as a recognition site for the amidation recation. The pairs of basic amino acids C-terminal to the glycine (with the exception of the melittin precursor) are assumed to be pro-hormone processing signals for trypsin- and carboxypep-tidase-B-like cleavage sites.

III. The Rat Arginine-Vasopressin Gene

A. The Brattleboro Rat—A Model for Gene Expression

Knowledge of the structural organization of the AVP gene could help one to understand the molecular mechanism underlying the defect in the expression of AVP in the Battleboro mutant strain (1). Studies of this hereditary hypothalamic diabetes insipidus show that these animals lack biologically active AVP as well as the respective neurophysin carrier (1). Characteristically, resorption of water in the distal kidney tubules is greatly impaired; these animals show a high water uptake accompanied by excretion of an excessive amount of dilute urine. It is not known at which level of gene expression the defect occurs. Preliminary experiments analyzing supraoptic nuclear mRNA from Brattleboro rats either in cell-free translation experiments or by "blot" hybridization studies suggest that AVP-Np mRNA is drastically reduced, if not absent. This may indicate that the defect is at the level of transcription.

B. Structural Organization of the Arginine-Vasopressin Gene

Figure 9 shows a scheme of the arginine-vasopressin gene from wild-type rats. Comparison of the rat genomic DNA sequence with the cDNA encoding bovine AVP-NpII precursor has enabled us to locate three exons and two introns in the rat gene (34). Exon A encodes a putative signal peptide, the hormone and the variable N terminus of neurophysin; exon B encodes the highly conserved middle part of neurophysin including nearly all cysteine residues essential to secondary structure (35, 36); and exon C encodes the variable C terminus together with the glycoprotein. Thus, the rat DNA sequence predicts a protein precursor similar in structure to the bovine one.

The two introns are inserted in the protein coding sequence specifying the rat neurophysin (37). Intron I (approximately 10^3 bases) exactly separates the variable N terminus and the constant part of the neurophysin at position 21 of the precursor. The second intron occurs between the first and second nucleotides of the GAG that encodes Glu-89 of the prepro-AVP-Np precursor. This is very close to where the highly conserved region of the rat neurophysins (37) ends (Ser-87 of the precursor). The sequence encoding the variable C-terminal part of

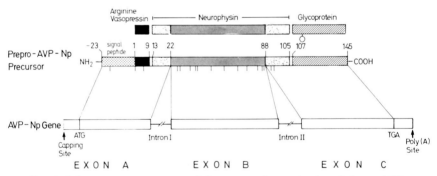

FIG. 9. Schematic representation of the structural organization of the rat AVP-gene and the deduced protein precursor. Dotted bar, putative signal peptide; black bar, AVP; shaded bar, neurophysin (dark shading shows the conserved region); hatched bar, glycoprotein. The open bars of the protein precursor present the amino acids involved in posttranslational processing. The positions of significant amino-acid residues are numbered; cystine residues are marked by vertical lines under the protein precursor; ♂, position of the glycosylation site. The sites of capping, translational initiation, and termination, and the poly(A) site are indicated.

neurophysin and the glycoprotein as well as the 3' noncoding region are uninterrupted. As indicated by nuclease S_1 digests, there are no introns in the 5' untranslated region or in the sequence encoding the signal peptide. Table III compares the rat glycoprotein deduced from the nucleotide sequence with that from other species (28, 29). The glycosylation site Asn-Al-Thr and the leucine-rich central parts are well conserved, which may indicate a defined function, possible processing signals (28), preserved during evolution.

In principle, the functional domains—AVP, NP, vasopressin, and the glycoprotein—are located on three distinct exons similar to other split genes (38–40). The processing signals Gly-Lys-Arg, essential for the release of a functional hormone, are located together with AVP on exon A. The other signal, an arginine residue between neurophysin and the glycoprotein is preserved in exon C. Genes encoding other large proteins, like the pro-enkephalins (4, 8–10), apparently adopted a mechanism in which repetitive enkephalin units together with spacer regions and proteolytic cleavage signals are encoded in a single exon. In these cases, preexisting introns separating the functional units might have been lost during evolution after repetition of an ancestral gene. Except for an ancient gene duplication within the neurophysin exon (B), this mechanism does not appear to have played a significant role in the evolution of the AVP-Np gene, which better fits an exon shuffling model (39, 40).

Comparison of the rat gene sequence with the bovine cDNA indicates striking homologies not only in the protein-coding sequence but also in the 5' and 3' untranslated regions. This finding, together with the remarkable sequence homology of 197 nucleotides encoding the conserved part of bovine NpI and NpII (6, 7), supports the notion that AVP and OT genes were subject to a recent gene conversion event (32). At least in the AVP-Np gene of the rat, an alternative splicing mechanism (41) appears to be unlikely since the AVP- and OT-associated neurophysins show three amino-acid replacements in their conserved regions.

IV. Concluding Remarks

The two precursors to the hormones AVP and OT can be considered as typical representatives of "cellular polyproteins" (Fig. 1). Processing of these proteins, composed of several distinct biological entities, is carried out by proteolytic enzymes often directed by pairs of basic amino acids. The maturation process is accompanied by modification of the biologically active peptides, e.g., amidation of the hormones.

TABLE III

COMPARISON OF THE GLYCOPROTEIN SEQUENCES FROM VARIOUS SOURCES[a]

$$\overset{\rightarrow}{}$$

Rat	A R E Q S N A T Q L D G P A R E L L L R L V Q L A G T Q E S V D S A K P R V Y
Ox	—N D R——L————S G A————A P—PAEP—Q—G—
Pig	—S D R——L————S G A————A P—PAEP—Q—G—
Sheep	—S D R——L————S G A———A A P—PAEP—Q—G—
Human	—S D R—————————G A————A P—PFEP—Q—DA—

[a] The arrow indicates the site of glycosylation.

This amidation reaction requires a glycine residue C-terminal to the hormones and is found in precursors to amidated peptides.

The structures of the two precursors indicate, however, that they have additional interesting features. First, both hormones are located immediately after the "pre" sequence without being separated by basic amino acids. One interesting speculation is whether signal and hormone sequences alone would have sufficient length, as a nascent polypeptide, to reach and traverse the membrane of the endoplasmic reticulum. Second, in the AVP precursor, NpII, and the glycoprotein are separated by only a single arginine residue, which is recognized as a processing signal by the heterologous proteolytic enzyme of the oocyte. In contrast, the pair of basic amino acids connecting AVP and Np is not cleaved in this system. A simple explanation would be to assume the existence of sets of processing enzymes with different specificities. Third, the precursors do not include long "spacer" sequences separating functional units, such as are found in the opiocortin and enkephalin precursors. Although a physiological role for the glycoprotein of the AVP-Np precursor has not yet been identified, its high sequence conservation between species implies some function.

Nucleotide sequence analysis and gene-cloning technology are promising tools for understanding regulation and control of neuroactive peptides, as well as their processing and modification into functional peptides. Analysis of the genomic DNA encoding the AVP-Np gene in Brattleboro rats should provide further insights into the problem of how regulation of such composite precursors is monitored.

ACKNOWLEDGMENTS

The cooperation of H. Schmale and R. Ivell during various parts of this research project is gratefully acknowledged. This work was supported by grants from Deutsche Forschungsgemeinschaft.

REFERENCES

1. H. Valtin, J. Stewart, and H. W. Sokol, *in* "Handbook of Physiology," Vol. 7, p. 131. Hanover, New Hampshire, 1974.
2. A. V. Schally, D. H. Coy, and C. A. Meyers, *ARB* **47**, 89 (1978).
3. D. de Wied and J. M. van Ree, *Life Sci.* **31**, 709 (1982).
4. E. Herbert, *Trends Biochem. Sci. (Pers. Ed.)* **6**, 184 (1981).
5. G. Koch and D. Richter (eds), "Biosynthesis, Modification, and Processing of Cellular and Viral Polyproteins." Academic Press, New York, 1980.
6. H. Land, G. Schütz, H. Schmale, and D. Richter, *Nature* **295**, 299 (1982).
7. H. Land, M. Grez, S. Ruppert, H. Schmale, M. Rehbein, D. Richter, and G. Schütz, *Nature* **302**, 342 (1983).
8. M. Noda, Y. Furutani, H. Takahashi, M. Toyosato, T. Hirose, S. Inayama, S. Nakanishi, and S. Numa, *Nature* **295**, 202 (1982).

9. U. Gubler, P. Seeburg, B. J. Hoffmann, L. P. Gage, and S. Udenfriend, *Nature* **295**, 206 (1982).
10. H. Kakidani, Y. Furutani, H. Takahashi, M. Noda, Y. Morimoto, T. Hirose, M. Asai, S. Inayama, A. Nakanishi, and S. Numa, *Nature* **298**, 245 (1982).
11. R. Acher, *Angew. Chem.* **91**, 905 (1979).
12. M. J. Brownstein, J. T. Russell, and H. Gainer, *Science* **207**, 373 (1980).
13. H. Sachs, P. Fawecett, Y. Takabatake, and R. Portanova, *Recent Prog. Horm. Res.* **25**, 447 (1969).
14. J. T. Russell, M. J. Brownstein, and H. Gainer, *PNAS* **76**, 6086 (1979).
15. M. Lauber, M. Camier, and P. Cohen, *FEBS Lett.* **97**, 343 (1979).
16. D. Richter, H. Schmale, R. Ivell, and C. Schmidt, *in* "Biosynthesis, Modification, and Processing of Cellular and Viral Polyproteins" (G. Koch and D. Richter, eds.), p. 43, Academic Press, New York, 1980.
17. D. F. Steiner, P. S. Quinn, C. Patzelt, S. J. Chan, J. Marsh, and H. S. Tager, *in* "Cell Biology" (L. Goldstein and D. M. Prescott, eds.), Vol. 4, p. 175. Academic Press, New York, 1980.
18. C. D. Lane, *Cell* **24**, 281 (1981).
19. H. Schmale and D. Richter, *Zp Chem* **362**, 1551 (1981).
20. H. Schmale and D. Richter, *PNAS* **78**, 766 (1981).
21. H. Schmale and D. Richter, *Neuropeptides* **2**, 47 (1981).
22. D. Richter and H. Schmale, *in* "Regulation of Gene Expression by Hormones" (K. W. McKerns, ed.), p. 235. Plenum, New York, (1983).
23. M. Kozak, *Cell* **15**, 1109 (1978).
24. R. Ivell, H. Schmale, and D. Richter, BBRC **102**, 1230 (1981).
25. H. Schmale and D. Richter, *FEBS Lett.* **121**, 358 (1980).
26. H. Schmale and D. Richter, *Neuropeptides* **2**, 151 (1981).
27. J. T. Russell, M. J. Brownstein, and H. Gainer, *Neuropeptides* **2**, 59 (1981).
28. D. G. Smyth and D. E. Massey, *BBRC* **87**, 1006 (1979).
29. N. G. Seidah, J. Rochemont, J. Hamelin, S. Banjannet, and M. Chrétien, *BBRC* **102**, 710 (1981).
30. Y. Yamawaki-Kataoka, T. Kataoka, N. Takahashi, M. Obata, and T. Honjo, *Nature* **283**, 786 (1980).
31. R. Acher, *Proc. R. Soc. London Ser. B* **210**, 21 (1980).
32. D. Baltimore, *Cell* **24**, 592 (1981).
33. D. Richter, in "Molecular Aspects of Neurological Disorders" (L. Austin and P. L. Jeffrey, eds.). Academic Press, New York. In press.
34. H. Schmale, S. Heinsohn, and D. Richter, *EMBO J.*, in press.
35. P. Cohen, P. Nicolas, and M. Camier, *Curr. Top. Cell. Regul.* **15**, 263 (1979).
36. E. Breslow, *ARB* **48**, 251 (1979).
37. M. T. Chauvet, J. Chauvet, and R. Acher, *BBRC* **103**, 595 (1981).
38. R. Breathnach and P. Chambon, *ARB* **50**, 359, (1981).
39. W. Gilbert, *Nature* **271**, 501 (1978).
40. F. Crick, *Science* **204**, 264 (1979).
41. S. G. Amara, V. Jonas, M. G. Rosenfeld, E. S. Ong, and R. M. Evans, *Nature* **298**, 240 (1982).

Index

A

Amino acid sequences, of arginine vasopressin and oxytocin precursors, 255–258

Archaebacteria, evolution of ribosome structure, 183–189

Arginine vasopressin, biosynthesis, processing and modification, 248–252

Arginine-vasopressin gene, rat
  Battleboro rat as model for gene expression, 261–262
  structural organization of gene, 262–263

B

Bacteriophage T4, processing of tRNA of, 22–26

B-Deoxyribonucleic acid, nearest neighbor effects
  helical repeats, 78
  other studies, 78–79
  solution NMR studies, 76–77
  X-ray diffraction studies, 73–76

Brattleboro rat, as model for gene expression, 261–262

C

Capping, gene expression and, 201–204

Cell(s), wild-type, RNA processing in, 14–15

Codon-anticodon interactions
  origin of interaction between stacking and coding, 57–58
  platform of small ribosomal subunit and, 169
  redundancy in genetic code, 56–57
  structural model for duplexes, 53–56
  two-out-of-three reading, 52–53

E

Enzymes, RNA processing, mRNA and, 21–22

Escherichia coli

lactose repressor, application of RY model to, 67–68

mutants, altered *tuf* genes in, 94

processing of tRNA in
  cooperativity of, 20–21
  participation of RNase III, RNase E and RNase P in, 18–20

ribosome, structure of, 163–166

RNA polymerase, application of RY model to, 70–71

Eubacteria
  evolution of ribosome structure, 183–189
  ribosomal exit domain of, 175–177
    in same relative region as in eukaryotes, 177–181

Eukaryotes
  ancestors, comparison to prokaryotic, 189–190
  evolution of ribosome structure, 183–189
  ribosomal exit domain, in same relative region as in eubacteria, 177–181
  RNA processing in, prokaryotic cells and, 30–36

Exit domain, ribosomal, function of, 175–183

F

Factor EF-Tu
  genes encoding
    conservation and duplication of *tuf* genes in prokaryotes, 94–98
    mutants of *E. coli* with altered *tuf* genes, 94
    organization of *tuf* A and *tuf* B, 92–94
    structure and function in *E. coli* mutants, 98–99
    mutant species derived from *tuf* A, 99–107
    mutant species derived from *tuf* B, 107–112

267

Contents of Previous Volumes

273